P9-CSB-236

LIFE SCIENCE LIBRARY

LIGHT AND VISION

LIFE SCIENCE LIBRARY

LIFE NATURE LIBRARY

LIFE WORLD LIBRARY

GREAT AGES OF MAN

THE LIFE HISTORY OF THE UNITED STATES

TIME-LIFE LIBRARY OF ART

TIME READING PROGRAM

INTERNATIONAL BOOK SOCIETY

LIFE Pictorial Atlas of the World
The Epic of Man
The Wonders of Life on Earth
The World We Live In
The World's Great Religions
The LIFE Book of Christmas
LIFE's Picture History of Western Man
The LIFE Treasury of American Folklore
America's Arts and Skills
300 Years of American Painting
The Second World War
LIFE's Picture History of World War II
Picture Cook Book
LIFE Guide to Paris

LIFE SCIENCE LIBRARY

LIGHT AND VISION

by Conrad G. Mueller, Mae Rudolph
and the Editors of LIFE

TIME INCORPORATED, NEW YORK

ABOUT THIS BOOK

VISION AND THE LIGHT that makes vision possible have been two of the most fascinating subjects throughout the history of science. Long before the Christian era, men knew enough about the anatomy of the human eye to perform cataract operations with crude instruments, and Hero of Alexandria had discovered one of the physical laws governing light. During certain periods in the years that followed there was little or no progress in the studies of light and vision. At other times, there were dramatic advances. There was, for example, a German biologist who learned a fundamental secret of the visual system by peering into the eye of a frog. And there was the British scientist, Sir Isaac Newton, who found the composition of light by taking it apart with one prism and restoring it with another. This book tells what science has learned through the ages about light and vision, describes the vital findings and charts the areas still to be explored.

Each chapter has a supplementary picture essay that may be read independently. For example, Chapter 5, "Exploring the Spectrum," deals with the behavior of colors and is followed by a picture essay, "The Paradox of Color," that shows how man studies and uses the laws of color.

THE AUTHORS

CONRAD G. MUELLER, Professor of Psychology and of Neural Science at Indiana University, was formerly chairman of the Psychology Department at Columbia University. He is a scientific adviser to the National Research Council Committee on Vision, author of *Sensory Psychology* and coauthor of *Vision and Visual Perception* and of *Modern Learning Theory.* He also served as an officer in the U.S. Navy's Medical Research Division.

MAE RUDOLPH is a writer whose byline has appeared in scientific and general publications for more than a decade. A graduate of the University of Illinois School of Journalism, she has been a newspaper reporter, managing editor of *Medical World News,* and a contributor to such magazines as *Today's Health, Life and Health, American Baby* and *Geriatrics.* She has also written booklets and brochures for the Albert Einstein Medical School.

THE CONSULTING EDITORS

RENE DUBOS, a member and professor of The Rockefeller University, is a microbiologist and experimental pathologist famous for research in antibiotics. He has written, among other books, *Mirage of Health* and *Man Adapting,* and is coauthor of *Health and Disease* in this series.

HENRY MARGENAU is Eugene Higgins Professor of Physics and Natural Philosophy at Yale, and an authority in spectroscopy and nuclear physics. He wrote *Open Vistas, The Nature of Physical Reality,* and is coauthor of *The Scientist* in this series.

C. P. SNOW has won an international audience for his novels, including *The New Men, The Affair* and *Corridors of Power,* which explore the effects of science on today's society. He was formerly Parliamentary Secretary to the British Ministry of Technology.

ON THE COVER

The blue eye of a pretty girl acts as a camera to register the world of light and color around her. On the back cover, a stylized convex lens bends light to create an image.

Published simultaneously in Canada. Library of Congress catalogue card number 66-27561.
School and library distribution by Silver Burdett Company.

CONTENTS

INTRODUCTION 7

1 **VISION: MAN'S LINK WITH THE WORLD** 8
Picture Essay: Versatile Eyes of the Animals 16

2 **THE SCIENCE OF LIGHT** 30
Picture Essay: Rays That Bounce and Bend 40

3 **THE EYE AS A CAMERA** 52
Picture Essay: Pioneers Who Captured Images on Film 62

4 **FROM LIGHT TO SIGHT** 74
Picture Essay: How Vision Begins in the Eye 82

5 **EXPLORING THE SPECTRUM** 96
Picture Essay: The Paradox of Color 104

6 **SENSING LIGHT'S MANY SHADES** 118
Picture Essay: The Mystery of Color Perception 126

7 **THREE DIMENSIONS OF VISION** 138
Picture Essay: More Than Meets the Eye 148

8 **SEEING WITH THE BRAIN** 166
Picture Essay: The Craft of the Artist 178

The Evolution of the Eye 193
A Vocabulary for Vision 194
Further Reading and Acknowledgments 196
Index 197
Picture Credits 200

This book, from its conception to final editing, was under the professional direction of Conrad G. Mueller. The text chapters were written by Mae Rudolph, the picture essays by the editorial staff. The following individuals and departments of Time Inc. were helpful in the production of the book: Fritz Goro and Dmitri Kessel, LIFE staff photographers; Doris O'Neil, Chief of the LIFE Picture Library; Richard M. Clurman, Chief of the TIME-LIFE News Service; and Peter Draz, Chief of the Time Inc. Bureau of Editorial Reference.

INTRODUCTION

STUDIES of vision and physical optics began almost as early as civilization itself. Scientists have not been alone in exploring these fields. Vision, in particular, has interested men of many viewpoints—the poet, philosopher, artist and engineer as well as the physicist, physiologist and psychologist. Perception, originally a philosophical concept, inevitably led to investigation of the structure and functioning of the eye and the nervous system. But anatomy and physiology could not cover all the phenomena of vision, and in the 19th Century psychological experiments on man were added to the general area of investigation.

This book is concerned not only with the separate areas of light and vision, but also with their interrelationship. In recent years, there has been a spectacular growth of information in these fields, a growth that has come from an interplay of theory, data and improved techniques. New methods of recording nerve impulses and measuring absorption of light by the eye, among other developments, have played an important role in this progress.

But modern visual science continues to owe an enormous debt of gratitude to the past. The theories and experiments of such pioneers as Newton, Goethe, Young, Helmholtz, Hering and Mach continue to exercise major influences in research today. Rarely have scientific foundations proved so durable.

I believe that the readers of this book will find in its treatment of light and vision an eminently satisfying presentation of a great and continuing adventure in man's intellectual progress.

—DR. CLARENCE H. GRAHAM
Department of Psychology
Columbia University

1

Vision: Man's Link with the World

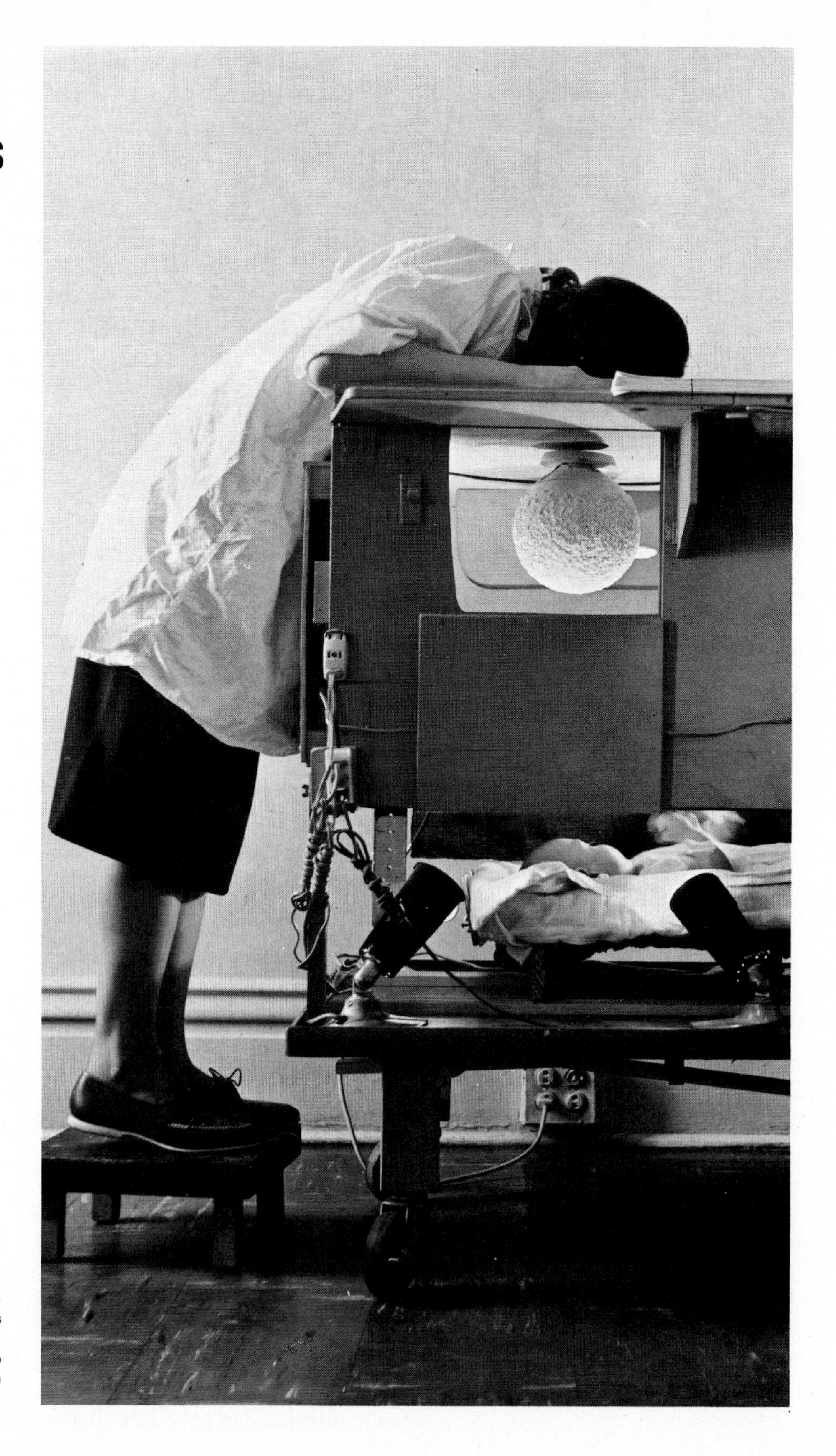

Checking an infant's visual reactions, a researcher holds an illuminated ball over its head in a special "looking chamber." Experiments have shown that, contrary to earlier belief, even a day-old infant can distinguish shapes, patterns and colors.

AT SOME TIME OR OTHER, almost everybody has closed his eyes and tried to grope his way across a room to find out how it feels to be blind. Few people can pursue the experiment for more than a few moments; a sudden uneasiness, a powerful urge and need to see are too compelling, and with a quick rush of relief, the experimenter opens his eyes. Something more than vision returns. He is once again in touch with the world.

For nearly all animals, vision is an instrument of survival, but for most of them, from those who stalk the jungle to those who flee, it is little more than that. For man, on the other hand, vision is not only an aid to survival but also an instrument of thought and a means to the enrichment of life. Even in prehistoric times men dwelling in caves painted pictures that must have been related to a compelling need to create visual images. The modern artist turns to his palette to express what cannot be said adequately in words. Because man is able to see in a certain way, he has been able to invent a written language that carries his message to large audiences and survives after the spoken word has vanished. The scientist, confronted with concepts too difficult to communicate verbally, constructs visual models of mathematical or chemical formulations. Albert Einstein, attempting to explain the most difficult ideas in modern science, often turned to images, particularly familiar ones such as railroad trains or elevators.

Among all the living species, man has the most complex visual system —a system that includes the eye and the related parts of the brain— which permits him to organize and understand the increasingly intricate elements of his environment. Because of his eye and his brain, man is able to ask certain questions and devise ways of answering them. He can speculate about his place in the universe, and build telescopes to extend his vision into space. He can wonder about the nature of life, and design microscopes that probe deep into living cells. A cat confronted by another cat on a television screen is baffled or simply not interested; a man looking at television can see another man floating in space and can understand the meaning of the Astronaut's achievement.

Sometimes the task that confronts man's vision stretches its ability to its limits. This is because man, using his vision, has been able to create ever more complex conditions in his environment. Consider, for example, a motorist traveling through New York City's Queens-Midtown Tunnel under the East River, and the problem of the lights in the tunnel. These are placed at even intervals in a double row along the ceiling—but as he moves along they seem to move, and the closer he gets to them the larger the intervals between them seem to become. The lights appear to move slowly when they are far ahead in the tunnel, but they speed up as he passes, receding suddenly beyond his side windows, and then slow down again as they drop behind his rearview mirror. Quite a problem in accommodation and adjustment? Indeed so, but this is only the beginning.

These rows of tunnel lights and the mosaic of ceiling tiles are reflected in turn on the polished surface of the car's hood, presenting the driver with an inverted—and distorted—image of the moving pattern above. Alongside the tunnel's roadway, the upright supports of an iron railing on the policeman's catwalk flash by like closely spaced telephone poles outside a speeding train. Ahead of the driver are more cars, their red taillights blinking in broken rhythms; in his rearview mirror he sees the headlights of following cars; in the adjacent lane other cars pass, their headlights and then their taillights flickering by, the ceiling lights reflecting once more off their shining hoods. Patterns multiply: wall tiles, the white center stripe of the roadway, the evenly spaced glass booths for policemen. All these visual stimuli and more assail the driver as he rushes along the narrow lane at some 40 miles an hour. More information is poured into his eyes in a few minutes than is put into a bank of computers for a rocket launching. And yet he handles it all with ease. Some two million drivers, all of them dependent on receiving accurate and coherent visual clues to safe passage, travel through this tunnel every month, with no more than 50 accidents a year.

This visual triumph is achieved by an apparatus whose first ancestor, some 300 million years ago, was a simple light-detecting spot on the body of an animal. This spot did little but signal whether it was dark or light. In the course of its evolution since then, the visual system has taken some unusual turns and has become more complex and specialized in the process.

Different eyes for different uses

The eyes of all living creatures are cut from the same basic mold, but their forms are as varied as life. Some eyes are designed for seeing at night, others in the daytime, still others for both. Some are best for defensive maneuvering, others for hunting. Each has its special advantages—and its disadvantages. The squirrel's eyes are on each side of its head, placed in its forward-sloping cheeks so that it has sharp vision ahead, but they are near enough to the top of its head so that it can look back over its head and down its spine while running up a tree to see if it is being pursued. It can also look upward for hawks while running along the ground, but it cannot roll its eyes for easy vision sideways. By contrast, a fish, which is constantly being turned and twisted by currents as it pursues its prey, keeps its eyes aimed at the object like a gyro-controlled drill, while its body rolls and turns around it. Since the robin cannot see anything clearly within a few inches of its eyes, it has had to adapt in another way: it stands erect and stretches its neck in order to see a worm. There is a remarkable fish, of the genus *Periophthalmus* (Greek for "revolving eye"), that has developed large bulging eyes on a turret that rises from the top of its head and scans

LIKE TWIN PERISCOPES, the eyes of a mudskipper pop up above the water's surface. The mudskipper is a small fish that spends most of its time on land, hunting for food there. As a consequence, its eyes are specialized for land use—they cannot focus under water—and each is mounted on a muscular turret that can rotate independently and scan in all directions. On sighting prey, both eyes zero in on it, giving the mudskipper such visual acuity that it can spot a tiny termite at 10 feet. For protection, the bulging eyes are lowered into a hammock of muscle and covered with a layer of skin.

the shore like a periscope while the fish is submerged. Finding prey, it flips ashore and eats it. When it again enters the water the fish relaxes certain muscles, lowers its visual turret, and covers it with a lid of tough skin.

Toads use their eyes in even stranger ways. They live mostly on earthworms, a difficult meal even for an animal with both sets of teeth. Possessing only uppers, a toad with a mouthful of squirming worm closes its eyelids, lowers its eyes through a trapdoor in the roof of its mouth, and holds the earthworm down with its extremely tough eyeballs. For this maneuver, the toad uses the same set of muscles that man uses for rolling his eyes. This solves the toad's feeding problem, but prevents its watching out for enemies while dining.

Vision for a hunter

While there are many similarities among all eyes, man's visual system is closest to those of tree-climbing animals or the hunters—for man's immediate ancestors came down from the trees where their eyes had become adapted for rapid focusing while swinging from limb to limb. The eyes of most tree creatures and ground stalkers face forward in their heads, so that their owners can look at a point with both eyes at once. These eyes also are equipped with aiming and focusing mechanisms for bringing the images of the two eyes together so that the picture is three-dimensional—and in sharp outline.

Man's eyes have traded certain advantages for others: they are versatile and highly accurate, but they are less acute than a hawk's and less wide-sweeping than a deer's. They are not ideally suited for seeing underwater, nor are they as efficient at night as an owl's. Yet with all the compromises, they retain a staggering degree of adaptability and precision. They are capable of extremely rapid movement, of instantaneous shifts in focus from a book in hand to a distant star, of adapting to bright or dim light, of distinguishing colors, of estimating distance, size and direction of movement.

Human vision also has a rich relationship with the other senses. Unlike animals that rely chiefly on touch, such as insects with sensitive antennae, on sound, like the night-flying bat, or on smell, like the pig who sniffs out truffles underground, man's five senses cooperate with and augment each other. The eye, the skin and the ear give man information about space; the skin and the eye also tell him about an object's shape and texture. The balancing mechanism in the inner ear, responding to gravity and to the speeding or slowing of bodily motion, provides orientation in space, which the eyes correct or corroborate. Under ordinary circumstances, the inner ear and eye work together harmoniously, but sometimes they provide inconsistent information.

In one psychological exploration of sensory perception, a man is taken into an ordinary-looking room, seated on a chair, and then blinders are put on him. However, this is neither an ordinary room nor an ordinary chair: both can be tilted. While the subject has the blinders on, both the room and the chair are tilted. Then the blinders are removed, and he is asked to order an adjustment of the chair which will make him upright. In some instances, the subject believes his eyes and directs an adjustment that lines him up with the walls and floor of the tilted room. Other participants rely on their sense of balance and ask for an adjustment that makes them feel erect.

The language of sight

For an infant, learning about the cooperation and corroboration of the senses is essential. When a child is born the physical apparatus for seeing is fairly well developed, and the visual processes are about the same as in the adult. But much of vision is like a language that has to be learned, word by word and sentence by sentence.

Exactly what a child sees and how his visual sense develops is difficult to ascertain. The initial development of human vision seems to begin with a response—to something bright. This is fairly easy to observe because even the youngest infant starts and blinks at a sudden light. Beyond this point, however, investigation is handicapped because the young infant cannot talk or even reveal his visual responses through behavior—as the laboratory animal can by pressing buttons for food or running through mazes. Scientists have had to devise special methods of getting information from this noncommunicative creature. Robert L. Fantz of Western Reserve University, for example, has built an elaborate box in which babies can be placed comfortably on their backs and their eye movements photographed while they are shown various objects. He has found that even very young babies show more interest in pictures of faces than in pictures of similar shapes with haphazard patterns. Small babies also seem to be more interested in actual round objects than in two-dimensional pictures of these objects—an indication that depth and form vision begins to develop fairly early or may even be partly innate.

An even more dramatic proof of the early development of depth vision was the experiment of Mrs. Eleanor Gibson. She wondered whether a young child would fall off a ledge or a cliff if left alone, so she built a safe "cliff" consisting of a deep hole covered by a glass sheet connecting the solid floor with supports on the other side. Babies, she found, will crawl across the floor to the edge of the "cliff" but in no circumstances will they crawl forward onto the glass, not even when lured by their mothers or their favorite toys. Clearly, depth sense is already present in babies still in the crawling stage. However, Mrs. Gibson noticed that the same babies will turn around and move backwards so that their legs are well out on the glass; the hole they so carefully avoid when they see it holds no terrors when it is outside their field of vision.

From such studies as these, and from careful, long-term observation of infants at home, scientists have sketched a general outline of the stages through which the infant's vision grows toward adult perception. The connection between sight and other sensory systems begins fairly early. At first an infant begins to suck only when a nipple touches his lips, but after a time he begins to suck when he sees the nipple moving toward him. Later he smiles at his mother's face. At three months he has learned to turn his head to look directly at objects from which sounds are coming, and by the fifth month he reaches out to an object dangling before him. After a while he can tell visually which objects are within his reach and which are beyond his grasp. This is the beginning of a rewarding period of exploration. By experimenting, touching, reaching, tasting in the months that follow, the infant will build up a store of experience and information which will one day allow him to make judgments on the basis of his eyes alone.

One of a child's first discoveries has to do with the physical world. He learns that certain things are solid, and that some are movable while others are not. By the end of the first year he begins to grasp the idea of identity and permanence—things which were square and solid yesterday are square and solid today. Things which are out of sight do not cease to exist; at first if a toy is covered up with a blanket he will forget it and look surprised when it reappears, but later he will lift the blanket to find it.

HOW CHILDREN TRANSLATE the world around them is illustrated by their drawings. In the above picture, drawn by a four-year-old, the house is portrayed by a series of curved lines because, to the child, a circle represents a solid form. A child's visual sophistication soon grows, however. In the drawing by a five-year-old below, there is a truer, more angular representation of a house.

Recognition in a complex world

Then he begins to learn that an object is the same even when presented from a different viewpoint. A very young baby will not recognize a bottle or a toy given him wrong-end-to, but later he can recognize objects backwards or upside down just as readily as in their "proper" position. And he begins to learn about size and distance, to understand that a large toy across the room is not the same thing as a small toy nearby, although their physical images are about the same.

A critical aspect of this development is the child's changed viewpoint: from a single, simplified version of whatever he sees he is moving toward an awareness of general principles and outstanding features. He no longer thinks of a red ball and a white one as two utterly different kinds of objects, nor does he call every smiling adult "mama." Things that were once lumped together as animals are now recognized as two-legged or four-legged and later as horses, dogs or chickens. And he can tell the character of many things merely by looking. With his eyes alone he knows that a dog is furry and a brick is too heavy to pick up. At the most sophisticated stage he is able to recognize and classify things he has never seen before. A poodle is seen immediately as just as much "dog" as the family dachshund.

Long before psychologists evolved the techniques for learning about the development of vision in the child, much attention was paid to the relatively rare cases of adults blind from birth who are given sight through surgery. The hope that careful observation of these people might provide better understanding of the normal development of vision has not been fulfilled. However, the study of such cases has revealed many other interesting facts.

Richard L. Gregory, director of perception studies at the Cambridge University Department of Psychology, has described in detail a recent case of a man who saw for the first time in his life at the age of 52. Like most such patients, he could see little at first and could only apply to the objects he was seeing for the first time what he had learned by touch. His depth perception was not as good as that of the babies who avoided the glass sheet over a hole. For example, he felt he could easily step out of his window and put his feet on the ground although the window was some 30 or 40 feet up. He was much better at judging the size and distance of objects that he already knew by touch. He never learned to read by sight and continued to rely on Braille.

But perhaps the most telling thing about Gregory's patient was that he became deeply depressed after he was able to see. He loved colors but was oversensitive to drabness or things like peeling paint. He became fearful of crossing streets that he had crossed with confidence when blind. He began reverting to his life without light, neglecting to turn on lamps in the evening and often just sitting in a dark room. Within three years after the operation, he died.

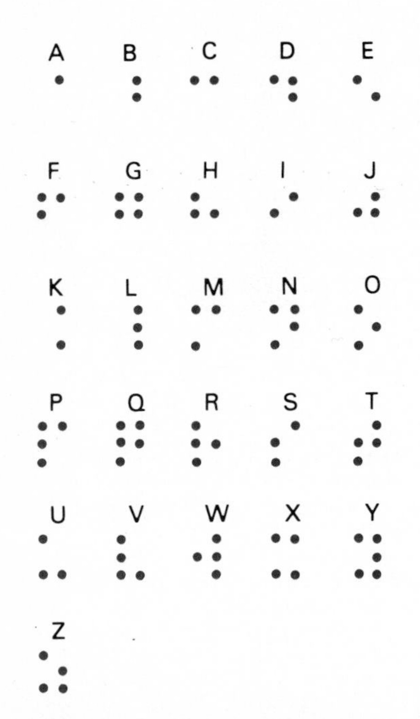

AN INGENIOUS ALPHABET of raised dots developed by a Frenchman, Louis Braille, in the first half of the 19th Century, enables the blind to read. In the Braille system, various combinations of from one to six dots are used to represent letters and short words. By running his fingers over the raised points, an experienced blind person can read at the rate of 50 words per minute. Braille, who was blinded in an accident at age three, developed the reading system when he was teaching at the Institution for the Young Blind in Paris.

Memory's role in vision

Vision is not a straightforward, direct affair. Man tends to think that a picture of the world enters the eye and he sees it. But that is only part of the story. Things retain their identity, are recognizable, because he sees them and has always seen them that way. The visual system is not simply a camera, a direct receiver and recorder of information. Together, the eye and brain are an organizing apparatus that analyzes and processes the large mass of data coming from the outside world.

The eye sees sharply only what it is concentrating on at any given moment. This choice is at least partly directed by the brain. William James, the eminent American philosopher and psychologist, said: "Millions of items of the outward order are present to my senses which never properly enter into my experience. Why? Because they have no *interest* for me. *My experience is what I agree to attend to.* Only those items which I *notice* shape my mind—without selective interest, experience is an utter chaos." But this selectivity is physical as well as mental. The eye actually focuses sharply only on small segments of the visual world. Look at the title of one book on a long shelf of books; the title stands out sharply and clearly, while the names of other books are indistinct and do not distract the eye from its main purpose. As part of the process of organizing, the eye physically eliminates the unnecessary and the redundant.

The eye is also mobile; a turn of the eye or head brings other parts of the field in view. The visual world cannot be perceived all at once; man perceives a succession of images. But the eye blends these so remarkably that all awareness of the episodic character of vision is lost.

This useful mobility is also combined with an essential stability. When a moving visual impression passes across the eye, man usually knows whether it is moving or whether he is. And when he himself moves, the world does not seem to move around him; it stands still visually while he moves about in it.

This stability runs through all of visual experience. In spite of the changing pattern of selective focus and the moving eye, in spite of the fact that man sees things from every angle and in a multitude of lighting conditions, things usually remain recognizable. A dinner plate is readily identified whether he sees it as a circle from above, or an ellipse when he reaches for it on the shelf.

Filling in visual gaps

The visual apparatus is not only capable of eliminating the irrelevant and of recognizing the unfamiliar, it is also able to operate with limited information. It "fills in" where there are gaps. A skilled artist can draw a few lines on a piece of paper and the viewer immediately sees a whole face. An artist draws a few completely detailed trees in the foreground of a landscape, then spots in some blobs and bits of color behind them, and the viewer sees a whole forest. This may be called "the etcetera principle," meaning that when man sees a few members of a series and an indication of the rest, he assumes the existence of them all. Much of art is based on this tendency to fill in, to complete, to organize—and so is much of ordinary vision. Man's eyes cannot see behind him, but he does not think of the visual world behind his head as black or empty. The brain fills in this unseen space, and he tends to "see" the world as continuing around him. The human eye demands completeness.

It also tends to see things in ways that make sense in the framework of experience, expectations and knowledge. When a man sees a field of wheat, its nearby rows widely separated but blending into an almost solid wall in the distance, he sees it as something extending into space. The eye and the brain constantly analyze the information received and compare it with past experience. Fortunately, the visual system is usually provided with plenty of information on which to make decisions. Like all good communication services or intelligence agencies, man's visual system rarely relies on one signal alone, but makes use of what engineers call "redundancies," the mutual confirmation of messages by repetition or cross-reference. Any single stimulus reaching the eye may be inadequate or ambiguous, but the interaction of a great many clues is a powerful instrument for weeding out wrong guesses.

Most of this process of visual organization, or what has been called "an effort after meaning," resides in the highly developed brain that sets man apart from all other species. His brain is capable of winnowing the mass of information, selecting what is needed, using the rest for comparison or background, making decisions, and achieving stable, consistent and meaningful vision of the universe in which he lives.

Versatile Eyes of the Animals

From the one-celled amoeba to the great bald eagle, virtually every form of animal life responds in some way to light. The simplest animals—such as the amoeba—react only to changes in light and dark. The night-crawling earthworm is eyeless but its entire skin is covered with light-sensitive cells; sunshine—or even the beam from a powerful flashlight—sends it burrowing into the ground.

More highly developed animals, such as birds and mammals, have evolved complex eye structures which register detailed pictures of the world about them. Hawks and eagles, which have the keenest sight of all, can spot a rabbit hopping through underbrush a thousand feet below them. The giant eyes of these birds of prey actually outweigh their brains. The harassed rabbit has eyes placed on either side of its head in such a way that it can see a hawk swooping down from behind. An owl has huge saucerlike eyes to help it see at night, and the eye structure of the dragonfly gives it a keen ability to judge motion. In every case, the way an animal perceives light is dictated by its particular needs—the way it catches food, how it evades its enemies, if it flies, swims or crawls, and whether its day begins at dawn or dusk.

A CHAMELEON'S SWIVEL EYES

Like armored gun turrets on a battleship, the chameleon's eyes swivel independently as it searches for insects to eat. A slow-moving lizard, the chameleon perches motionless on a tree branch. When it sights its quarry, both eyes zero in on the target, thus providing the acute depth perception it needs to strike its victim with a lightning dart of a long, sticky tongue.

The Simplest Sight

The most elementary sight organs are not eyes at all, but light-sensitive areas called eyespots which can only detect differences between light and dark. Many simple forms of marine life, like the one-celled *Euglena,* have eyespots to orient them toward the light, which they use to manufacture energy in much the same way plants do. The eyespot, which contains one or more specks of pigment, also is useful in directing the organism away from the surface during periods of strong sunlight, when the sun's rays could injure it.

During millions of years of evolution, some marine creatures have developed highly specialized and often complex eyespots. The scallop *(below)* has from 50 to 200 such spots, each of which functions like a simple but unfocused eye.

Unique among microscopic marine life is the pinhead-sized *Copilia (opposite),* which can actually form images by means of its crude visual system. Some scientists think the *Copilia* may be an evolutionary link in the progression of the organs of vision from eyespots to more complex eyes.

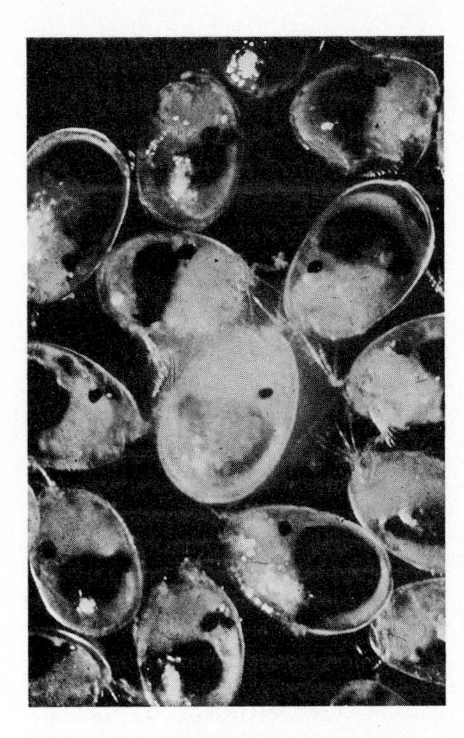

TINY LIGHT SENSORS
The black dots within the transparent shells of these minute cypridinids are light-sensitive eyespots. Cypridinids, microscopic crustaceans, use their paired eyespots to head them toward vitally needed light. Other simple marine organisms similarly distinguish between light and dark.

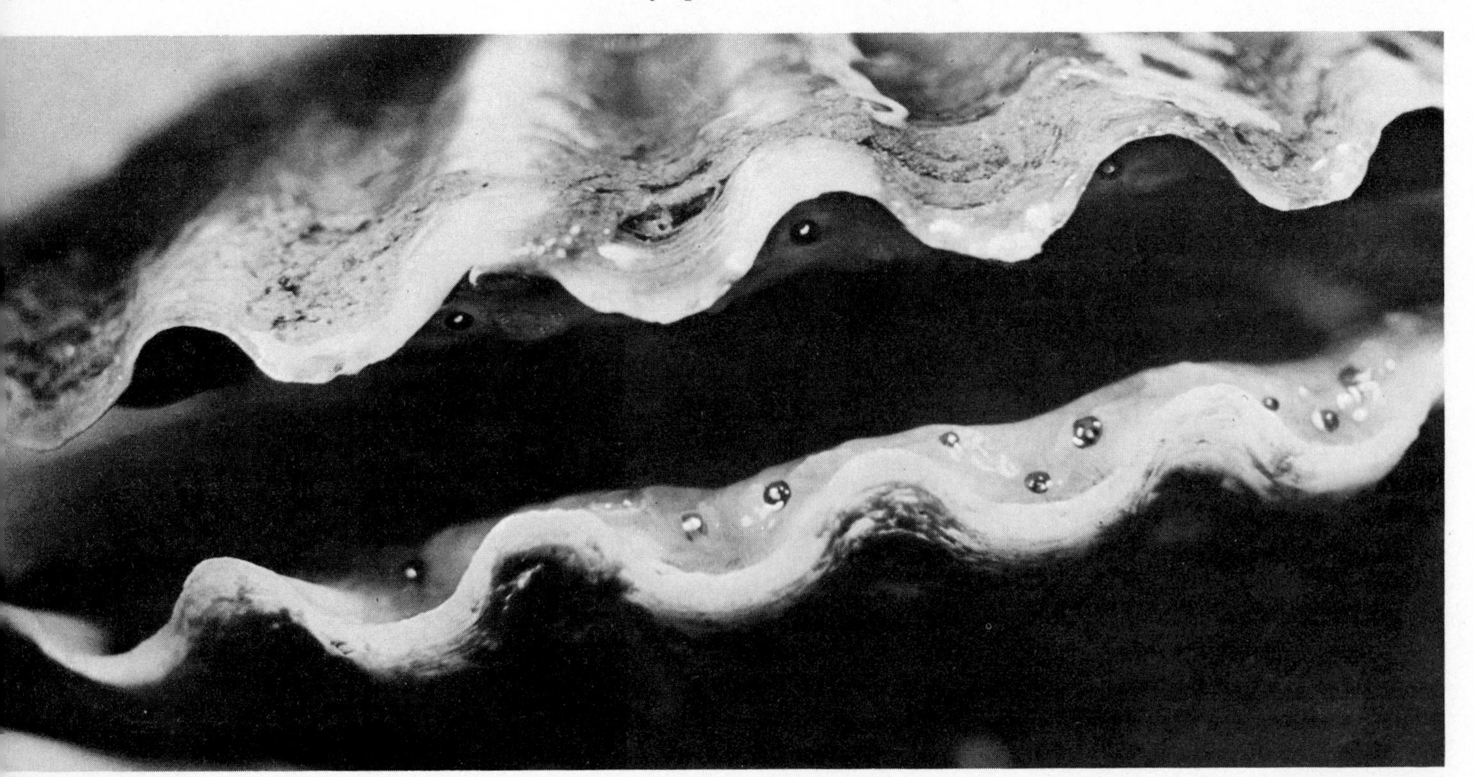

A SCALLOP'S BATTERY OF EYES
Two rows of gemlike eyes stud the fleshy mantle just inside this scallop's shell. Each eye has its own lens and group of light-receptive cells, giving the scallop exceptionally good vision for a mollusk. This is important because scallops, unlike clams and oysters, can actually "swim" across the ocean floor, propelling themselves by squirting jets of water from inside their shells.

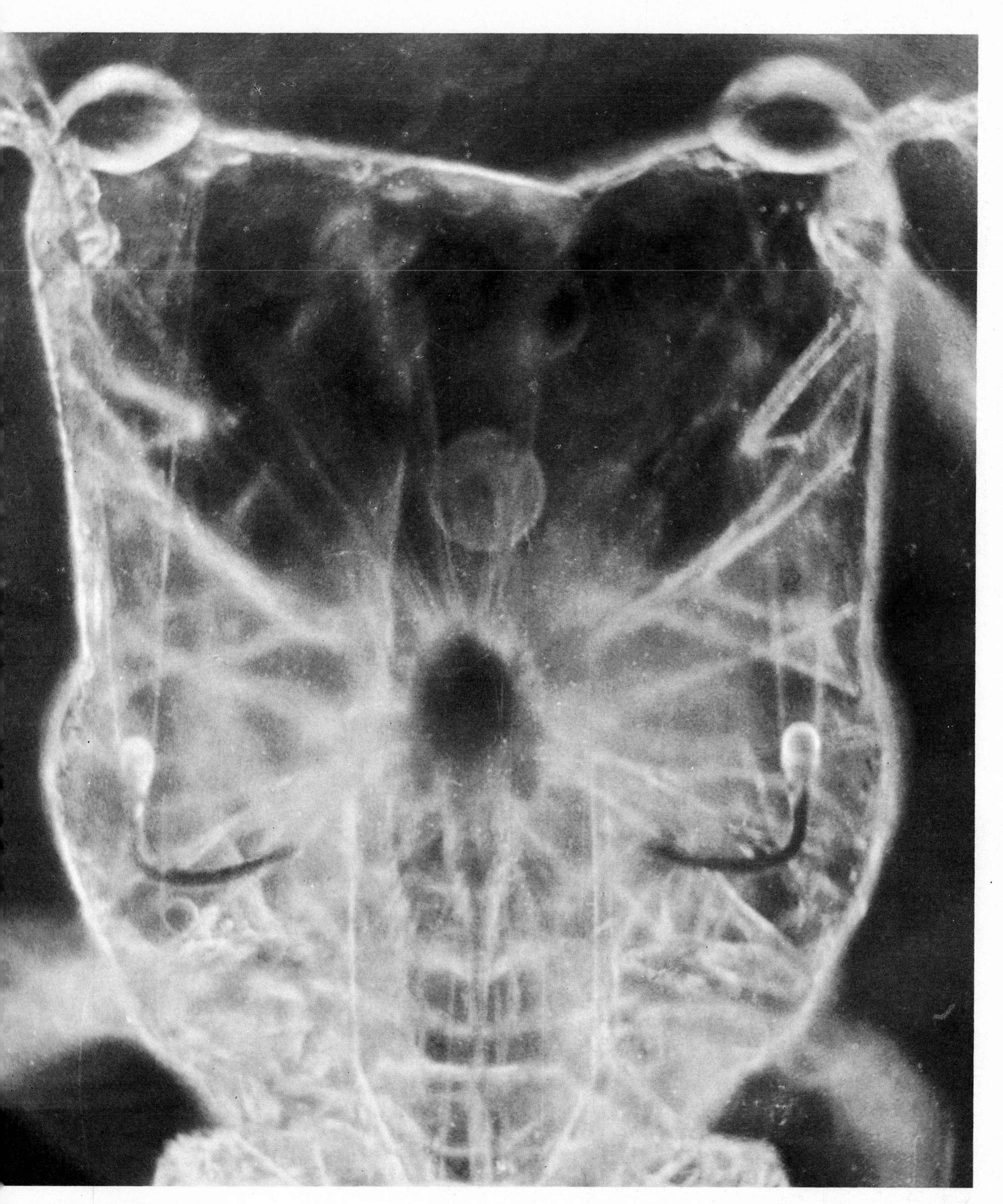

A SPECK THAT CAN SEE

The microscopic *Copilia,* shown here magnified 25,000 times, is the smallest organism capable of seeing images. The two bulges at the top are lenses which focus light into a smaller set of lenses set deep in the transparent body. The interior lenses, and the hook-shaped light receptors attached to them, sweep back and forth like scanning radars while sending signals to the brain (dark spot in center) along a single optic channel. Not until a scan is completed—which takes from a fifth of a second to two seconds —can the brain reconstruct an entire image.

Multiple Facets of Compound Eyes

Compound eyes, found in insects and some marine animals, are the type most often observed in nature. The world's oldest eye, preserved as a fossilized rock *(bottom left)*, has a compound structure much like the eye of a modern horsefly *(right)*.

Compound eyes comprise hundreds of relatively long tubes bunched together like a handful of soda straws. At the external tip of each tube is a fixed lens that focuses light rays toward a group of light-sensitive cells at the tube's innermost end. Since the tubes fan out slightly, the eye structure is rounded, giving an extremely broad field of vision.

Each tip, or facet, of a compound eye picks up a tiny image of the section of the world in front of it, and transmits this fragment to the brain as a nerve impulse, there to be fused with signals from other facets into an overall mosaic picture. Since facets cannot change focus, compound eyes are unable to form precise images. A wasp cannot tell the difference between a fly on a wall and a nailhead. But compound eyes are extremely efficient at detecting movement. Honeybees always head toward flowers swayed by a light breeze; predatory dragonflies are able to make precise calculations of the speed of smaller insects darting through their visual fields.

The simple eyes of most spiders are like separated facets of a compound eye. They are usually arranged in clusters along the spider's back, in such a way that they can register the movement of images passing in sequence from one eye to the next. Spiders which sit quietly in their webs are not so dependent on their vision as hunting spiders, and therefore can get along with very nearsighted eyes.

A SPIDER'S CLUSTER OF EYES
Eight simple eyes dot the back of this hunting spider. Each has a fixed lens and cluster of light-receptive cells. Though no spider can perceive an object beyond one foot, or form sharp images at any distance, the hunting spider can track the slightest motion from one eye to the next.

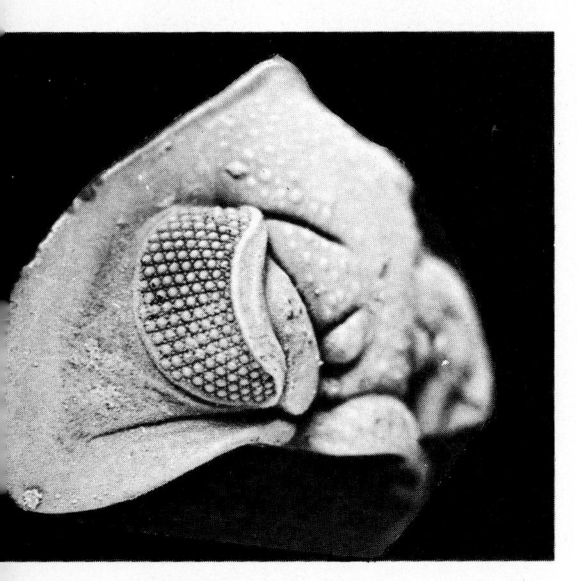

THE WORLD'S OLDEST EYE
This fossil segment shows the dimpled, curved surface of a trilobite's compound eye. Trilobites were tiny creatures, now extinct, which roamed the ocean floor some 500 million years ago.

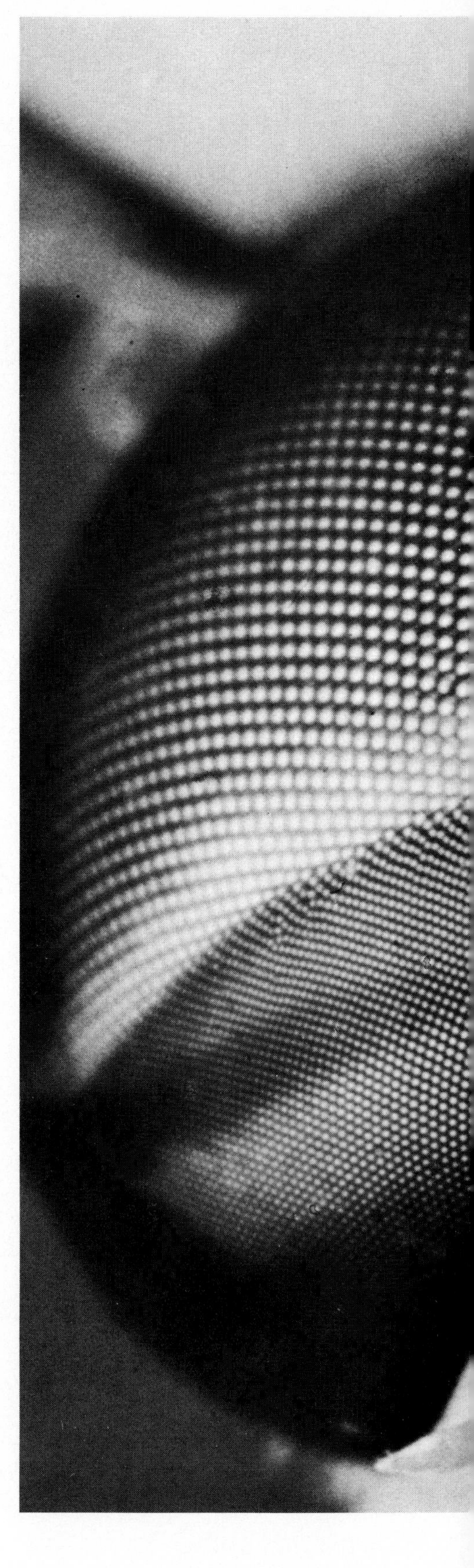

A HORSEFLY'S HONEYCOMB EYE

Some 7,000 separate facets form the compound eye of this male horsefly, here magnified 2,000 times. The eye, which covers most of the horsefly's head, has facets of two sizes. The larger ones, on top, give a broad but indistinct view. Vision is sharper with the smaller facets *(below)*. Since they are more densely concentrated, they register images in greater detail.

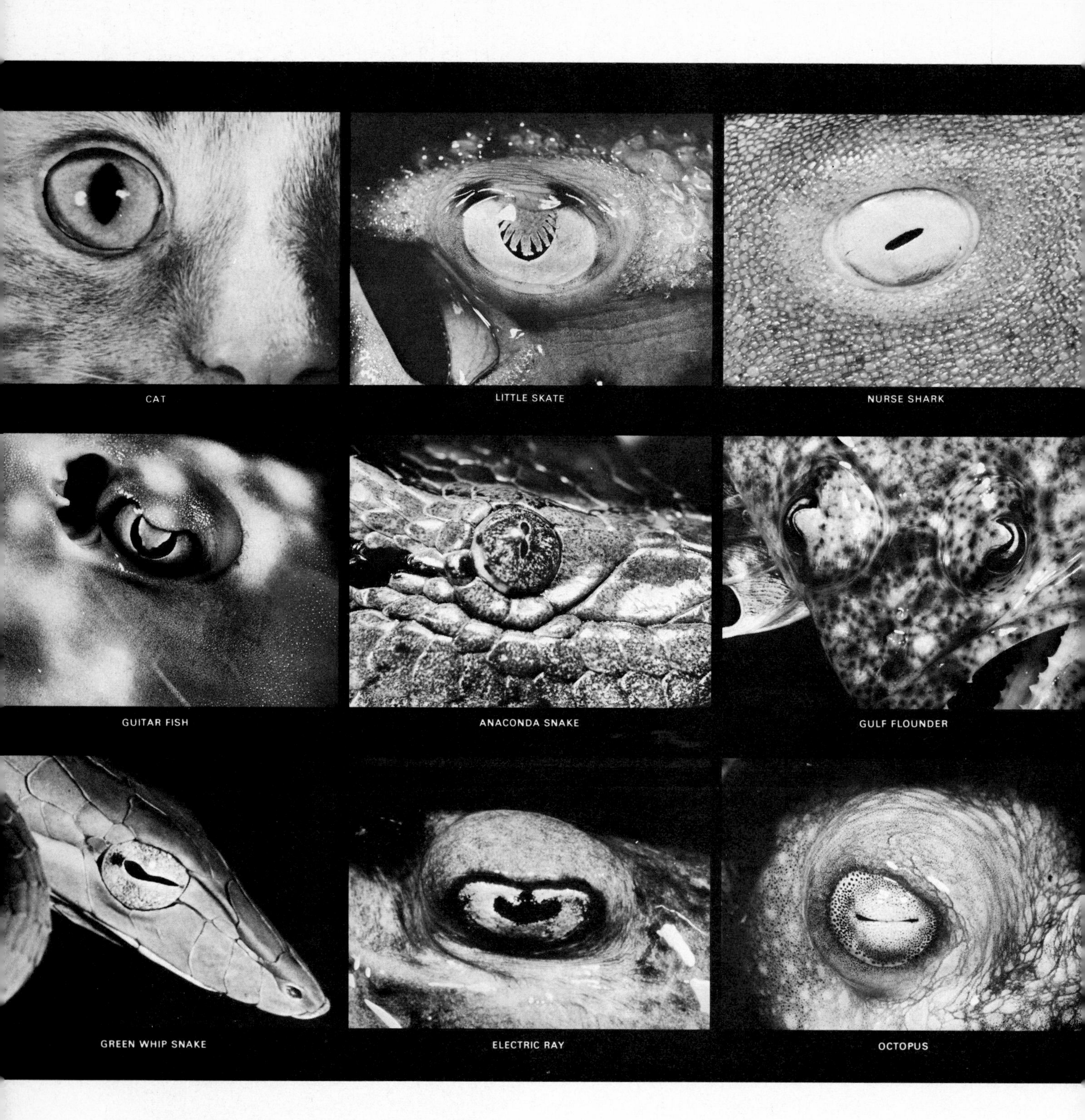

CAT

LITTLE SKATE

NURSE SHARK

GUITAR FISH

ANACONDA SNAKE

GULF FLOUNDER

GREEN WHIP SNAKE

ELECTRIC RAY

OCTOPUS

A Gallery of Animal Eyes

The most complex and efficient eyes belong to higher animals—especially vertebrates such as fish, birds and mammals. Like humans, most animals have adjustable lenses and myriads of light-sensitive cells for recording sharp images.

But while human eyes are basically the same except for the color of their irises, the eyes of animals take on an almost infinite range of colors, shapes and sizes—as shown by the sampling above. The variations reflect evolutionary adaptations to the animal's habits and environment.

Night-prowling animals most often have large, circular pupils because their eyes must be able to catch every

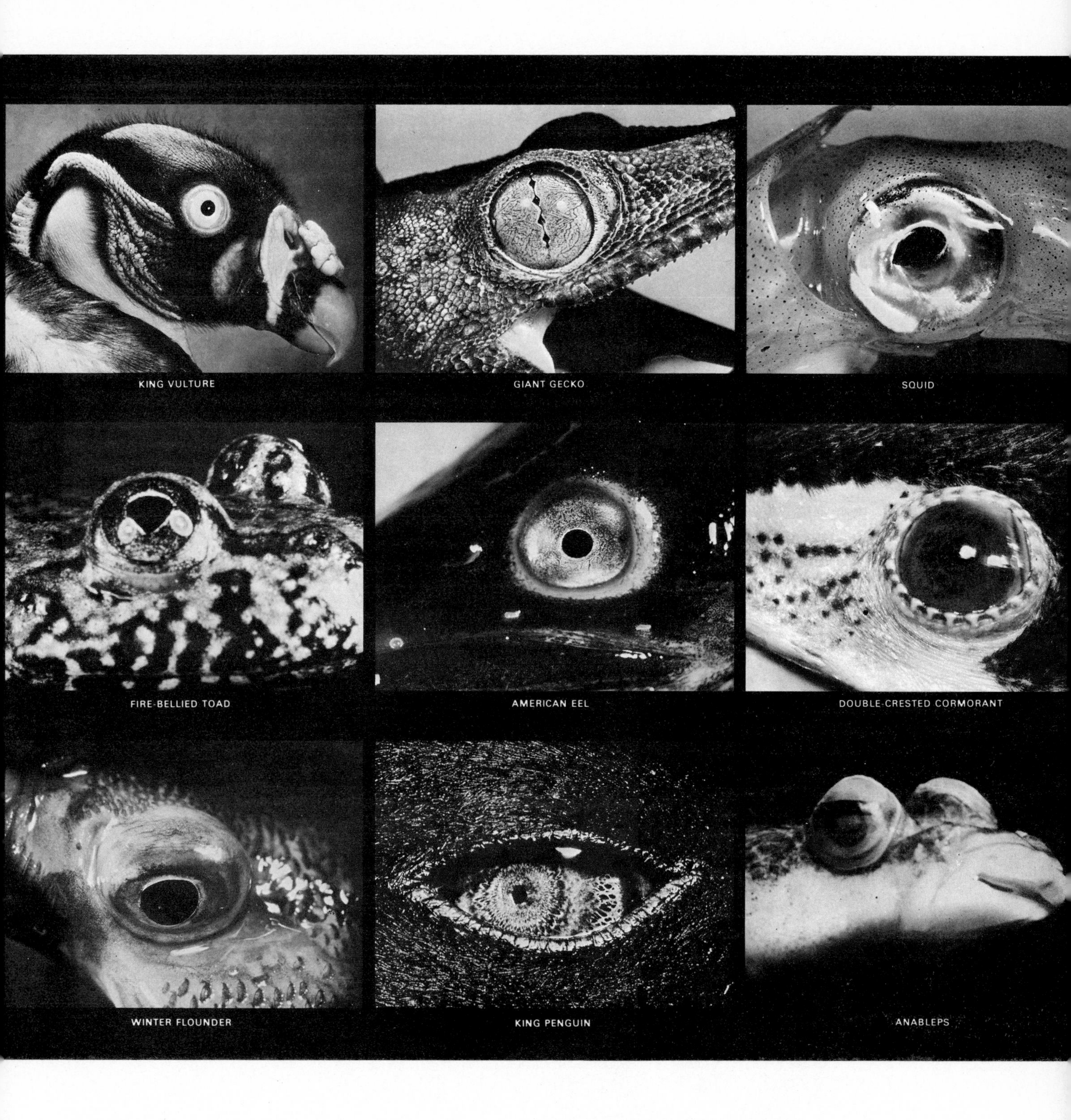

KING VULTURE | GIANT GECKO | SQUID

FIRE-BELLIED TOAD | AMERICAN EEL | DOUBLE-CRESTED CORMORANT

WINTER FLOUNDER | KING PENGUIN | ANABLEPS

stray glimmer of light. But animals like the cat, which hunts both night and day, have made special adaptations to allow them to see clearly in both dim and intense light. The cat's pupil is not round but oval-shaped. At night the oval opens wide, but in strong light it closes to a tight slit. Similarly, the gecko—a lizard which feeds at night—shuts its pupil in daylight but leaves four tiny diamond-shaped holes to admit light.

The green whip snake has an odd pupil shaped like a keyhole, allowing it a sweeping view forward through a horizontal slit and a more direct view to the side through the round portion. Among sea dwellers, the skate has a fringed awning to protect its eyes from strong sunlight. But the oddest adaptation of all belongs to a tropical fish, the *Anableps*, which swims along the surface with its eyes half in and half out of the water. Each eye has two pupils, one for looking upward into the air and the other for gazing down into the water.

Eyes in Strange Places

Many marine creatures can see in all directions at once. Most fishes have eyes placed at opposite sides of their heads, permitting sight through a full sweep of 360°. Other creatures, like the fiddler crab *(right, top)*, have eyes on stalks, which can be moved about to extend their visual horizons.

The queen conch *(right, bottom)*, a large, seagoing snail, has its eyes at the ends of two long tentacles. The more familiar land snail also has two hornlike tentacles which are somewhat light-sensitive and supplement the eyes at the base of its tentacles.

The way fishes' eyes are placed—pointing up, down or sideways—depends on environment. The flounder is an unusual case, however. It starts life swimming upright in the ordinary way, with an eye on either side of its head. But as the flounder grows, its body becomes round and flat, and it swims along the bottom on what formerly was its side. At the same time, one eye migrates to the other side of the head, so that the full-grown flounder has two upward-looking eyes.

Years of selective breeding produced the bulging, heaven-facing eyes of these two Japanese goldfish, hence their name, "celestial."

A FIDDLER CRAB'S ROVING EYES
Compound eyes on movable stalks give this fiddler crab a sweeping 360° visual horizon. When buried in the sand for protection, it can raise its eyes like periscopes, retracting them at the first signs of danger. Though less acute then human eyes in forming images, the fiddler crab's eyes are so sensitive to motion they can discern the slow movement of the sun across the sky.

EYES ON TENTACLES
Eyes at the tips of two tentacles peer out from under the curving shell of a queen conch. Each eye has its own lens and a rich concentration of light-sensitive cells to help the conch in its search for food along the dimly lit ocean bottom.

Lids and Lashes for Protection

Any sudden movement in front of a human eye causes it to blink. The single eyelid snaps shut in a swift reflex action to protect the eye. In many other types of animals the eye's protective system is far more elaborate. Some creatures—including most birds—possess three eyelids to help guard their eyes against dust, sand and twigs, as well as to carry cleansing tears across the eye surface. The third eyelid is a semitransparent tissue—the nictitating membrane—that flicks across the eye from the inside to the outside corner. Birds seldom close their upper and lower lids except in sleep, but use their nictitating membranes to blink. Tiny feathers on the inside surfaces of the membrane act as miniature brushes to "dust" the eyes. In ducks and some other waterfowl, the third lid serves another purpose. It houses a clear, gogglelike lens which improves the ability of the eye to focus underwater while searching for food, a task for which these birds' normal vision, adapted for flying, is too farsighted.

Snakes and most fishes have no lids at all; the eyes of both are protected by a tough, glassy coating. When a snake sheds its skin, it sheds the coating too. In fishes, the coating is permanent and the water constantly washes it clean.

Eyelashes of different kinds also protect the eye, shading it from glare and filtering out dust. Long, thin feathers act as lashes for birds; similarly, rows of scales circle the lids of lizards. Desert animals, which must protect their eyes from the whirling fury of sandstorms, often grow unusually long lashes. A camel's lashes may measure as much as four inches.

CAMOUFLAGING AN EYE
Two fleshy upper lids project like visors of a helmet from the brow of the South American Wied's frog *(top)*. When menaced, it partially closes the lids *(bottom)* to hide its eyes' normally bright sparkle—an easy giveaway for a hungry crocodile or heron. Like most frogs, it uses only a translucent lower lid for normal blinking, but shuts both its lids when asleep.

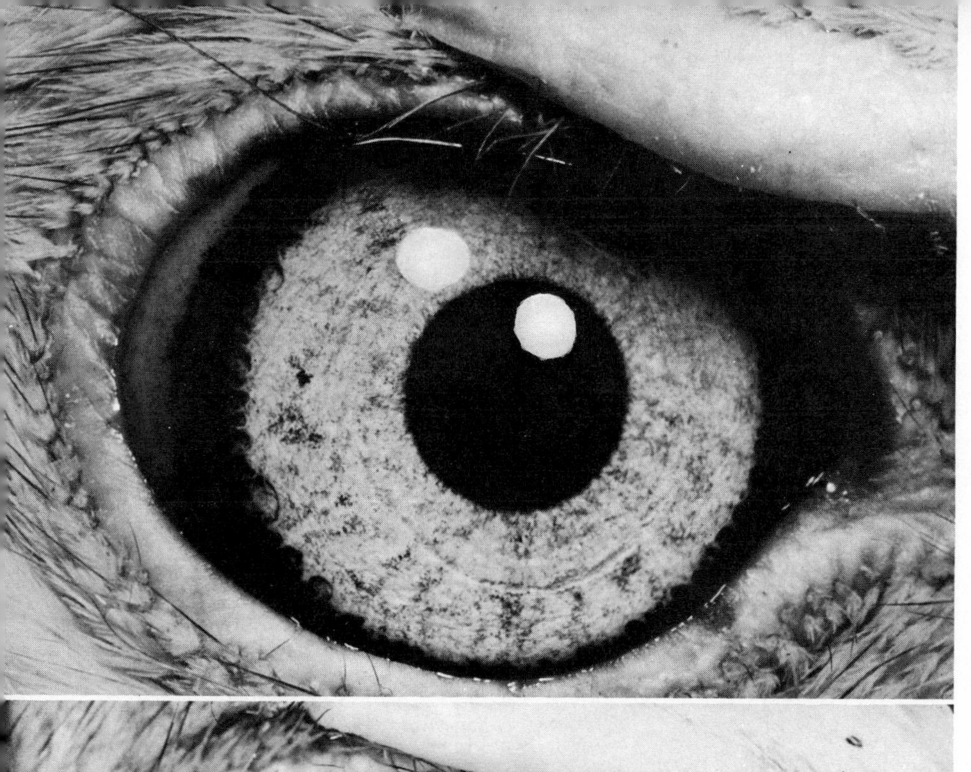

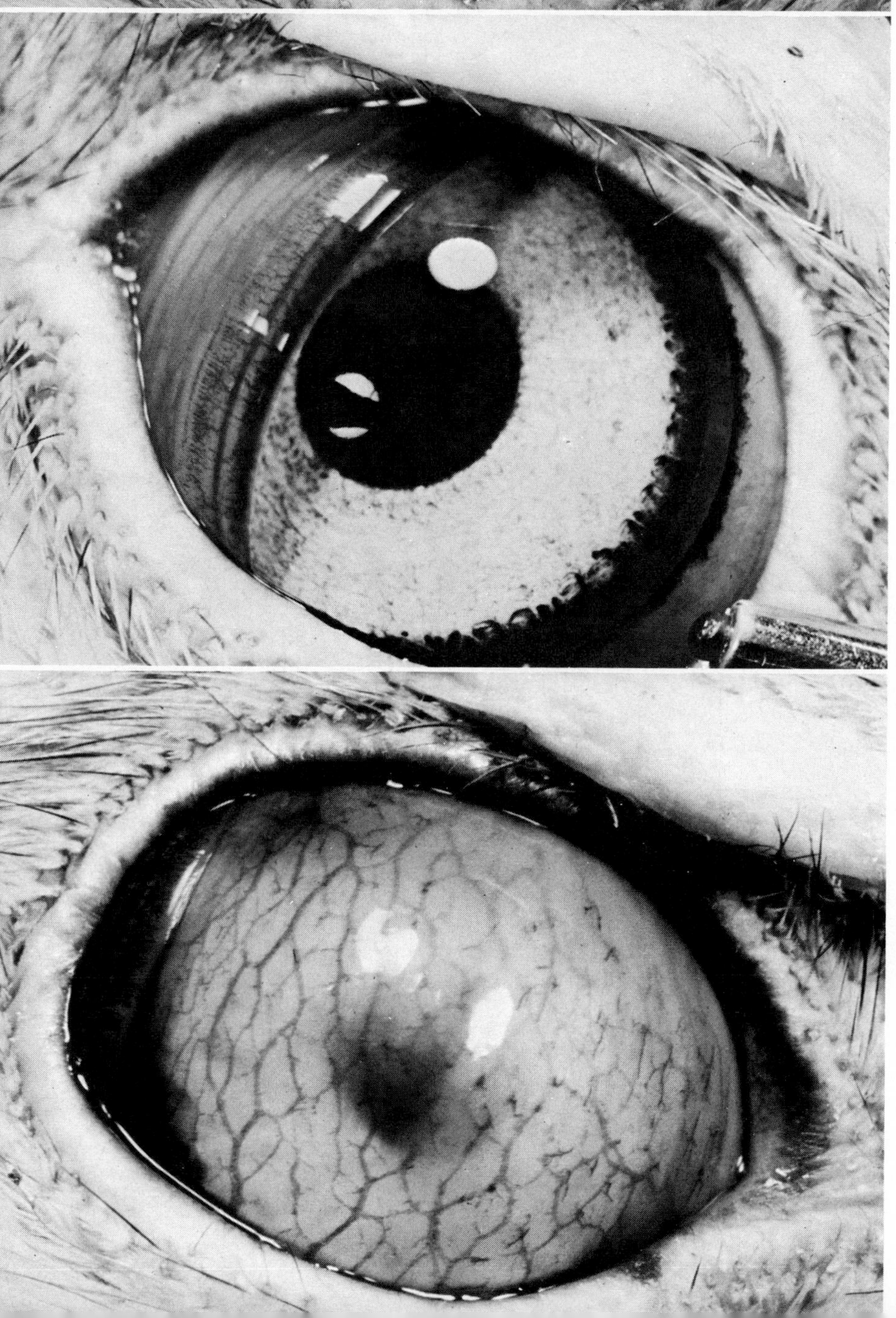

THE WINK OF AN EAGLE EYE

These sequence photographs, taken 1/50 of a second apart, catch the nictitating membrane of a bald eagle as the huge bird blinks its left eye. The membrane can be seen as a small crescent at the inside corner *(top, left)*, which then sweeps outward until it covers the entire eye *(bottom)*. A bony hood, seen at the upper right in each photo, provides additional protection.

A LIZARD'S SCALY LASHES

An orderly row of projecting scales serves as eyelashes for the iguana, a large but harmless desert lizard common to the southwestern United States. Unlike snakes, lizards have eyelids; when blinking, they raise their lower lids instead of lowering the uppers, as humans do.

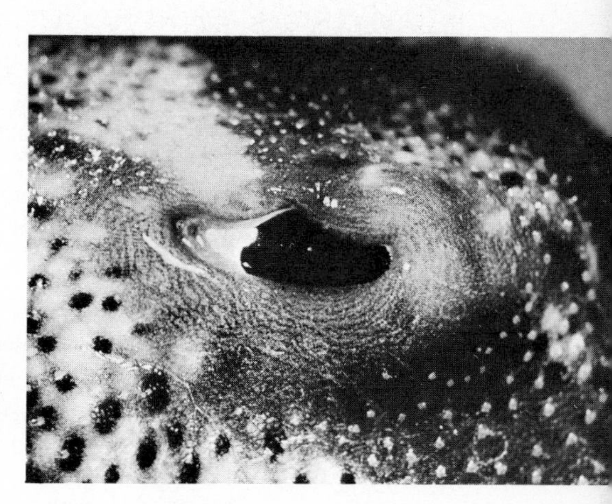

A FISH'S SIMULATED LID

Although most marine creatures have no eyelids, the pufferfish can manufacture a set when alarmed, as shown here. Sensing danger, the puffer blows itself up with water. The muscles circling the eye contract, forming lidlike pouches which reduce the opening to a protective slit.

The Eyes of the Night Creatures

A CONTRAST IN EYES
A tiny slit in a mole rat's furry hide *(top)* shows the position of its seldom-used eye. A rodent that has lived underground for millions of years, the mole rat is able to do little more than tell light from dark. But the flying squirrel *(below)*, whose head otherwise resembles the mole rat's, uses eyes that take up most of its skull to see as it leaps from branch to branch in pitch-darkness.

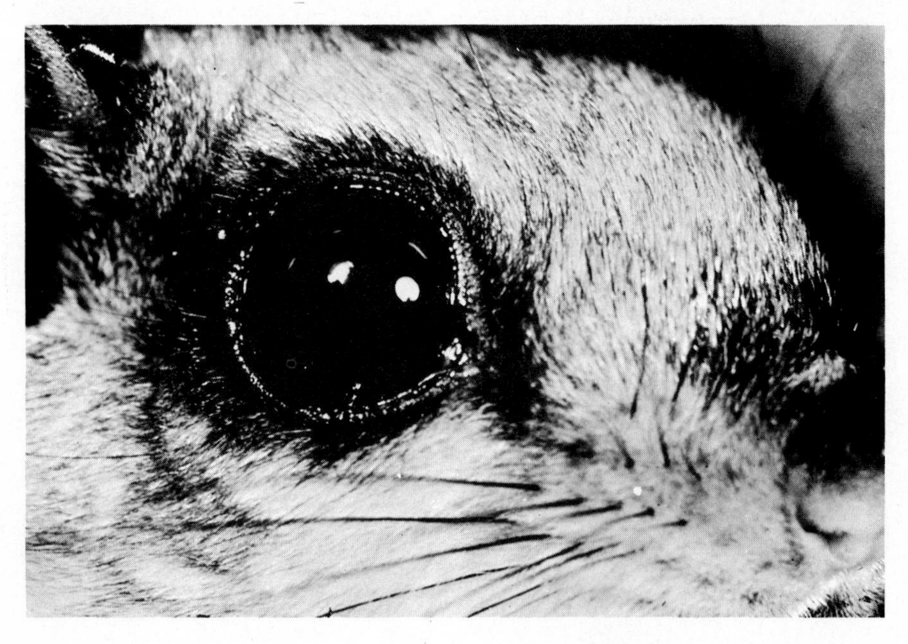

Animals that must live in darkness—in the gloom of caves, underground burrows and the night world—have special sight problems. Over millennia of evolution, they have been solved either by the development of oversized eyes or by the sharpening of other senses to supplement weak, ineffective eyes.

The night-hunting owl has eyes so large they cannot turn in their sockets. To follow the path of a scurrying field mouse, the owl swivels its head, and can twist it around to look directly backwards. Certain owls have eyes which are so sensitive that they can detect shapes in light many times dimmer than the minimum required by human eyes.

There are other adaptations that help nocturnal animals to see in the dark. A cat's eyes glow in the beam of approaching headlights because a mirrorlike lining at the rear of each eye reflects the light forward again, giving the receptors in the cat's eye a second chance to register each particle of light. The cat also has an especially large number of cells sensitive to dim light, although it cannot distinguish colors.

Moles, bats and shrews, which live in almost complete darkness, have eyes which have degenerated to such an extent that they are almost sightless. The mole rat *(left, above)* is virtually blind; its two rudimentary eyes, no bigger than pinheads, detect only shades of light and dark, and are useful mainly as a danger signal when its burrow is broken into from above.

THE BUG-EYED TARSIER
The tarsier, a sharp-sighted cousin of the monkey, has the largest eyes—in proportion to its head—of any known mammal. Shown here at twice its actual size, the tarsier sleeps in hollow tree trunks during the day, emerging at night to search for insects and lizards to eat.

2

The Science of Light

Rays of early morning light, traveling in straight lines from the sun to the forest floor, would streak by unseen except for the phenomenon of reflection. They become visible only when they are bounced by mist particles toward a viewer's eye.

THE EYE RESPONDS TO LIGHT. Every object viewed is seen with light—either the light emitted by the object or light that is reflected from it. But what is light—that mysterious glowing stuff that gushes forth in infinite color and variety from the sun, from light bulbs, from candles, fireflies and fireworks? The question has troubled man for centuries.

The Greeks pondered it and arrived at several conclusions. The Pythagorean school assumed that every visible object emits a steady stream of particles. Aristotle, on the other hand, concluded that light travels in something like waves.

Even though these ideas were gradually modified as man began to study light with more sophisticated equipment some 20 centuries later, the essence of the dispute established by the Greeks remained. One point of view held that light is wavelike in nature, that it is energy gliding through space the way ripples spread across the surface of a still pond. Another faction argued that light must be a flight of particles—like drops of water shooting in a stream from a nozzle. At times, one view prevailed; at times, the other. Only in the first half of the 20th Century was something like a comprehensive answer found. And oddly enough, both theories turned out to be right.

To identify anything—solid, liquid, gas or pure energy—scientists study its properties. Using this approach, the ancient Greeks discovered that light travels in straight lines. The second important discovery about light was made by Hero of Alexandria. Experimenting with mirrors, Hero noticed that any beam of light that was angled in toward a mirror would bounce off again at an equal angle. This made possible the following fundamental rule: the angle of incidence (or striking) and the angle of reflection (bouncing off) are always equal. Although many thinkers continued to reflect on the nature of light, progress was slow until early in the 17th Century.

For centuries people had been noticing another odd but obvious fact: a straight pole stuck in the water at an angle no longer appears straight to an observer. The underwater part seems to slant off in a different direction. In 1621 a Dutch mathematician named Willebrord Snell finally explained this phenomenon. A ray leaving one transparent medium and entering another, he said, is usually split at the surface. One part is reflected, in keeping with Hero's rule. The other part continues into the second medium. The reason that the stick appears to bend on entry into the second medium is that the light rays bringing its image to the eyes are suddenly bent at that point.

Well, if light rays are bent when they enter the water, does this not dispose of the Greeks' old idea that light always travels in straight lines? Not at all, said Snell. All it indicates is that light may be deflected somewhat if it enters a new medium. The light was traveling in a straight line through the air; when it reached the water it changed direction, but continued in a different, deflected straight line under the water. Snell tried to measure this deflection in various transparent substances such as air, glass and water. He found that each one varied in the amount that it could bend light. Whereupon he gave a name to the bending itself—refraction. It took him a long time to work out the principle, because it seemed terribly contrary and slippery until he also discovered something else: the angle of incidence of the light also had something to do with the amount of refraction. For example, a ray of light striking water vertically will not bend at all. But if it enters at a slight slant it will bend a little; at a greater slant it will bend a lot. Later researchers were able to give numerical values—called refractive indexes—for the various bending powers of all transparent substances. What Snell never discovered is *why* light bends.

A formula for bending light

It remained for another Dutchman, Christian Huygens, to suggest an answer. In 1678 he worked out the mathematical formula for Snell's observations and theorized that the refractive index of any material is determined by the speed with which light travels through it. He visualized light as a wavelike phenomenon. If this were true, he calculated, then the greater the refractive index, the more slowly the light would travel through the medium—another basic discovery whose truth still stands up.

With the principle of refraction in hand, it became possible for man to understand, and improve, the relatively crude optical instruments he had been using—the telescope, for example. The first telescope had been invented around 1600, and credit usually goes to the Dutch lens grinder, Hans Lippershey. Although the instrument was developed further by Galileo and others, a full understanding of its principles had to wait until Snell, Huygens and others had worked out the theory.

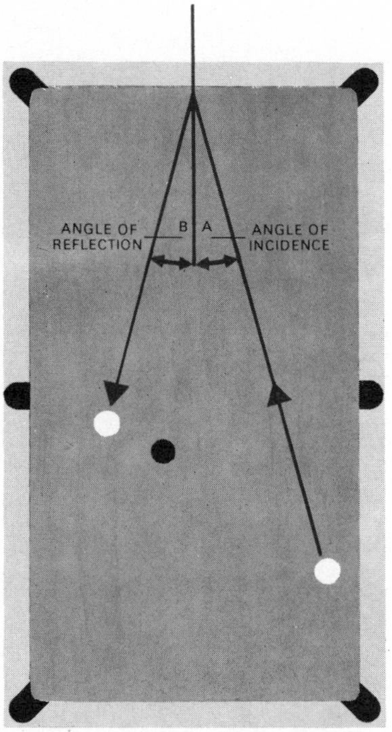

Any lens—or any combination of lenses, as in a telescope—works on precisely the same principle that makes a stick appear bent when it enters the water at a slant: light bends as it goes from one medium to another. The difference is that optical instruments usually contain lenses with curved surfaces. If the lens is convex (thin edges, thick middle), parallel rays of light reaching the lens at different angles are bent into a pattern of converging rays and focused on a single spot. Hence the heating ability of a burning glass. Conversely, if the lens is concave (thick edges curving in to a thin center), the rays are spread.

Visualize a beam of light traveling from a small electric bulb through the center of a convex lens to a screen. At the center of the lens, the rays strike the glass at a 90° angle. Head on, at 90°, there is no refraction, and the beam passes through the lens in a straight line.

But the light bulb, of course, is emitting rays that hit all over the lens, as well as in its exact center. One of these, for example, strikes the lens a small distance from the center. Since the lens at this point has begun to curve away from the light bulb, the beam hits it at a slight angle. The ray is refracted, or bent. Still other rays leaving the light source hit the lens at other points on its surface. And the greater the distance from the center at which they strike, the more acute is the angle they form with the lens surface, and the greater the angle of refraction. In a well-

ANGLE OF REFLECTION B A ANGLE OF INCIDENCE

THE REFLECTION OF LIGHT obeys the same fundamental law of mechanics—the angle of incidence is equal to the angle of reflection—that governs other kinds of bouncing. Its operation is easy to see on a pool table: the angle at which the cue ball on the right strikes the elastic cushion of the table will be equal to the angle at which the ball bounces off. Therefore, to hit the white ball on the left, the player must select the spot on the rail where angles A and B will be equal.

designed lens, the curvature is arranged so that all rays originating from a single source of light on one side of the lens are regathered—or focused —at a single point in space on the other side.

In practice, of course, a light source is not a point, but an object with physical dimensions. Every point on its surface acts as did the points in the example. All the rays from a point at the top of the bulb, for example, are forced to converge at a single point in space on the other side. Similarly, all light rays from points at the bottom of the bulb are focused to reform *their* original image. The result is that the total image of the light bulb is re-created on a screen.

There is one odd quirk worth noting in the law of refraction. Huygens' mathematics showed back in the 17th Century that if light starts from a substance with a high refractive index to one with a low index—glass to air, for example—and if it strikes the surface between them at a very glancing angle, it is bent so much that none escapes and all is reflected. This phenomenon is called total internal reflection, and is best illustrated by certain rods of glass fibers. When light enters the end of such a rod, it does not shine out through the sides of the rod, but is reflected back to the inside. This internal reflection continues again and again, zigzagging down the length of the rod until it gets to the other end. With precise engineering, rods can be made so that they can even carry light around corners. Medical scientists are particularly interested in this phenomenon, since it is beginning to provide them with a way of lighting up and looking inside parts of the body that otherwise could not be examined.

One final, and very important, point about refraction: the amount that light bends will depend not only on the substance it is passing through but also on the color of the light itself. If two rays, a red and a blue, are beamed at the same angle into a thick piece of glass with parallel faces, they will be affected differently—the blue will be bent more than the red. But none of this was understood until the great English physicist, Sir Isaac Newton, discovered another basic property of light: he found that white light contains colors.

Discovering the spectrum

Newton passed a narrow beam of light through a prism in a dark room, projected the emerging rays on a panel, and got the brilliant display we know as the spectrum—a series of colors starting with red at one end and going on through orange, yellow, green, blue and indigo to violet at the other. Then Newton directed the colored beams through another prism and recombined them, thus getting back to the original white light. This proved that white light is a combination of all colors and that it can be taken apart and reunited at will. Finally, Newton isolated the colors one at a time and demonstrated that nothing could be done to change any of them in any way. The basic nature of light, consequently, was not changed by passing through glass, as had been thought.

By this time, the old argument started by the Greeks as to whether light was a wave or a stream of particles had matured into a full-fledged

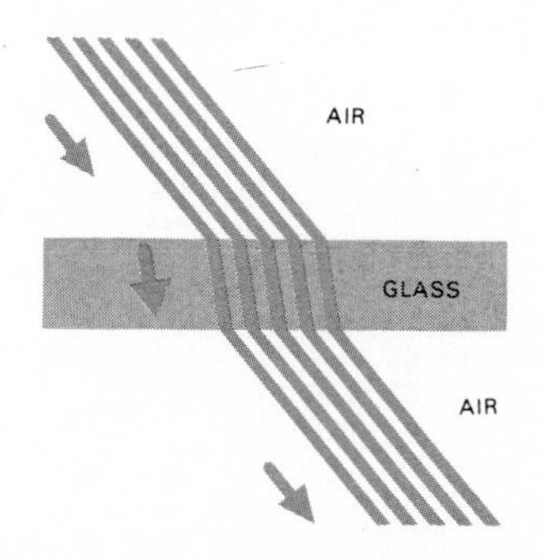

LIGHT IS BENT TWICE as it passes from a less dense to a denser medium and back again, as in the air-glass-air example above. In this behavior, light resembles the action of wheels meeting a patch of sand on an otherwise hard road *(below)*. As they approach the sand at an angle, one wheel hits the patch first. The sand slows it down, but the other wheel, which is still on the hard surface, keeps moving and swings the axle onto a new angle. Now both wheels are in the sand, moving at the same speed, and the new course is held. But the first wheel to enter the sand is the first out; it begins moving faster than the other. The action on entering is now reversed, and the axle reverts to its original angle.

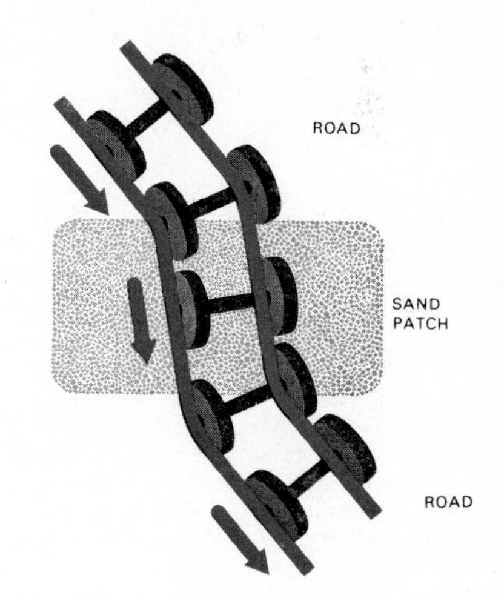

verbal war, with scientists sharply divided. Newton himself, while somewhat undecided, tended to visualize light as a shower of particles shot from a luminous object, with each particle traveling in a straight line until it was refracted, absorbed, reflected, or somehow acted upon. While there was some evidence that light could be a wave—energy transmitted like a series of ripples spreading from a pebble dropped into a pond—it seemed more likely that it was made up of fast-moving particles.

The battle over the nature of light

Newton had serious qualms about his position, but his followers had none. So powerful was his reputation that for the next hundred years his corpuscular theory held sway—despite vociferous protests that there was indeed a way of settling the argument. Why not, it was said, go back to Huygens' theory of refraction? According to Huygens, who believed in the wave theory, the velocity of light in any substance was inversely proportional to its refractive index; i.e., the more light was slowed down, the more it would be bent. But if light were made of streams of particles, the reverse would be true. Light entering a denser medium would be attracted by the molecules and therefore would speed up. The solution was to measure the speed of light in air and then in glass. If it was faster in air it was a wave; if it was faster in glass, it was a stream of particles. But the argument continued—it would be 150 years before the speed of light could be measured accurately enough to prove that Huygens was right. With the devices available at the time, light seemed to move at a constant speed, no matter what medium it was passing through.

Meanwhile, despite Newton's prestige, not all scientists agreed with his conclusions. Huygens argued that if light were corpuscular, it could be likened to a flight of arrows. And if two flights of arrows crossed, some would collide with one another. When two beams of light crossed, though, they appeared not to affect each other. Conclusion: no corpuscles.

However, the corpuscular theory remained supreme until a series of discoveries in the early 19th Century. The basis for these developments, though not recognized at the time, was laid back in Newton's day by an Italian named Francesco Grimaldi and by Newton himself.

Grimaldi directed a beam of light through a narrow slit and found that he could not keep the beam from spreading on the other side. He also found that there was no such thing as a truly sharp shadow. Large light sources like lamps obviously made shadows with fuzzy edges because the light was originating over a wide area. But even the tiniest light made a fuzzy shadow, as a look through a magnifying glass proved. All along the shadow line the light dropped off gradually, not sharply. Also, just inside the shadow there was a bright line. Neither Grimaldi

THE SHIMMERING MIRAGE *(below, colored drawing),* often seen in the distance during hot weather, is the result of refraction. Some of the light rays *(black lines)* reflected from objects like the sky and trees are bent when they leave the high-density cooler air and enter the lower density of warmer air. Because the viewer is accustomed to light's traveling in a straight line, he interprets these bent rays as coming from another source *(colored lines).* Thus he receives an inverted image in which the blue sky looks like a lake that is reflecting the tree. Some other rays from the sky and tree which do not penetrate the thin band of warmer air come directly to the viewer's eyes, and therefore he sees the original scene as well.

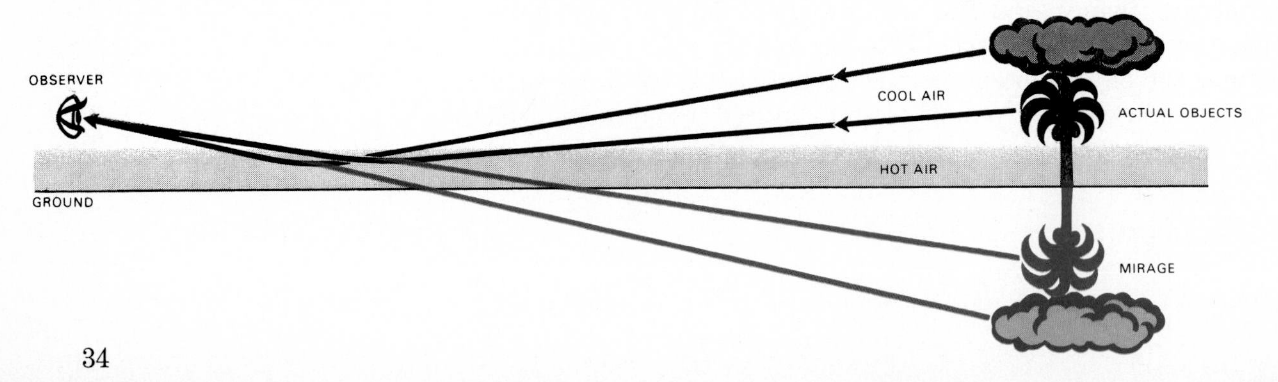

nor anybody else could explain these phenomena, but being a conscientious scientist he did give them a name—diffraction.

Even stranger things were noticed by Newton. About 1665 he began experimenting to find out why soap bubbles, made from a colorless liquid, displayed brilliant dancing colors on their surfaces. Reasoning that this might be related to the closeness of the inner and outer surfaces of the bubble, he placed a very thin convex lens on a flat piece of glass. The result astonished him. Around the center contact point, he saw a succession of colored rings: black, faint blue, strong white, orange, red, dark purple, blue, green, bright yellow, and so on. This was no ordinary spectrum; the colors were wildly mixed up according to some strange logic of their own. But this was not all. If he lit the glass with a pure red light he got alternating red and black rings; with blue light the rings were black and blue. The spacing between them depended on color; blue rings were closer together than red ones. These spectacular circles came to be known as "Newton's rings," and they puzzled everyone until 75 years after their discoverer's death, when Thomas Young put his mind to them. A physician-turned-physicist, Young favored the wave theory of light, and reasoned that if light did travel like ripples on water, then there would be some kind of interaction where two ripples met. If the two were in step, they should combine to make a larger ripple. If they were out of step, so that the trough of one coincided with the crest of the other, two ripples of the same size should cancel, and there would be no ripples at all.

Young set up an ingenious experiment to test this hypothesis. He knew that if a single source of one-color light were directed toward an opaque sheet in which two small slits had been cut, the light coming out the other side and hitting a screen would spread, as shown by Grimaldi's diffraction experiment. If the slits were fairly close together, then the spreading beams of light should overlap on the screen.

Waves in and out of step

Now, Young theorized, if light were composed of waves, a wave from the source would reach the two slits, equidistant from the light, at the same time. The slits would divide the original wave into two new waves perfectly in step with each other. If they traveled to a single point on the screen exactly midway between the slits, they should reach *that* point perfectly in step. The resultant waves then should be bigger than either wave alone, creating a bright line halfway in the overlap on the screen.

But a point at either side of this spot of maximum brightness would no longer be equidistant from the two slits. The wave from the closer slit would follow a shorter path than the wave from the far slit, and consequently, one wave should arrive slightly before the other. At some

THE TWO BASIC LENS SHAPES differ in the ways they refract light. The convex lens *(below, left)* bends the light rays *(black and colored lines)* inward and creates an inverted image on the other side of the lens.
The concave lens *(below, right)* has an opposite effect on the rays, diverging them so that they cannot actually meet to create an image. However, when some of these diverging rays enter the eye, they seem to produce an image. The refracted rays are perceived as if they had traveled in straight lines *(dotted lines in drawing)*, and thus the eye sees an image closer to the lens and smaller than the object.

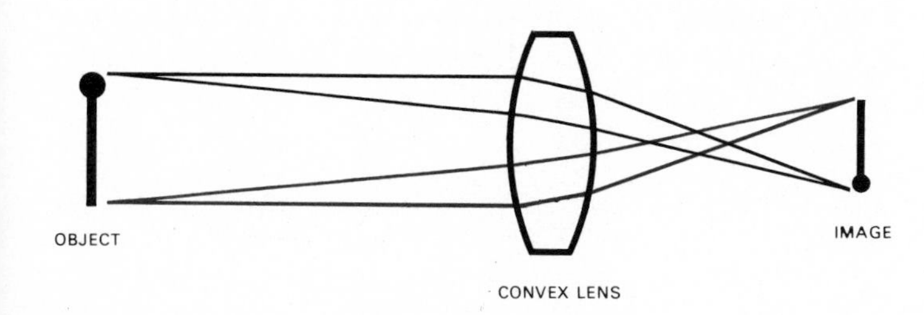

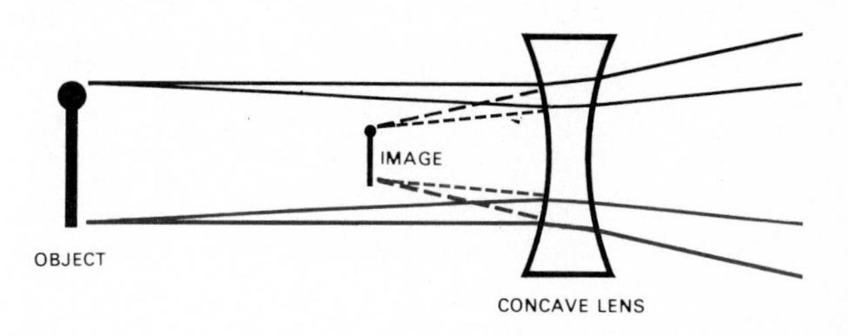

point on the screen, therefore, the lengths of the different paths would be such that one wave would be completely out of step with the other, so that a crest of one would coincide with a trough of the other. There, the waves should cancel each other and the result should be darkness.

The experiment was spectacularly successful. What Young observed on the screen was a series of light and dark lines—now called an interference pattern—caused by the alternate cancellation and reinforcement of the waves arriving at different times.

Young's success was a powerful argument in favor of the wave theory. It also focused attention on the behavior and shape of waves, and makes it appropriate at this point to examine some of the properties of light waves—and see how they are measured.

In speaking of light, wavelength and frequency are simply alternate ways of expressing the same physical fact. Returning to the example of a pool of still water, let us suppose that ripples are created and start to move outward across the water. At any given point on the water before the first ripple reaches it, the surface is flat. Then the surface gradually rises to build up the front edge of the arriving ripple. As the moving ripple crests, the water rises higher and higher to a peak. Then, as the ripple passes, the peak will subside and the next ripple comes along. A wavelength is the distance between the crests of two ripples. Frequency is the number of such ripples that pass a certain point in a second. There is, of course, a direct relationship between velocity and the wavelength and frequency of the ripples. The formula is simple: wavelength times frequency equals velocity. With light, velocity in any given medium is constant.

Obviously, then, the more waves that are packed into a single second, the less distance any one of them will have time to travel; and therefore, the shorter their wavelengths will be. This explains the relationship of wavelength and frequency: if the frequency is doubled, the wavelength is cut in half, and vice versa.

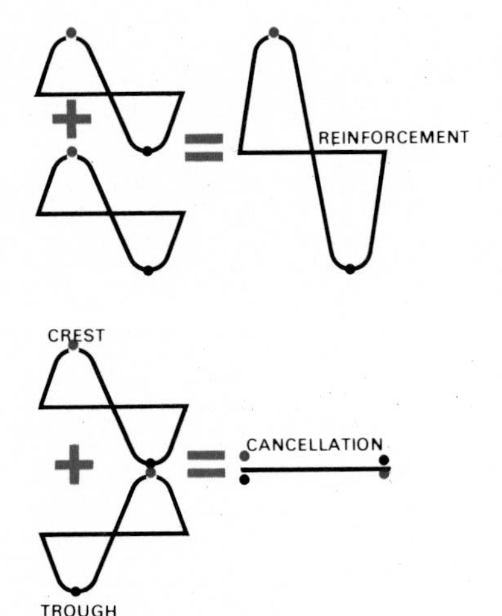

HOW WATER WAVES REACT on one another gives a clue about the behavior of light waves. When, for example, two waves of water meet crest to crest *(colored dots in top illustration)* or trough to trough *(black dots)*, they reinforce each other, forming a larger wave. However, if they intersect crest to trough *(bottom)*, the two waves cancel each other out—the water is smooth. Thomas Young reasoned that if light traveled in waves, the waves could have the same effect on each other as water waves. His successful experiment to test the wave theory of light is shown on the opposite page.

Solving the mystery of the rings

Inasmuch as waves of various lengths exist, it now begins to be easier to understand that color is simply one way of expressing those differences. Not only did Young's experiments clarify the problems of wavelength and frequency and their relationship to color, but they also explained the phenomenon of Newton's rings and even that of rainbow colors in soap bubbles. In both cases the spectacle results from the fact that there are two reflecting surfaces very close together. In one case it is caused by two touching layers of glass, in the other by the inner and outer surface of the soap bubble itself. In both cases different wavelengths reinforce and cancel each other. The glass, being regular in dimensions, makes regular patterns: concentric rings of bright color (where waves reinforce each other) and darkness (where waves cancel each other). The irregular rainbow effects produced by a soap bubble result from the fact that the wall of the bubble is slightly uneven in thickness.

Young's experiment also made it possible to explain diffraction—and why shadows do not really have sharp edges. To understand this it is necessary to realize that light is propagated in all directions. From a light source such as an electric bulb not only does light radiate out in every direction, but in every direction from every point on the bulb. Obviously there will be millions of tiny interferences between each tiny wavelet and its neighbor. However, the wavelets combine smoothly to produce one progressing wave front for light of any given wavelength and frequency. It is only when such a wave hits a narrow slit in a wall that the tiny components of the wave assert themselves. Each is a source of expanding ripples, and as they crowd through the hole the ones at the edges send their waves not only forward but out to the sides as well. Thus the energy appears to spread as it leaves the hole—almost to turn a corner as it goes through. With some waves spreading farther to the side then others, there cannot be a sharp shadow cast by the edge of the hole.

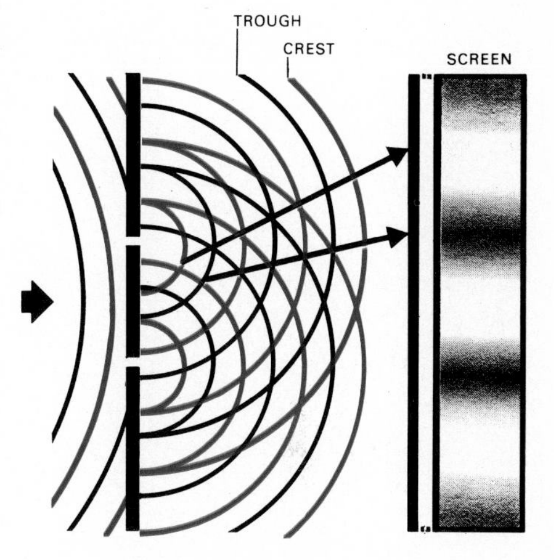

A FAMOUS EXPERIMENT to test the wave theory of light was performed by Thomas Young. He set up a board with two small holes, then beamed light from a single point *(arrow, left)* through the holes and onto a screen *(shown at right, both edge on and head on)*. He reasoned that as the light waves radiated from the two holes, their peaks *(curved colored lines)* and troughs *(curved black lines)* would intersect in a regular pattern. Wherever color crossed color, or black crossed black, it would mean that light from the two holes was in phase and reinforcing itself at that point —an effect that should show up as a bright area on the screen. This is demonstrated in the drawing by the arrow at upper right, which does cross several of the in-phase intersections and points to a bright area on the screen. The lower arrow, however, crosses only black-color intersections, indicating that peaks and troughs are out of phase at these points. This should show up as a dark area on the screen, and the arrow indicates such an area.

More evidence for the wave theory

There remained one aspect of the behavior of light to be cleared up, and this too, when it was understood, further strengthened the wave theory. This was the matter of polarization. Light waves normally vibrate in three dimensions. However, certain transparent materials have a curious effect upon light passing through them; the waves are forced into a two-dimensional form instead of the usual three. This phenomenon was first observed in certain crystals in the 17th Century. The change in the movement of the light waves occurs because of the molecular structure of the substance.

In effect, the structure is somewhat like that of a venetian blind with a great number of tiny slats with a small opening between each of them. Assume that these slats are horizontal. Because of the smallness of the space, light waves entering cannot vibrate vertically; only horizontal movement is possible. However, because of the many slits, the light can pour through almost unimpeded, even though the waves are moving only in one plane.

Now imagine a second venetian blind with the same number of slats and the same-sized openings aligned directly behind those in the first. There is no added obstruction with the light. But if the second blind were mounted on a wheel, partial blocking would occur as soon as the wheel was turned; the slits of the two blinds would no longer be lined up. If the wheel were turned slightly, only a little of the light would be blocked by the slats of the second blind. But the more the wheel is turned, the more light is shut out, until the slats of the second blind are completely vertical. Now no light at all can get through. The light waves, which were forced into only horizontal movement by the first blind, are faced with a blind with only vertical slits.

If the wheel is turned past the vertical, some light begins to get through again, and the amount of light gaining passage continues to increase until the slits are again aligned horizontally.

Thus two crystals with the same peculiar molecular structure can be placed face to face in one position and will transmit light freely. However, if one is turned, light will be diminished until, at one point, no light will pass through the second. It is by this simple principle that polaroid glasses reduce glare. They cut out all random light from bright reflections and admit only rays in one plane.

These insights about polarization assured clear superiority for the wave theory of light. No manipulation of the corpuscular theory had been able to explain either interference or diffraction—now seen to be two different aspects of the same phenomenon.

By the mid-19th Century, investigators had deduced the physical laws governing the behavior of light and established its wavelike character. They had not, however, answered the basic question: what is it? That task was left to the great English theoretical physicist, James Clerk Maxwell. Maxwell identified light as part of a vast, continuous spectrum of electromagnetic radiation. Light is distinguished, of course, by the fact that the eye is sensitive to it.

The connecting link pointed out by Maxwell was that all electromagnetic radiation—including light—travels through a vacuum at precisely the same speed, some 186,000 miles per second. (Later researchers learned of the vast range of the electromagnetic spectrum, from wavelengths miles long on the low-frequency end of the radio range to unbelievably small fractions of a millimeter on the upper, gamma-ray end.) With Maxwell's work came the complete triumph of the wave theory.

By the dawn of the 20th Century, light and optical theory seemed complete and perfect. Wave theory explained virtually every phenomenon that had been observed. The scientific world, consequently, was completely unprepared for a series of dramatic developments that started with the new century.

Chipping electrons with light

As early as 1887, it had been observed that a clean zinc plate exposed to ultraviolet light acquires a positive charge. Philipp Lenard, a German physicist, in 1900 explained this effect. The ultraviolet light was literally knocking electrons out of the zinc. With a loss of these negatively charged particles, the zinc took on a positive charge. Other researchers quickly found that this so-called photoelectric effect was common among metals. Further, the number of electrons ejected per second was proportional to the intensity of light radiation. (The photoelectric effect is most commonly seen today in two applications: the electric eye that opens supermarket doors, and television. Light falling on a highly sensitive photoelectric plate in the TV camera creates an electric current proportional to the brightness of various parts of the scene. This varying current of electrons is re-created as a pattern of light and dark areas on the TV screen to form the picture.)

But there was an odd quirk to this photoelectric phenomenon. Although electrons ejected from the metal had varying energies—as pieces of ice chipped away from a block with an ice pick fly away at different speeds—the *maximum* energy of the escaping electrons was determined not by the intensity of the light, as would be expected from the wave theory, but by its wavelength. A beam of short wavelength, in other words, would eject electrons with high energies. A beam of light of longer wavelength, on the other hand, would produce electrons at lower energies. Intensity of the beam affected the *number* of electrons dislodged per second, but not their maximum energy. Nothing in the theory of light developed so far could explain how this might be so.

A revolution in physics

In 1905, Albert Einstein, applying Max Planck's quantum theory, postulated that the wave theory of light might be incomplete; that light might have some of the characteristics of a particle after all. Einstein worked out a mathematical picture of how an electron in metal could absorb one bit of light energy, which he called a light quantum—later called a photon—and thus have the energy to escape. Further, if the energy of a photon were inversely proportional to wavelength—the shorter the wavelength, the greater the energy—then it would be clear that light of short wavelengths could impart to the ejected electrons the high energies that Lenard had observed.

By 1923, the American physicist Arthur H. Compton had demonstrated that photons have momentum, and consequently mass—strong support for Einstein's theory. X-rays had been investigated, and although it had been shown that they have a wavelike character, the particles also have great penetrating power, allowing them to be used for taking pictures through matter opaque to light. The particlelike nature and high energy of X-rays could be explained by the photon theory. Other experiments followed, showing that when light interacts with matter, many events that take place can be understood only by considering light as separately packaged bits of energy.

These developments were upsetting theoretical physics. The wave theory had been spectacularly successful in explaining a variety of phenomena—interference, diffraction and others—that could not be explained by corpuscular theory. Yet many recently discovered phenomena could be understood only in terms of photons. What was the true answer?

The answer came from a complex physical theory called quantum mechanics, developed by the joint efforts of some of the great men of modern physics: Max Planck, Niels Bohr, Louis de Broglie, Werner Heisenberg, Erwin Schrödinger, Max Born and others. In general, the theory shows how electromagnetic radiation can have both wavelike and particlelike traits. At times, one predominates; at times, the other.

Thus light, that commonplace but mysterious stuff that fills the universe, is only a small visible segment of the electromagnetic spectrum. It is wavelike and particlelike at the same time, these two qualities being complementary aspects of a single reality. And by means of this luminous energy, the beauty of the universe is transmitted to man's eyes.

Rays That Bounce and Bend

Since light is a visual phenomenon, its characteristics are more easily explained with photographs than with words. But in trying to take pictures of light, a peculiar problem presents itself: unless its energy is directed right at the eye or the camera, light is invisible. A man suspended in outer space, with the sun behind him, would see nothing; all would be blackness (save the distant planets and stars) because the energy of the sun would be streaming past him, with nothing to bounce it back to his eye. Standing on the earth's surface, however, he can see trees, houses—even the atmosphere—all made visible by light bouncing off them and back to his eyes. This phenomenon is exploited in some of the photographs that follow. So that the bouncing and bending paths of different-colored beams of light can be traced, the air has been filled with smoke. The smoke particles help to catch the light and reflect it back toward the camera lens. Similar phenomena often occur in nature: a beam of sunlight can be seen slanting through a room because it is glancing off dust particles in the air; the shafts of sunlight that are sometimes seen coming down through gaps in clouds are made visible by particles of haze or moisture present in the atmosphere.

NEW LIGHT ON AN OLD TRICK

Making light travel in circles is actually an ingenious use of total internal reflection. Light rays, when beamed into one end of a glass fiber cable, strike the sides at such a slight angle that, instead of passing outward, they bounce back and ricochet repeatedly until they emerge as a beam at the other end of the cable, here illuminating the scientist's face.

Reflection: Relaying the Image

Although all light can be traced to certain energy sources, like the sun, an electric bulb or a match, most of what actually hits the eye is reflected light—rays that have bounced off various objects and kept right on going. Nearly everything that light strikes reflects a certain amount of its rays, and smooth, shiny surfaces—like the still pool of water at the right—reflect almost as much light as they receive. In fact, it is possible to line a room with mirrors angled in such a way that they will reflect the feeble light of a single candle dozens or even hundreds of times, filling every corner with a brilliance considerably greater than would be possible if the room were covered with black felt, a light-absorbent material which reflects almost nothing.

Light can bounce in many ways, but it always follows a simple rule: the angle of incidence (approach) is equal to the angle of reflection (departure). Despite appearances to the contrary, this rule is being observed by both the flat mirror below, which predictably returns images at equal and opposite angles, and the curved mirror, far right, which sends three identically angled beams leaping outward in three different directions.

IMPACT EQUALS REBOUND

An ordinary flat mirror, a protractor and three beams of light illustrate light's fundamental law: the angle of incidence equals the angle of reflection. Rays of colored light shine down from the left at angles of 40°, 30° and 20°; they bounce off the mirror at those same angles. Pins stuck in the path of each beam cast shadows to show the direction of the beam.

LIGHT ON A CURVED SURFACE

On a curved or irregular surface *(right)*, the rule of light reflection still applies. The blue beam, hitting the parabolic mirror at dead center, is reflected back on itself. But the parallel red and green beams strike the curve at different points. The angles of incidence are different, and so the beams bounce in different directions.

REFLECTIONS FROM WATER

This building is seen as a real object and as a reflection. The second image is created by light angling from the dome to the surface of a reflecting pool, then bouncing at the same angle to the viewer's eye. If the water were rippled, the image would be distorted by irregular reflections.

Refraction: Bending the Light

Light not only bounces off surfaces, it goes through some of them, often slowing down and changing direction in the process. This directional change, or "bending," is known as refraction, and it occurs at the point where light passes from one medium to another of different density. In the air, light travels at 186,000 miles per second; but water, which is denser than air, slows light down by about one fourth. Glass, which is denser yet, slows it down by a third, and diamond still more. However, for any sort of refraction to take place, the light must strike the new medium at an angle, not head on. The size of this angle determines the amount of bending, a phenomenon illustrated in the photograph above with transparent plastic blocks. Entering from the left, the three light beams hit the first block head on and pass through without bending. But they hit the next block at an angle, causing some of their light to be reflected upward. Most of it, however, enters the block where, slowed by the greater density of the plastic, the beams are bent downward—only to resume their original direction and speed as they leave the block. The third block's two concave surfaces spread the beams apart, but the last block acts as a convex lens and refracts them back together so sharply that they actually cross each other at the right.

The refraction of light produces mirages, rainbows and such bizarre optical effects as the distortion of the girl sitting by the pool at extreme right. It makes a thick-walled glass beer mug look fuller than it really is, and makes the sun appear to set several minutes later than it really does. It also makes it possible to remedy the often faulty refraction in the human eye with corrective eyeglasses.

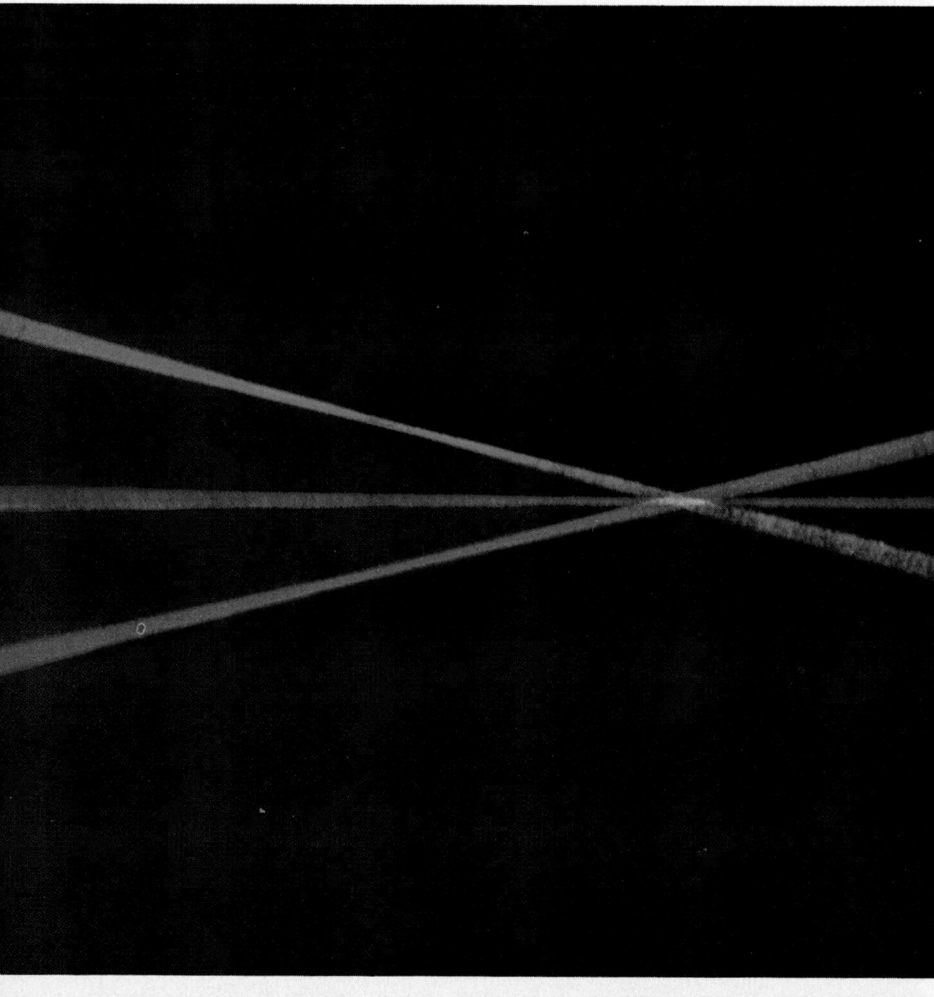

REFRACTION IN ACTION
The glass lens of a camera *(above)* has convex surfaces, like the block of plastic at left. It refracts light waves in the same way, bending them inward so that they come together and eventually cross each other to produce a smaller, upside-down image of the rose at the back of the camera. The same kind of inversion can also be seen at left, where the red ray emerging from the bottom of the lens crosses the green ray, reversing their previous positions.

ANATOMY OF AN ILLUSION
A light beam *(above)* shines into the tank and is reflected off three differently tilted mirrors. Two of the reflected rays are refracted out of the water; the third, hitting the surface at too great an angle, is totally reflected back in. Combinations of refraction and reflection also account for the strange sight *(right)* recorded by an underwater camera: a girl sitting on the edge of a pool and dangling her legs in the water.

Diffraction: Turning a Corner

The trick that light sometimes plays with shadows, giving them bright bands inside their edges, is caused by diffraction—the result of light's traveling in waves.

If you wiggle a stick in water, a series of waves will flow out in all directions. When they encounter an obstacle, like a plank sticking out of the water, the part of the wave that strikes the very edge of the plank sets up a new series of ripples from that point. Some of the ripples will fan out around the edge—in effect, turning the corner.

That is also what light does. When the waves from a distant pinpoint of light strike an opaque object, they bend around the edges, curving both into the shadow and into the path of other waves from the same light source. Waves bending behind the object create a bright line where the shadow would ordinarily begin. But the waves moving in the opposite direction overlap opposing light waves. Where the crests of the waves meet, they tend to reinforce each other and create bright lines. But where crest meets trough they cancel each other, and dark bands result. This overlapping is visible in the picture of a shadow on the opposite page, which has bright edges and distinctive patterns of alternating light and dark bands.

WAVES IN WATER
A stick moved in water sends out ripples in all directions. Until they hit something, they will keep going, diminishing as the friction of the water molecules saps their energy. Light waves, unlike water waves, need no medium; they can travel in a vacuum without ever diminishing.

A STUDY IN DIFFRACTION
This is a laboratory photograph of water ripples hitting a barrier. Their tendency to turn the corner around the edges of the barrier is clearly visible, as is their spreading out after they go through a hole in the center of the barrier. Eventually the various sets of waves run into each other and set up new and complex patterns.

FUZZY EDGES TO A RAZOR BLADE

This photograph of the shadow cast by a razor blade shows the effects of diffraction very clearly. A thin beam of light has spilled through the slit in the center of the blade and turned outward, producing a fringed effect along the edges of the slit. The crisscrosses and circles are the result of interference, as the light waves alternately reinforce and then cancel one another.

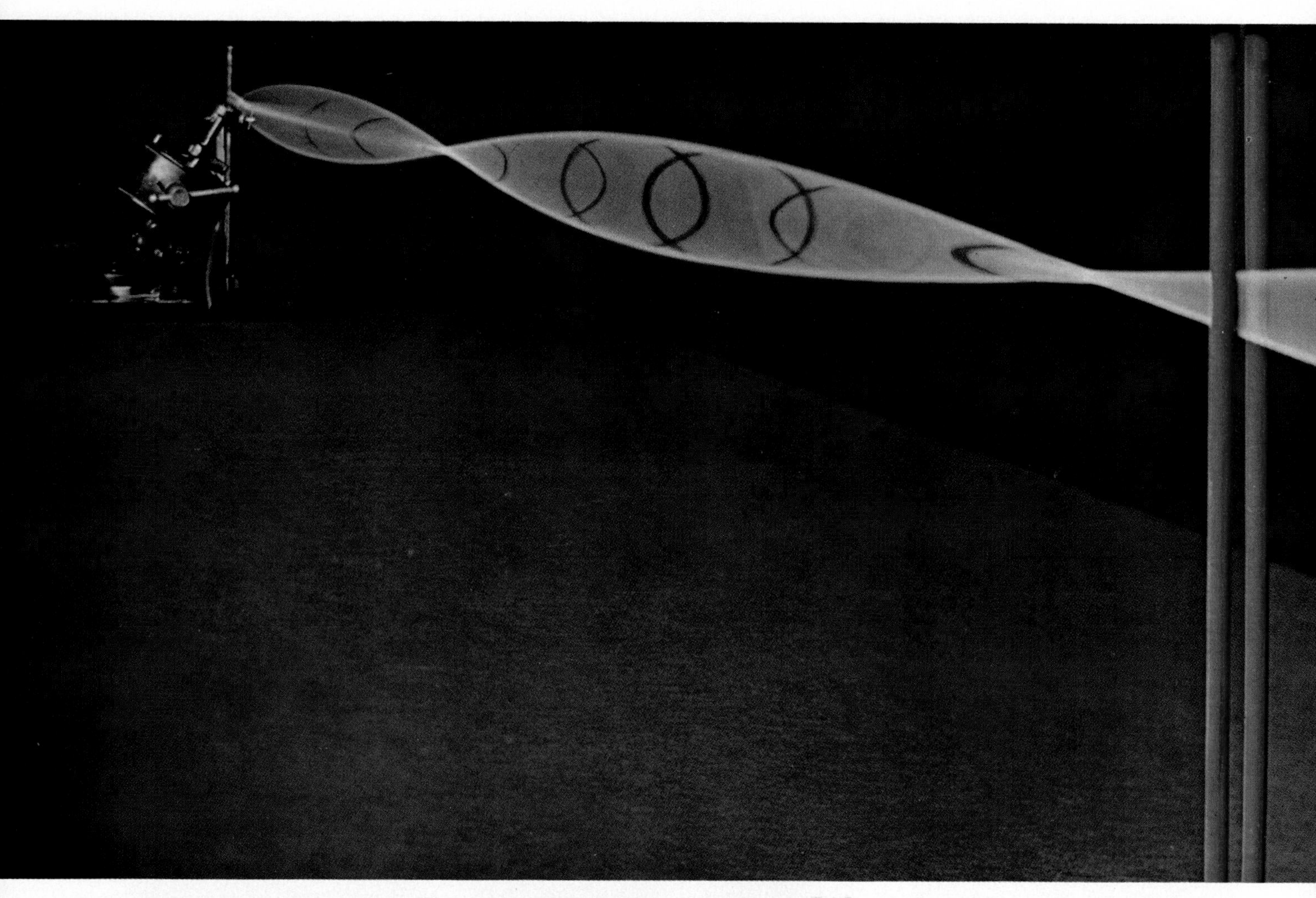

POLARIZING A WAVE
What looks like a ribbon in this picture is actually a time exposure of a string vibrating freely in all directions—just as a traveling light wave does. But when the string passes through a vertical slit, its vibration wave is polarized in a single vertical plane, with all other vibrations absorbed.

FROM GLARE TO GLOOM
This polarizing filter has had four strips cut from it, showing the difference between filtered and unfiltered light. When these strips are positioned at increasing angles to the filter, they block off more and more light until finally *(bottom)* virtually no light gets through the combined filters.

SCREENING UNWANTED LIGHT
The glaring reflection arising from the glossy page at right makes it very difficult to read the print under strong light. But when the same page is viewed through the polarizing lenses of the sunglasses, the troublesome glare is eliminated and the text can be read without difficulty.

When Light Becomes Glare

A motorist driving over a highway, with the sun in front of him, finds himself squinting in order to see better. A bather at the seashore shades his eyes even on overcast days. In both cases their eyes are being hit by about 10 times as much light as they need, a painful amount. Such concentrations of light, called glare, may result simply from intense sunlight, but more often glare is caused by sunlight reflecting off surfaces like water, snow or sand. Instead of diffusing the light in many directions, these surfaces absorb some of it and reflect the rest—especially the waves which vibrate in a horizontal pattern. Scientists have a word for this selective light-filtering process: polarization.

Polarized glare can be virtually eliminated by sunglasses fitted with polarizing lenses. Such lenses contain a tinted plastic filter with tiny crystals that have been "stretched" into a series of lines, like the slats of a picket fence. The annoying horizontal light is blocked by these lines, but enough of the vertical light vibrations get through the filter so that the sunglass wearer can see to drive or even read. However, if a second set of polarizing lenses is superimposed on the first, so that their lines cross at right angles, so much light is blocked that the wearer is virtually blind. Such an arrangement is often used in space capsules to shield Astronauts from the sun's glare during their naps.

Particles of Light

One of the most surprising discoveries about light is that it is made up of tiny particles of packaged energy called photons. If a tremendously magnified beam of light could be imagined, it might look like the picture opposite: a barrage of photons *(blue)* striking a surface and passing on their energy to surface electrons *(orange)*, which then break off and streak away. The liberated electrons, with energy to burn, can be harnessed to produce electricity that can move the needle of a light meter *(below)* or signal a supermarket door to open. This photoelectric effect of light had puzzled scientists for years until Albert Einstein was able to explain it in 1905. Einstein reasoned that light traveled as streams of energy "packets," which are now known as light quanta or photons. A later theory explained that light can be created by electrons changing orbits around an atomic nucleus. The energy they release assumes the form of photons, which combine into beams of light.

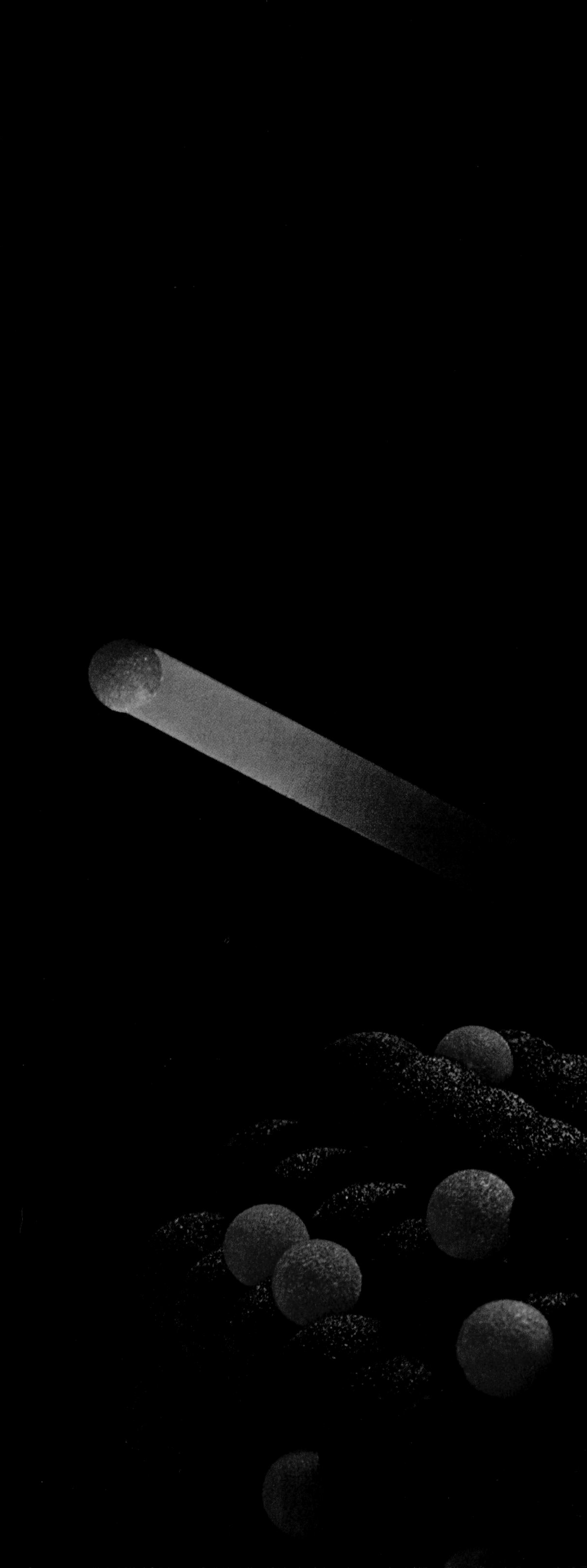

MEASURING LIGHT WITH LIGHT
The photographer's light meter in effect counts photons of light striking it. The more intense the light, the more photons hit a metal plate inside the meter, sending its electrons flying. The total electric charge is calibrated on the meter's scale to indicate variations of light intensity. The circular device then allows the photographer to relate the meter reading to his lens opening and the type of film he is using.

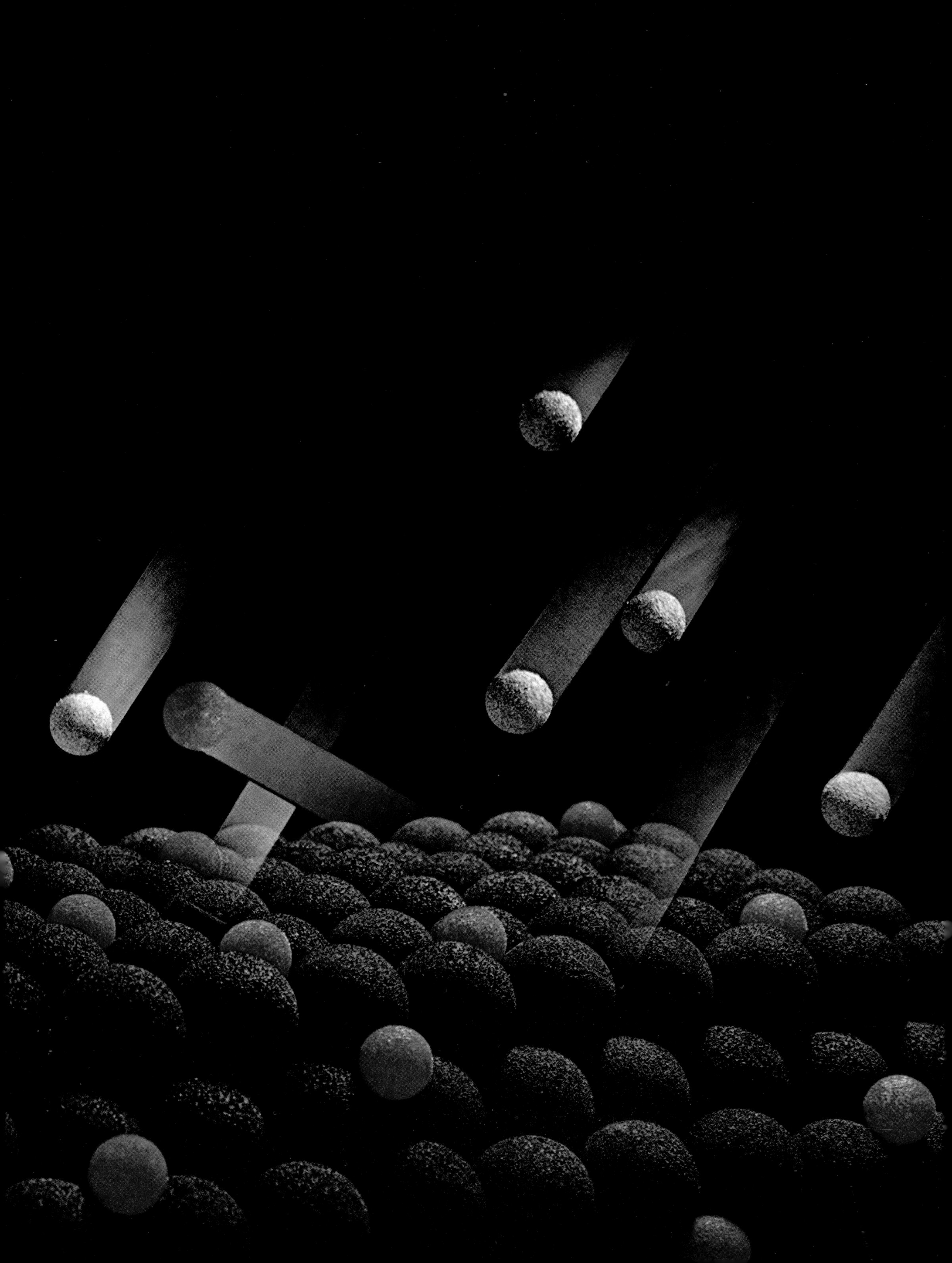

3

The Eye as a Camera

Two wooden eyes were used by the great German physiologist Hermann von Helmholtz to demonstrate eye movement. When the eyes are moved, the attached strings and weights also move, simulating the action of ocular muscles.

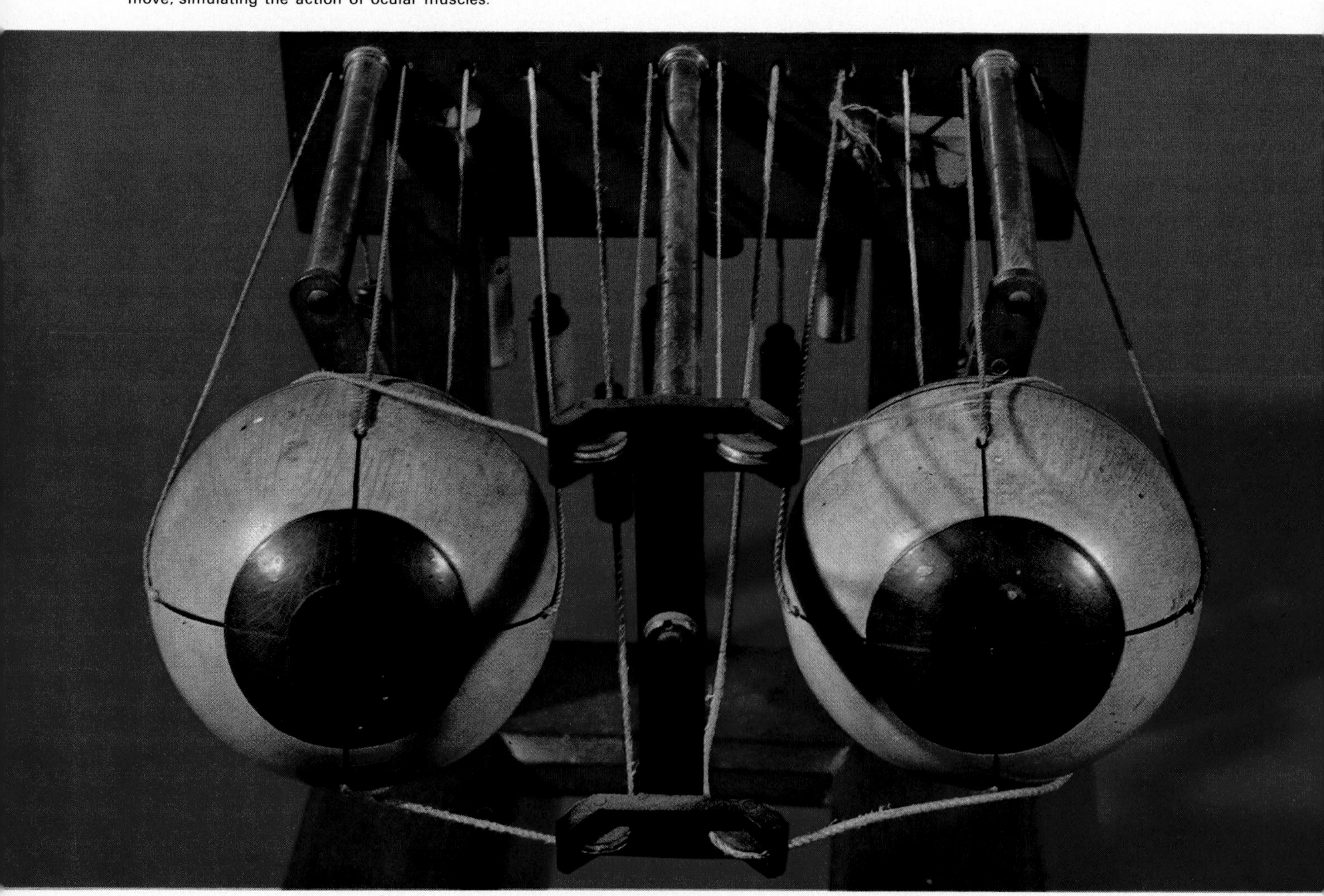

"How does the eye function?" is a question that has fascinated man for thousands of years. Although a number of theories were advanced at various times, the basic fact about the eye—that it is an image-catching device—was not established until about 300 years ago.

Even the ancient Greeks, who had a fairly accurate knowledge of the structure of the eye and could perform delicate surgery on it, did not understand this fundamental point about vision. About 500 B.C., they developed the curious concept that man saw because lightlike rays streamed from his eyes like feelers, touched an object, and thus made it visible. It made sense to the Greeks to assume that since things appeared "out there"—a manuscript held in the hand, a table across the room, a ship on the horizon—the visual process must be taking place "out there." Even the precisely mathematical Euclid accepted the emanation theory. Aristotle did attack the concept by asking a flawlessly logical question—if eyes are the source of light, why are things invisible in darkness?—but his reasoning was ignored. And apparently no one put the concept to a test until the 17th Century, some 2,000 years later.

It was a German Jesuit named Christopher Scheiner who is credited with bringing an end to this misconception about vision in 1625, by clearly demonstrating that light enters the eye and carries with it the image that man sees. His proof was simple and direct. He removed the coating from the back of the eye of a newly slaughtered animal. With the transparent inner wall, or retina, of the animal's eye thus exposed, Father Scheiner was able to look into it from behind, as it were, and see miniature reproductions of objects that were out in front of the eyeball, just as a modern photographer can see objects in the ground-glass viewing screen of a camera.

Today it is universally accepted that the eye is an image-catching device. No matter how greatly the apparatus for seeing may vary from one kind of animal to another, vision is always the same in one fundamental respect: the process begins with light entering the eye and bringing with it the information it has picked up in touching or passing through the objects in its path. These light patterns travel through the various parts of the eye until the image is cast upon the back wall, or retina, of the eye just as a picture is thrown upon film by a camera.

But getting a clear, intact image to the retina is no simple matter. First, the amount of light entering the eye must be controlled. If there is too much, the image will be uncomfortably glaring; if there is too little, it will be indistinct. Next, the image must be focused sharply on the retina, as a subject must be focused on film to make a good picture.

In the human eye, the tasks of controlling and focusing light are performed by a delicately engineered system of devices whose coordination and ability to adapt to various conditions make the most sophisticated camera seem a child's toy by comparison. At the very front of the eye is the cornea, a transparent tissue rising from the opaque white of the eye. The cornea bends light and is, therefore, part of the focusing arrangement. Behind the cornea is a clear fluid called the aqueous humor, which also plays a part in focusing. Next in order is the doughnut-shaped iris with its hole, the pupil, lying almost directly in line with the cornea. The iris governs the amount of light entering the eye by increasing or decreasing the size of the pupil opening. After the light has passed through the cornea, aqueous humor and pupil, it goes through the lens, which does the fine focusing for near or far viewing. Finally, the light proceeds through a jellylike substance known as the vitreous—which maintains the degree of bending set by the lens—and reaches the retina. However, there is one other factor which plays an indirect role in focusing: the muscles that move the eyeball to the left and right, and up and down, enabling man to look directly at what he wants to see.

Controlling the amount of light that enters the eye is done solely by the iris. The iris—from the Greek word for rainbow—is the most distinctive part of the eye; it has the eye's coloring, the blue, brown, gray or green which has inspired generations of lovelorn poets. The iris is a diaphragm made up largely of circular and radiating muscles. These muscles, by contracting or stretching, are able to shrink or enlarge the size of the light-admitting hole, the pupil.

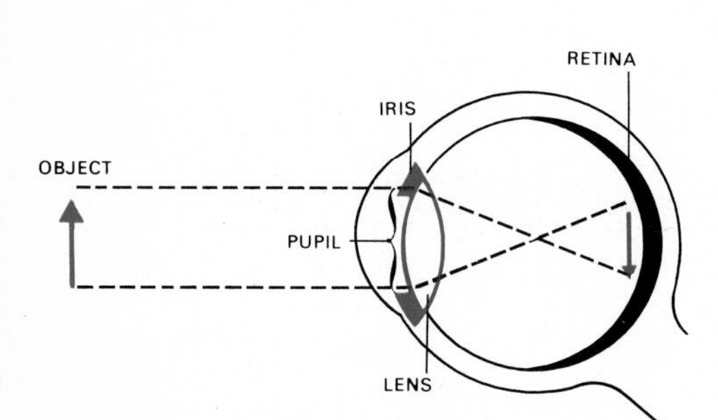

THE EYE AND THE CAMERA are strikingly similar optical instruments. The amount of light entering the eye *(above)* is controlled by the circular iris, whose muscle fibers regulate the opening of a window called the pupil. The cornea and lens focus the inverted image on the retina. The camera *(below)* also has an adjustable iris diaphragm to govern the amount of light entering through the aperture, and a lens for focusing the image on the film. However, the camera's lens must be moved forward or backward for every change of focus; the eye's stationary lens changes its shape to achieve a sharp image.

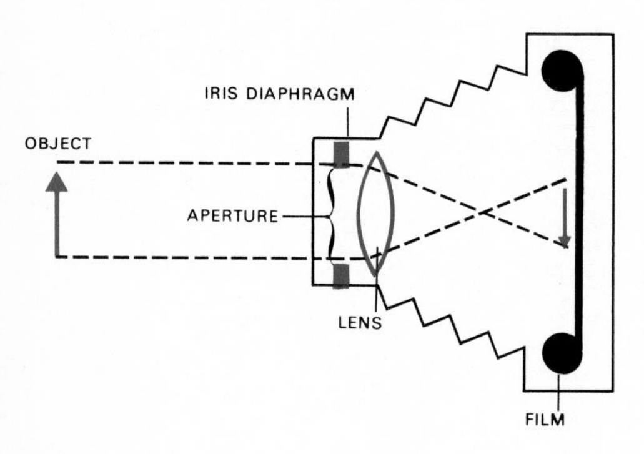

A hole that looks solid

The pupil does not look like a hole. In fact, it appears to be an almost-black solid because behind the opening is the dark interior of the eye. The size of this hole is automatically adjusted to varying degrees of light by nerve signals to the muscles of the iris. In darkness, the opening may be as large as an eraser on a pencil. In bright, glaring sunlight, the pupil may be reduced to about the size of a pinhead. However, the opening is never closed entirely. When the light is painfully bright, the eyelids close automatically. The iris works so efficiently that man is rarely aware of its importance to vision unless he happens to have an eye examination in which the doctor uses special drops to enlarge the pupil artificially. Then everything he looks at seems glary because too much light is being admitted to the eye.

But the amount of light is not the only factor which governs the functioning of the iris; signals from the eye's focusing equipment also affect the size of the pupil. When an individual is doing close work, such as reading, the pupil shrinks slightly to sharpen the image. A photographer uses his camera in the same way when he wants to get a picture with sharp focus. He employs the smallest aperture that can be used with the light that is available to him. Because reduction in pupil size has this sharpening effect in near vision, a farsighted person doing close work tends to squint when not wearing corrective glasses. A pinhole punched in a piece of paper and held up to one eye will sharpen the vision even further by artificially reducing the effective area of the pupil. On the other hand, the pupil becomes larger to admit more light when one is looking at a distant object.

Recent studies have shown that there is still a third element which influences the size of the pupil at a given moment. That element is an emotional response to what is being seen. When, for example, a man is looking at a picture of a pretty girl in a bikini, the pupil tends to widen a tiny amount instead of becoming smaller. This change is unnoticeable except on close observation, but the scientists who noted the phenomenon point out that Chinese jade dealers have been aware of it for centuries. When offering several pieces of jade to a prospective buyer, the merchant carefully observes the customer's eyes. As soon as he sees a slight enlargement in pupil size, he knows the patron covets the piece being shown. The dealer then sets his price accordingly.

Benders of light

Once the iris has admitted the proper amount of light for the immediate purpose, the rays must be bent to come to a focus on the retina. In the human eye, there are four elements which must function together to provide a sharp image. These are the cornea, the fluid called aqueous humor, the lens and the jellylike substance, the vitreous.

The cornea is the first of these. Bulging slightly upward from the surface of the white of the eye, like a crystal from the face of a watch, is the curved, clear, transparent cornea. It causes the first and biggest light refraction, or bending, of the four focusing devices. The cornea reduces the speed of light by about 25 per cent and bends it sharply toward the center. Anyone who has played the old carnival game of trying to toss a penny into a cup resting on the bottom of a tub filled with water has witnessed a similar phenomenon—and probably enriched a pitchman. The penny slows down when it hits the water and then follows a changed path to the bottom, usually missing the cup. Like the course of the penny, the course of light can be determined with mathematical precision by the cornea's refractive index, i.e., the degree to which the cornea can bend light.

When the light rays emerge at the back of the cornea, they have been bent sharply inward toward each other. In this more tightly clustered condition they next encounter the aqueous humor, a fluid that occupies the space between the cornea and the iris. This fluid is virtually colorless, and it is optically matched to the cornea—that is to say, both bend light to approximately the same degree. Thus, the squeezing together of the light rays is not changed by their passing through the fluid. Rather, they go through about as they entered, and as a result the fine focusing job must—for man—be done elsewhere. That such a job is done, and done superbly well, is attested to by the extraordinary flexibility of human vision. A man can focus on things a few inches from his nose, and instantaneously switch to a clear, sharp view of the most distant star. The device that makes this possible, a piece of equipment far more sophisticated than any part of any camera ever invented, is the lens in the human eye.

The lens is a tiny crystalline structure about the size and shape of a small bean. Like any lens, it is a refracting device. However, it differs from glass lenses in two important ways. In the first place, it is not a

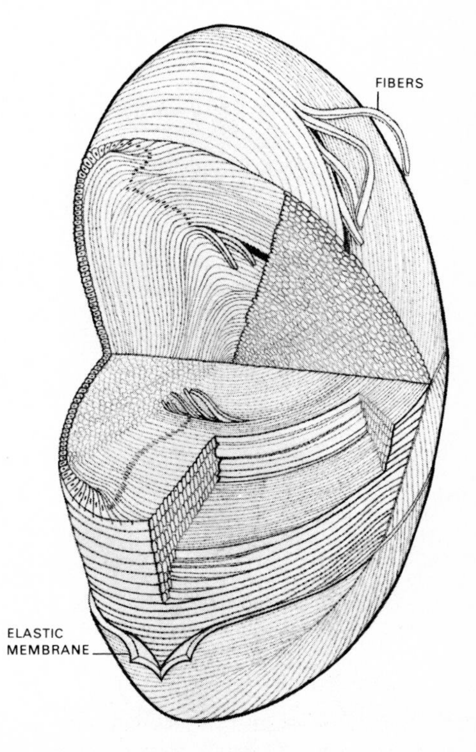

THE LENS OF THE HUMAN EYE *(shown in partial cross section)* is composed of numerous transparent fibers and is encased in a clear, elastic membrane. Because new fibers are constantly being created, the size of the lens increases with age: the lens of an 80-year-old man is more than 50 per cent larger than that of a 20-year-old. However, as the lens grows larger, it becomes less pliable, thus diminishing its ability to focus for near-vision.

uniform structure like a piece of curved glass. Instead it consists of about 2,200 infinitely fine layers, or lamellae. These layers lie on top of one another like the skins of an onion. As the light passes through each of these layers, it undergoes a minute degree of refraction in a series of little jumps. But because the change in the light path is microscopic in each instance, the effect is essentially smooth.

The second characteristic of the human lens is that, unlike its glass counterpart in a camera, it is not rigid; it is, in fact, highly pliable. This difference is fundamental; to understand it, it is appropriate to consider how a camera with an adjustable lens is focused.

Because the lens can be moved closer to or farther from the film, the photographer can get sharp focus at almost any distance he chooses. To make a closeup picture, he moves the lens away from the film; for a distance shot, the lens is brought closer. The eyes of many fishes operate in this way. To see something very close, the fish bulges the whole eyeball outward so that the lens moves away from the retina; to focus on far objects, the eyeball is flattened to bring the lens closer to the retina.

The amazing human lens

But few other animals can perform this engaging trick with their eyeballs. In an eye such as man's, the distance between the lens and the retina is fixed, unchangeable. Therefore, an entirely different method of focusing must come into play to provide clear vision at all distances. A pliant lens that can change its shape is the solution. By changing from a comparatively flat form to a more convex one, the lens increases its refractive power—its ability to bend light rays.

Rays from a light source very close to the eye are highly divergent; they are still widening out when they reach the eye, and the refractive power of the cornea is not great enough to bring them to a point on the retina. In response the muscles contract, thereby changing the form of the lens. By presenting a more curved surface for the light to pass through, the rays are bent to a much greater degree. On the other hand, light rays from a distant source are almost parallel as they enter the eyeball and therefore do not have to be squeezed together as much to come to a point. The cornea alone can do most of the job. Under the circumstances, the lens flattens out and thereby lessens its refractive power. This process of changing shape to meet the needs of near and far vision is known as accommodation.

Accommodation takes place almost instantaneously, enabling man to shift his gaze from near to far objects without a focusing problem. It must be remembered, however, that man can only focus on one thing at a time. This can be demonstrated with a simple experiment. If an open book is placed about two feet from the eyes and the viewer looks at it through a screen of mosquito netting held some six inches from the eyes, he can see either the mesh of the screen or the letters in the book with clarity, but not both at the same time. When the mesh is in sharp focus, the letters are blurred, and vice versa. In this particular example—

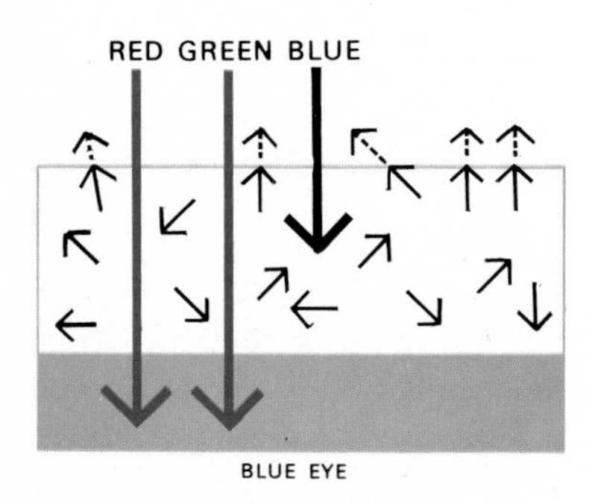

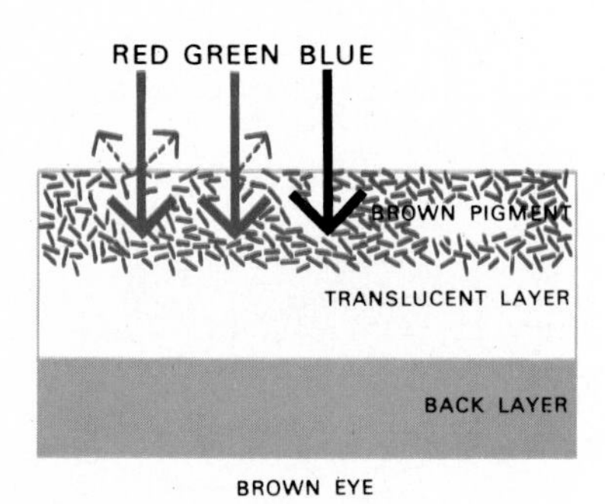

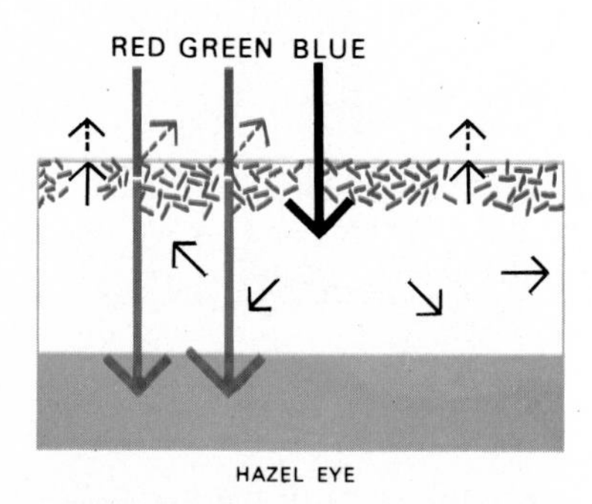

EYE COLORING depends on the amount and distribution of pigment at the front of the iris. When blue eyes *(top)*, devoid of such pigment, receive light *(large colored and black arrows)*, the longer red and green wavelengths are absorbed by the back layer of the iris *(colored block)* and the shorter blue wavelengths are scattered *(small arrows)* by tiny particles in the top layer of the iris. It is this scattering that gives the eye its blue color. Brown eyes *(middle)* have densely packed pigment. This absorbs all the blue wavelengths and reflects some of the others *(small colored arrows)* to create brown. Hazel, speckled and gray eyes *(bottom)* have a thin layer of pigment. Some of the red and green light is absorbed by the back layer and some is reflected along with some of the blue to produce various mixed light colors.

looking at two objects that both happen to be very close to the eye—focusing requires a conscious effort. However, in looking around us at things across the room or across the street, the lens makes the fine adjustment from near to middle to far distances with such ease and rapidity that man is unaware that his mind is directing a change of focus. Not even the most skilled photographer with the finest equipment can shift his camera's focus with anything like the speed of the eye.

Lens accommodation, which permits these adjustments in focusing, is controlled by the ciliary body, a ruff of muscles surrounding the lens. By contracting or stretching, these muscles change the shape of the lens. This change is surprisingly small, even when it must accommodate for the nearest and farthest distances man can see. The maximum change in thickness the lens makes is about 1/50 of an inch.

After the light has been sharply focused by the lens, the rays pass through the vitreous humor, the clear, jellylike substance that fills the entire space between the lens and the retina. This space is about two thirds of the entire volume of the eye. Just as the aqueous humor is optically matched to the cornea, so the vitreous is matched to the lens. Since the vitreous has about the same refractive index as the lens, it therefore keeps the rays on the course set by the lens.

In addition to the cornea, aqueous humor, lens and vitreous, there is another device that has an important role in getting a clear picture to the retina. This structure consists of three sets of muscles for moving the eyeball up and down, and from side to side.

Depending on what a person is looking at, the eye moves in long, smooth sweeps or small, abrupt jerks. When following a moving object across a broad visual field, or when taking in a large landscape, the movements are smooth and even. But in examining detail, as in reading or looking at a picture, the movements are rapid and jumpy. When reading, the eye makes a series of pauses and quick jumps along each line and from line to line, sometimes slipping back a little, moving ahead, pausing, jumping back and repeating a scan. These movements are related to concentration and understanding, but even when these are not involved, the eye tends to move almost all of the time. In experiments where volunteers deliberately attempted to fix their eyes steadily on a point, delicate measuring devices showed hundreds of slight movements away from the point, around it, back toward it.

Nerve circuits for error correction

The eye has an elaborate system for coordinating its various components and correcting their errors. Each of its major actions—light control, focusing, movement—is linked with each of the others by a complex system of interwoven nerve circuits, all cooperating so that mistakes in one are corrected by signals from one or more of the others. When, for example, the eye looks toward an object and the image falls on the peripheral part of the retina where vision is fuzzy, the muscles are signaled to move the eye so that the image is centered for a clear view. At

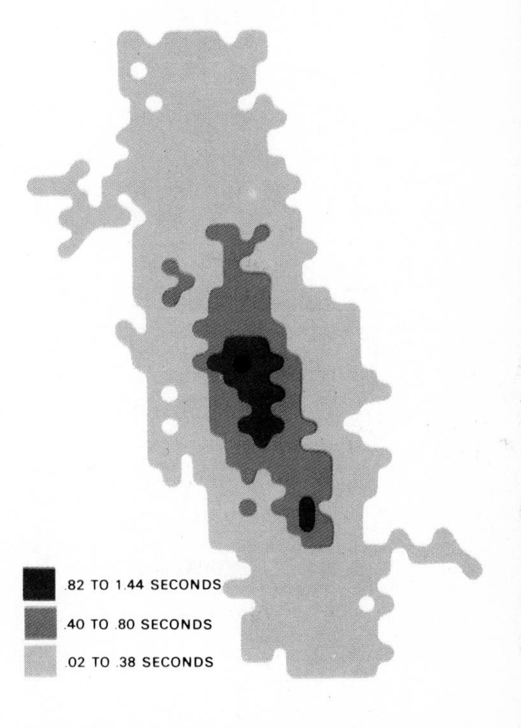

THE CONTOUR MAP above was created by man's wandering eye. A test subject, wearing a contact lens equipped with a tiny lamp, was asked to stare at a pinhole—represented here by a black dot—while the light was directed toward a photoelectric device linked to a computer. The amount of light received indicated the direction of the constant, unconscious eye movements. The map, drawn from the computer's analysis, shows dark tones covering points where the eye wandered most often during the two-minute test, and lighter tones where it wandered less frequently. The scale indicates the time spent at individual points within each area. The complete area of drift, from top to bottom, at normal reading distance, is less than two tenths of an inch —about the height of two lines in this caption.

the same time, another set of messages goes to the ciliary muscles, which adjust the thickness of the lens to clarify the focus. Similar control circuits change the diameter of the pupil to adjust the amount of light when the illumination is too dim or bright, and there is even an automatic circuit that moves the eyelids out of the way when the eyes look upward.

All of these adjustments and movements are made simultaneously for both eyes—for although it is generally convenient and accurate to discuss the working of "the eye," the human visual system is, after all, binocular. And it is binocular in a particular way which differs markedly from that of many other species: it is stereoscopic. The images of the two eyes fit together to produce roundness and depth in the scene.

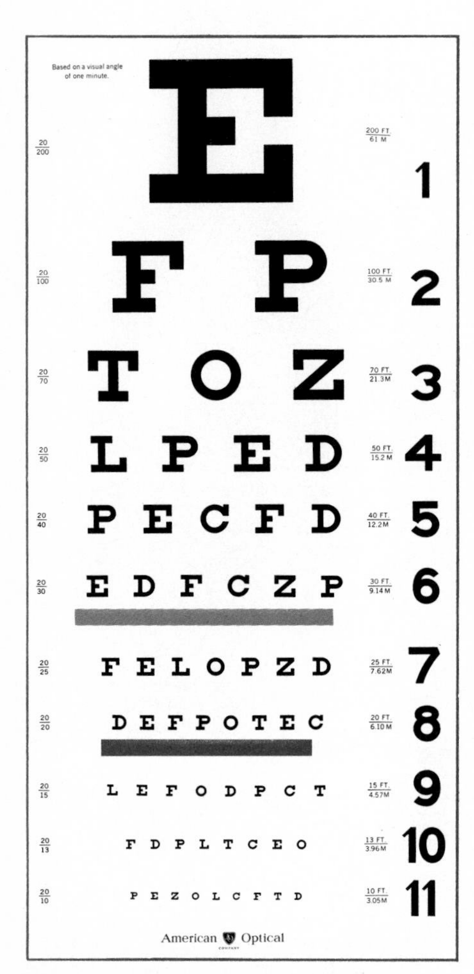

THE FAMILIAR EYE CHART, reproduced here at one fifth its actual size, was devised by Dutch ophthalmologist Herman Snellen in 1862, and is still the most common means of testing distance acuity. The subject stands 20 feet from the chart and reads as many letters as he can. If he can correctly read all the letters in the first eight lines, his distance acuity is considered normal, or 20/20. If he can read more than eight lines, he has exceptional acuity; less than eight may indicate a need for eyeglasses. For an informal acuity test, prop this page and measure off 20 feet. From that distance, a person with 20/20 vision should be able to read the two letters of line 2.

The cyclops and the eight-eyed spider

Nearly all animals from insects to man have two eyes. There are rare one-eyed creatures like the tiny freshwater crustacean cyclops, 1/25 of an inch long, and the saltwater copepods, measuring 1/6 of an inch, which are devoured in the millions by whales. Some species have three eyes. Spiders usually have as many as eight eyes. Still, two eyes is the general rule. But the possession of a pair does not guarantee stereoscopic vision unless the eyes are arranged to focus in concert and unless the two fields of vision overlap to some extent at the center and there is an exchange of nerve signals. For this to happen, of course, the eyes must be set in the head in such a way that they face more or less in the same direction—as they do in predatory animals like cats, wolves or owls, whose need for exact judgment of distance in hunting is obvious. Depth perception is also important among animals that pick up their food, like raccoons, and they too have their eyes set in the front of the head. Another large group, apes and monkeys, are similarly equipped because of their need to gauge distances accurately while scampering and swinging through trees.

Browsing animals like rabbits, horses and deer have their eyes set in the sides of their heads. For them, depth perception is not as important as an all-around view is—they are more concerned with avoiding attackers than they are with catching things. Thus, a rabbit can see in all directions without moving its head, but its view of the world must be a flat one, offering little information about distance.

Certain animals, though their eyes are placed to the side, may have some degree of stereoscopic vision if the fields of the two eyes overlap in the front. The tree shrew has a tiny overlap, the lemur a larger one. On the other hand, there are animals whose eyes are placed properly for stereoscopic vision but do not have it because their optic nerve trunks fail to permit a proper blending of the two images.

In movement as well as placement man's binocular arrangement differs from that of other species. A dog or a horse scarcely moves its eyes at all. Other species, like the keen-eyed birds, can match or surpass man's speed of movement, while the chameleon and the sea gull have the added advantage of being able to move one eye independently of the other.

Man's eyes always work together, and their movements are coordinated and in unison even when they are opposed, as when they turn slightly inward toward the nose for near focusing. Even when one eye is blindfolded, it continues to move in harmony with the open eye.

Thus all the eye's image-controlling structures—pupil, iris, refracting fluids, lens and muscles—make up a remarkably cooperative system for taking "light pictures" into the eye and throwing them back to the retina. Even the various protective devices which do not directly contribute to the processing of light nevertheless help in their own way. The front "window" of the eye is kept clean, for the unimpeded entrance of light, by lashes that keep out dust and by a continual flow of tears that wash the eyeball and run off into a small drainpipe at the inner corner of the lower eyelid.

The eyelid, which protects the human eye from injury, shuts off distracting stimuli and allows the eye's working parts to rest during sleep; it also sweeps away dust particles from the surface of the eyeball. Snakes and some lizards have no eyelids; instead they are equipped with an immovable scaly window covering the eye. When a snake sheds its skin it also sheds the covering of its eyeball. Certain lizards do have eyelids; they even have a third lid—a transparent membrane that moves sideways across the eye from the corner nearest the nose. It protects the eye under water. Man may have once had one; a degenerate and functionless remainder of the third eyelid can be seen in the small pink fold of tissue at the corner of the eye nearest the nose.

The wondrous but imperfect eye

Although the human eye is an awe-inspiring device, it does not always function perfectly. The most common flaw is astigmatism, usually resulting from an imperfectly curved cornea. Because of this lack of symmetry, for example, rays entering the eye are refracted to a greater degree in the vertical plane than in the horizontal, or vice versa, thus distorting the image. Improper focusing, often caused by the cornea, is another prevalent fault. With some individuals, the focus falls short of the retina, causing nearsightedness, the inability to see distant objects. With others, the focus point falls behind the retina, producing farsightedness, or difficulty in seeing near objects. Aging is also likely to bring about a change in the functioning of the eye. As man grows older, the lens loses much of its pliancy, and the muscles have an increasingly difficult time thickening and flattening it. When the lens can no longer focus for near vision, the condition is known as presbyopia.

The use of glasses to correct defects in focusing goes far back, long before the mechanism of the eye was fully understood. As far as is known, the first spectacles were invented in the 13th Century in northern Italy, although earlier generations are believed to have used jewels as lorgnettes to magnify something close at hand. Certainly the "burning glass" was used long before the Christian era to focus the sun's rays,

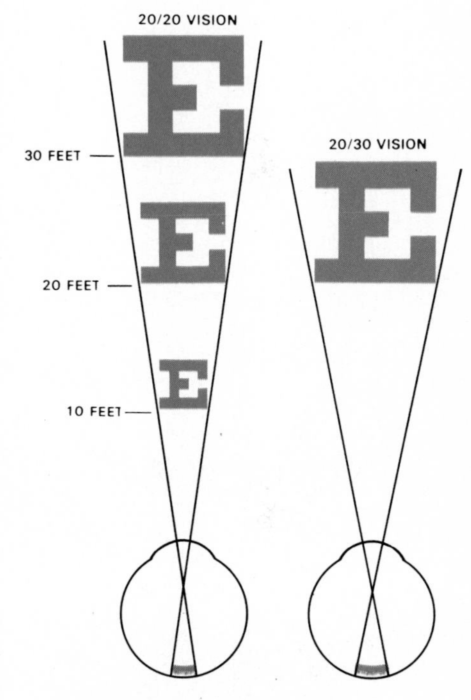

TO RATE DISTANCE VISION, the Snellen chart *(opposite page)* reproduces letters that a person with normal eyes can just distinguish at such distances as 10, 20 and 30 feet *(left)*. If the test subject, standing 20 feet away, can identify the appropriate letter for that distance, he is said to have 20/20 vision. If he fails, as in the diagram at right, and can read at 20 feet only the letter a normal person reads at 30 feet, his vision is rated 20/30.

but apparently no one thought of using the lens to improve vision.

For the first several hundred years of their history, spectacles were crude, expensive and the object of ridicule. As late as the 18th Century, proper Frenchmen considered their use in public as a breach of etiquette. The glasses were, of course, primitive. A person who needed them could only try out various lenses until he found some that served his purpose. The benefits of accurate glasses made to correct the specific flaws in an individual's vision had to await such developments as Hermann von Helmholtz' invention of the ophthalmoscope for measuring the defect precisely, and for modern techniques for mathematically exact lens polishing.

Probably because of the shortcomings of the glasses of his time, Samuel Pepys, the great 17th Century English diarist, often preferred to use what he called his "tubes," two cylinders, each with a pinhole opening that sharpened the image while excluding stray light from the sides. In the use of tubes, Pepys could have taken his cue from nature. The so-called compound eye, which serves a large number of lower organisms including most insects, consists of a great many tubes bundled together like a handful of tightly held soda straws. Each tube has a lens at the outer end and light-sensitive cells connected to nerve fibers at the inner end. The tube is wrapped with a pigment layer so that light cannot leak through the sides or flow from one tube to another, which would cause a blurred image. Each tube receives a tiny portion of the scene in front of the eye; put together, they make up a mosaic image.

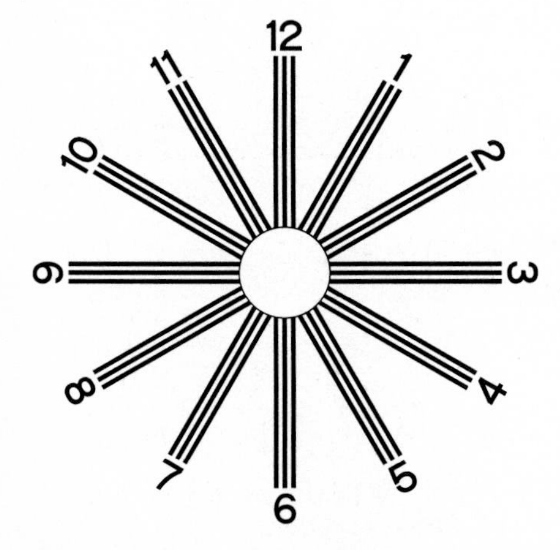

TESTING FOR ASTIGMATISM is sometimes done with this wheel of numbered lines. Astigmatism is usually caused by an imperfectly formed cornea which distorts the image by refracting light rays to a greater degree in one plane—the vertical or the horizontal, for example—than in another. By noting which lines the subject sees sharply and which are blurred, the examiner receives an indication of the type of astigmatism the subject has.

Dual lenses for dual faults

Some individuals have eyes that do not focus properly at either near or far distances, and need a separate lens to correct each flaw. Benjamin Franklin was the first man to conceive the idea of bifocals, a combination of the two lenses in one pair of spectacles. Before his time, a person with both visual faults had to carry two pairs of glasses. However, a small, four-eyed tropical fish, the *Anableps*, anticipated Franklin's invention by eons. The *Anableps* spends much of its time on the surface of the water looking for food. But larger fish, which might gobble up the *Anableps*, lurk below. This presents a difficult problem for the tiny fish. The refraction of light is much greater when it passes through air into the eye than when it passes through water into the eye. Two kinds of visual equipment are necessary if the fish is to have good sight in both media simultaneously, and the *Anableps* has both kinds. It has an iris that extends across the eye as a horizontal bar, dividing the eye into upper and lower parts exactly like bifocal glasses. The upper part has optical properties that are appropriate for seeing in air; the lower part is adapted for underwater refraction. Thus the *Anableps* can search for food on the top of the water, and also keep a wary lookout for enemies below.

But the human eye can suffer impairments which neither glasses nor tubes can correct by themselves. One of the most common, and usually associated with old age, is the severe cataract. A cataract is partial or total opacity of the lens. Surgery—removal of the lens—is the only known remedy. With the lens removed, there are only the cornea, the aqueous and the vitreous to focus light, but by themselves, these cannot provide sharp vision. Today contact lens or glasses can often provide a satisfactory substitute for the human lens. However, centuries before glasses were invented, surgeons performed cataract operations. Even perpetually blurred vision was preferable to blindness.

Sophisticated surgery, 1000 B.C.

It seems strange that this delicate operation could have been performed long before the Christian era by men who had limited knowledge of the structure of the eye, and only comparatively crude instruments, some of them made of stone. Yet there is evidence that in India there were operations for cataracts as early as 1000 B.C. In at least one country, Babylonia, the fees of eye surgeons were rigidly fixed by law and were quite generous. A successful operation on a rich freeman cost 10 shekels of silver, as much as a mechanic made in a year. The same operation on a slave was priced at two shekels. However, the life of the surgeon, while financially rewarding, was not without hazards. If the wealthy freeman lost the sight of his eye in the operation, the surgeon's hand was cut off; if the slave was blinded, he had to be replaced by the doctor.

Even the normal eye is not a perfect optical instrument. For example, the lens is not completely transparent, but contains fibers arranged somewhat like the whorls of a fingerprint. Very small, very dim sources of light, such as distant stars, which are neither strong nor large enough to pass unaltered by these whorls, are slightly deflected so that they seem to have tiny streams of light radiating from them. Perhaps it was this defect which inspired Alfred Lord Tennyson to write:

> *Many a night I saw the Pleiads, rising thro' the mellow shade,*
> *Glitter like a swarm of fireflies tangled in a silver braid.*

Another minor flaw in man's vision stems from the fact that the vitreous, the gelatinous fluid inside the hollow of the eye, is not totally clear either. The fluid contains microscopic particles—sometimes called "flying gnats"—that float freely about and are usually seen as the eye gazes upward and sideways toward a light-colored surface. Seeing them is somewhat like watching the movement of an amoeba through a microscope. If one attempts to fix the particles in view, however, they float capriciously away because the movement of the eye in attempting to focus on them sends them off in another direction.

Despite such shortcomings, the eye remains one of the most wondrous creations in nature. The astounding coordination of the various parts, the ability of the eye to adjust to the manifold demands of varying light conditions, its capacity to switch focus instantaneously from a book to a plane streaking across the sky at supersonic speed—these are reasons enough for man to regard his eyes with an awe bordering on reverence.

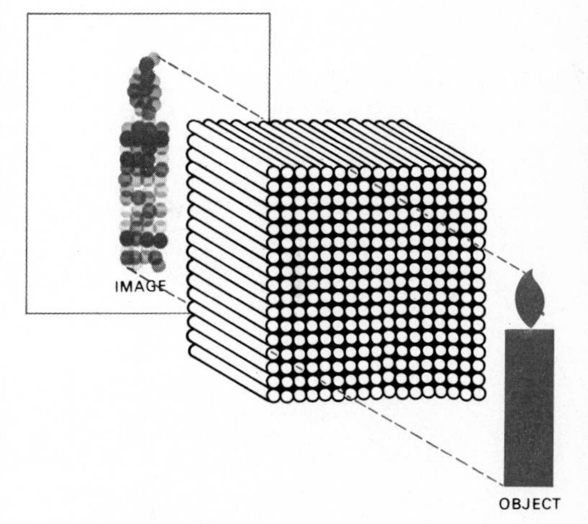

THE COMPOUND EYE, common to most insects, is simulated by this bundle of soda straws as it casts a blurred, mosaiclike image of a lighted candle on a screen. In the real insect eye, the straws are actually tubes which carry tiny parts of the image to the retina, where they are assembled into an overall scene. Because each tube is equipped with a lens, however, the final image is much sharper than the man-made model shown above.

Pioneers Who Captured Images on Film

Although men have used sculpture and painting for thousands of years to capture the images of what they see, the idea of doing this mechanically probably never occurred to anybody until the 18th Century, when investigators became interested in an ancient semiscientific device known as the camera obscura. This was a small room, dark except for the light that came in through a lens in a small hole in one wall. People in the room saw a view of the sunlit scenery outside, projected on the opposite wall. But this image was tantalizingly transient; when the light faded outside, it disappeared.

It was the effort to catch and keep these images that produced photography. The first experiments were made with metal plates coated with various silver solutions. These chemicals decompose slowly on exposure to light. When a plate so prepared was placed in a dark box (a miniature camera obscura) and set up in front of a scene or an object, gradually the ghostly shape of the object would reproduce itself on the plate. From this crude beginning came a whole procession of improvements in photoreceptors, in chemicals and in cameras, some of the high points of which are illustrated by the historic early photographs shown on the following pages.

A LENGTHY EXPOSURE

A silver-on-copper plate made light-sensitive with silver iodide recorded this image of a Paris street, a daguerreotype made by L.J.M. Daguerre in 1839. It includes the first human ever photographed—a man having his shoes shined *(right, foreground)*. The street was bustling but only this man was still long enough to be visible during the five-minute exposure.

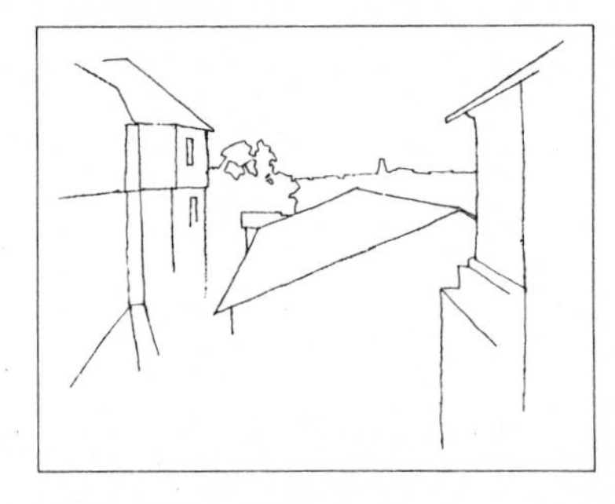

THE FIRST PHOTOGRAPH
The world's first photograph was made in 1826 by Nicephore Niépce from a window in his estate in France. For "film" Niépce used a sensitized pewter plate and he got a blurred image of the rooftops outlined above. This photograph is usually retouched to make it legible, but the version shown at left is what it really looks like.

In front of his laboratory-studio in Reading, England, Fox Talbot demonstrates in a photograph taken in 1845 what his new paper "film

A DAGUERREOTYPE OF DAGUERRE

Salient Experiments on Copper and Paper

The first successful efforts to capture visual images were made in France in the 1830s by Nicéphore Niépce, an inventor, and Louis J. M. Daguerre, a stage-set designer. To Niépce, in fact, goes the honor of taking the world's first photograph *(opposite)*, but Daguerre was the man who sent photography on its way by treating his sensitive copper plates with mercury vapor to bring out on them much sharper images than anyone had previously been able to produce. Although no copies could be made of the pictures, daguerreotypes were sensationally profitable, and made their inventor rich.

At the same time an Englishman, Fox Talbot was making his "film" by coating paper with silver chloride. The result was a paper negative that could reproduce many prints by being pressed against sensitized paper and allowing sunlight to shine through.

process could do: from left, copy a painting, do a portrait of a seated man, print plates in racks by sunlight, and photograph a sculpture.

Better Results with Wet Glass

Daguerreotypes and Talbot's paper negatives sank into oblivion by the 1860s with the introduction of chemically treated glass plates as "film." Glass was an excellent base for the sensitive chemical emulsion because it was completely transparent and did not hinder the passage of light, making possible sharp, clear prints. The problem of sticking the emulsion to the glass was solved by an Englishman, Scott Archer, in 1851. He managed it with a sticky liquid called collodion.

Wet plates had to be prepared, exposed and developed on the spot, before their sensitive emulsions had a chance to dry. This was a very clumsy process, but it was good enough to inspire photographers to lug heavy equipment to all parts of the world. Two such pioneers were William H. Jackson, who photographed America's West, and an Englishman, Roger Fenton, an early war photographer.

A PORTABLE WORKSHOP
Out West, William H. Jackson works with wet plates in a tent darkroom pitched here by railroad tracks at Echo Canyon, Utah. He took pictures of train crews in exchange for free rides.

JACKSON IN ACTION
Atop Glacier Point, in what is now Yosemite National Park, California, Jackson sets his wet-plate camera for a panoramic view. Between 1866 and 1879 he wandered throughout the Far West, taking thousands of pictures. These became tremendously popular; and his scenic shots were influential in persuading Congress to create Yellowstone and other national parks.

TOOLS FOR A WET PLATE

Here is what it took to make wet-plate pictures. The glass plate was locked in a vise *(left)* to be cleaned and polished. A tacky collodion was poured over the glass, which was then plunged into the plate bath *(center)*, where it received a coat of silver nitrate solution. The glass plate was then placed in a holder *(foreground)* so that it could be slipped into the camera *(rear, right)* without its sticky surface touching anything. After exposure, a pistol grip *(right)* was used to hold the plate in the developing fluid. All this equipment could weigh up to 120 pounds.

PHOTOGRAPHER OF THE CRIMEAN WAR

Roger Fenton was an English lawyer who, with an assistant *(above)*, took this mobile photographic laboratory to the Crimea in 1855. Inside his van Fenton stored five cameras, 700 glass plates, and chests of chemicals, as well as sleeping tents and food. He explored the camps and battlefields, often halted by British troops who insisted that he snap their pictures.

ACTION PHOTOGRAPHS IN SERIES
Muybridge made his motion studies in several ways. In the top two strips he took simultaneous front and rear views of a girl walking. In the lower three strips he used three cameras for different views of a girl tossing her handkerchief. These motion studies were invaluable to artists as well as to doctors who were teaching the handicapped to walk. Muybridge first worked with wet plates, but only with the faster dry plates could he develop the stop-motion technique that made him famous—and also notorious, for many of his strips were of nudes.

The Wonders of Dry Plates

The heroic trials of wet-plate photographers came to an end in 1876 with the advent of dry plates—glass squares as before, but this time with their sensitive emulsion held in place by a layer of fast-drying gelatin. The first gelatin formula was developed in 1871 by an English doctor, Richard L. Maddox. Not only could plates be prepared ahead of time, but the gelatin itself increased their sensitivity, making them up to 60 times as fast as the old wet variety. Now, for the first time, action could be reliably "stopped" by rapid exposure times.

The new plates immediately led to changes in camera design. Heretofore, photographs had been made by removing a lens cap from the camera, since exposures were measured in seconds or minutes, and the "film" was far too slow to record the blur made by the photographer's finger. Now, with the faster plates, complex mechanical shutters were needed to allow only a scrap of light through the lens.

Dramatic new action photographs quickly followed. One man, Eadweard Muybridge, made vital studies of locomotion, lowering the exposure time to fractions of a second. His pictures enabled men for the first time to see how they actually moved.

A LINE OF LENSES
A 12-lens camera was built by Muybridge for making complicated sequence pictures like those shown at left. The lens shutters clicked in series, a fraction of a second apart. What appears to be a 13th lens *(left)* is actually a focusing lens; it controlled the focus of all the others.

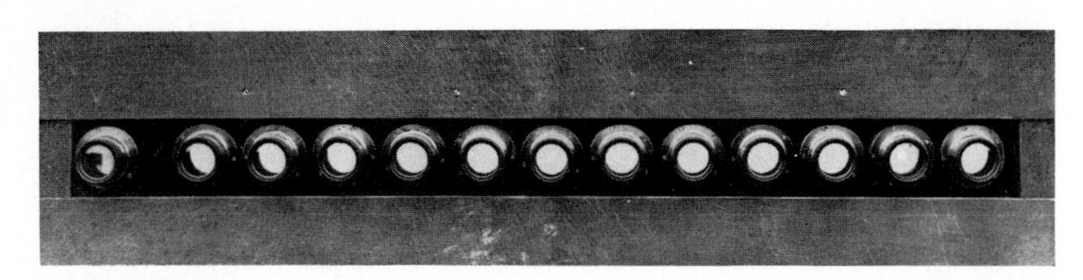

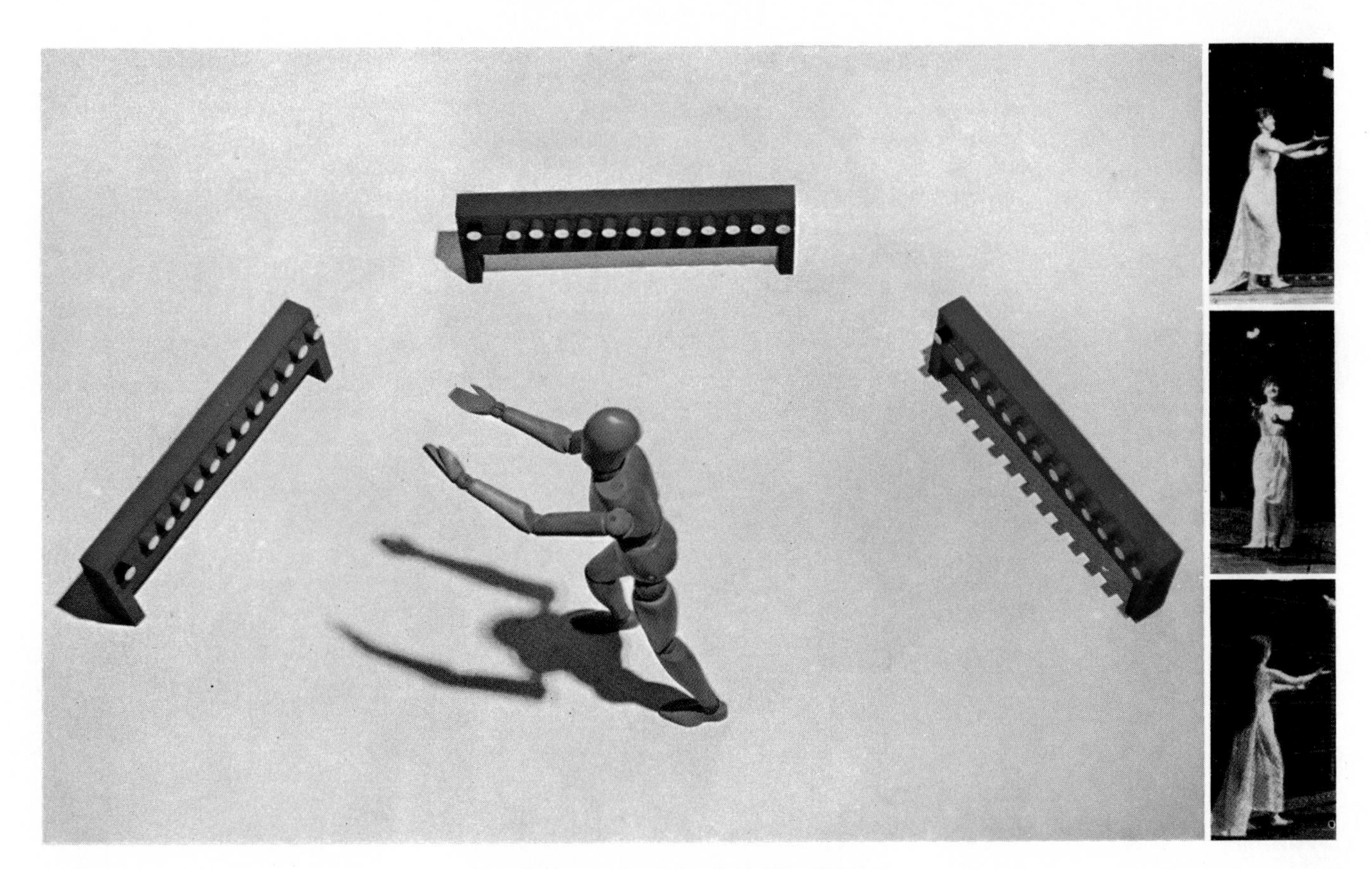

MUYBRIDGE'S THREE-CAMERA METHOD
To photograph the handkerchief-tossing girl opposite, Muybridge aimed three 12-lens cameras at his subject—one from the side, and one each at an angle from front and rear. The camera shutters were synchronized so that their lenses operated together. A single frame, taken by lens four in each camera, is shown above—giving an in-the-round view of the girl's motion.

THE FIRST KODAK

The original Kodak, shown here with its inside mechanism pulled out, was the ideal instrument for the newly invented roll film. The film could take 100 snapshots; a new frame could be twisted into position manually after each exposure. A circular mask eliminated the edges of the snapshots, which tended to blur. At right, George Eastman, aboard ship, aims his recent invention while a friend snaps his picture with another Kodak.

The Kodak made almost any scene a subject for permanent record, as seen in these random snapshots taken in the 1890s. Tourists arme

Photography for Everybody

The invention of roll film and an easily operated hand-held box camera opened photography to the amateur. One man, George Eastman, was pivotal in these dramatic innovations. A dry-plate manufacturer in Rochester, New York, Eastman began wondering why the heavy, fragile glass plate could not be replaced by something better. Glass, after all, was only a way of holding the emulsion in place. Why not use a flexible material, one that could be wound up on a spool and put inside a camera in such a way that one frame at a time could be exposed? By 1889 a man who worked for Eastman, Henry M. Reichenbach, had perfected such a backing for an emulsion. This was a mixture of nitrocellulose and wood alcohol. It proved so successful that it was used the world over until the 1930s—when a less flammable material, cellulose acetate, replaced it.

Meanwhile, Eastman perfected the film roll and the camera to hold it—the Kodak. Everything about the first Kodak was unique, including the name, which was coined by Eastman. A masterwork of simplicity, the Kodak reduced photography to two easy steps: sighting the subject through the viewer and clicking the shutter. The camera was small and light; its fixed focus lens brought in clearly everything over eight feet away. The film was installed at the factory and after 100 snapshots the camera was sent to the Eastman Company, where the pictures were developed, printed and then returned with the freshly loaded camera. The Kodak was a sensation—millions were sold around the globe. The Eastman slogan, "You press the button, we do the rest," became an international maxim, even popping up in Gilbert and Sullivan's operetta, *Utopia, Unlimited,* in 1893.

themselves with Kodaks and snapped away while natives took pictures of tourists. Everywhere people caught on film what their eyes saw.

Color Photography Gets Its Start

Surprisingly enough, some work was done in color photography as early as a century ago, when the Scotsman James Clerk Maxwell demonstrated that color pictures could be made by breaking a subject down into three primary hues—red, green and blue—through the use of filters. Unfortunately his system required three separate photographs, each recording one color. It was not until 1904 that anyone came up with a reliable color system that involved only one camera. This was accomplished in France by the Lumière brothers with a process they called autochrome. The secret was in their "film," a glass plate covered with microscopic grains of starch, each grain dyed either red, green or blue. This idea of getting different particles of color into the film itself is the one followed today.

COLOR IN ITS INFANCY
This photograph of a ceramic tile was made by the nephew of Nicéphore Niépce in 1867. His "film" was a sensitized silver plate that took on certain hues under the influence of sunlight.

AN EARLY AUTOCHROME
Titled simply *Young Lady with an Umbrella,* this autochrome *(right)* was taken by the Lumières at Evian, France, in 1907. The autochrome was one of several color methods that disappeared in 1935 when Leopold Godowsky and Leopold Mannes invented Kodachrome color film.

4

From Light to Sight

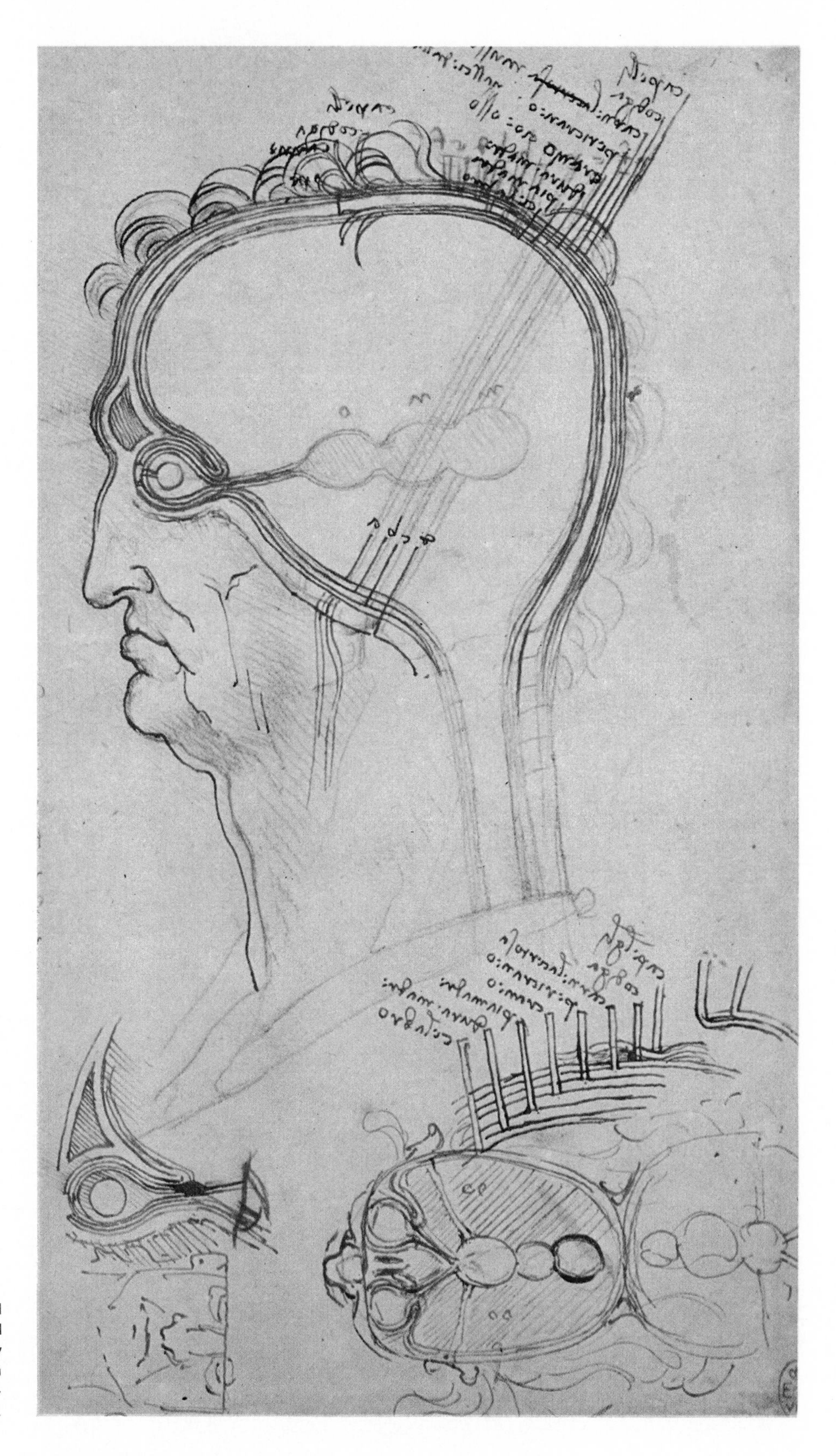

These cross sections of the human head were sketched by Leonardo da Vinci around 1500. Although his anatomy is basically correct—including a direct link between the eye and the brain—the three sausage-shaped "cerebral cells" are nonexistent.

FOR HUNDREDS OF YEARS it has been clear that man's vision takes place, not in his eyes, but in his brain. One proof is that severe brain injury can blind him, completely and permanently, even though his eyes continue to function perfectly. The eye does gather and focus light into images on its back wall, the retina. But when the light strikes there, a wholly new step in the visual process begins. Sensitive cells in the retina convert the energy of light into signals, and these signals are transmitted to the brain. Only now, after generations of physicists, biologists and psychologists have pieced together fragmentary—often contradictory—bits of evidence, is this part of vision beginning to be understood. It is one of the most delicate achievements of nature, operating with the smallest quantities of light that can possibly exist, initiating elusive chemical reactions in single molecules, and transmitting signals over networks more complex than any in the biggest electronic computer.

The first important clue to the way visual signals reach the brain was uncovered in 1877 by a German biologist, Franz Boll. One day Boll looked into a frog's eye he had just taken from a dark closet in his laboratory and noticed, far back in the eye, a reddish substance that quickly faded in the light. Other scientists had observed the same phenomenon but had dismissed it as a blood clot. This explanation did not satisfy Boll. If the red matter was blood, why did it disappear in the light? He returned the eye to the dark closet for a while and then repeated the experiment. Again the reddish substance was present when the eye was first removed, and again the color faded in the light. Soon Boll realized that he had made an important discovery: a chemical change takes place in the eye when light enters it.

Nearly a hundred years later, in 1959, David H. Hubel and Torsten N. Wiesel performed an experiment on a cat at The Johns Hopkins University. They inserted a microscopic electrode into the brain and recorded the activity of a single nerve cell of that part of the cat's brain where vision takes place. The electrode was connected to an amplifier and loudspeaker, as well as an oscilloscope—a device for showing electrical signals visually—so that if anything happened in the cell, no matter how slight, it would be heard and seen. Then the experimenters flashed a light in front of the cat. Immediately a distinct put-put sound came from the loudspeaker and a pattern appeared on the oscilloscope, both indicating an electrical response to the light in the brain cell.

These two experiments, separated by nearly a century, established the beginning and end of the crucial processes of conversion in vision. The first had detected the conversion of light into chemical reactions. The second had found the end result of those reactions: a signal stimulating one brain cell to "see."

Light passing into the eye remains essentially unchanged, although its path is altered so that it reaches the retina in proper focus. It is at this point that the dramatic conversion takes place, and light is transformed into signals, partly electrical and partly chemical in their nature. Although triggered by light, these signals can no longer be described in terms of light units. In fact, the light is gone—dissipated. It is used up just as the energy of a gun's hammer is used up when it strikes the bullet. At this point, it is important to keep in mind that light *is* energy. Light is not a substance nor a picture, but energy, the ability to do work. The eye harnesses light energy to see by the process of vision just as plants harness light energy to grow by the process known as photosynthesis.

In neither the eye nor the plant can the transfer of light energy be direct. In photosynthesis, sunlight must be transformed into life-sustaining sugars and starch before the energy is useful to the plant. In vision, light energy must be converted into electrochemical reactions. In both the plant and the eye, this transformation of energy is performed by special, light-sensitive pigments in the cells.

In vision, these pigmented cells, called photoreceptors, are part of the retina, which corresponds to the film in a camera. The retina looks like a pink net (its name comes from the Latin word for net, *rete*) and is about 1/50 of an inch thick, a multilayered coating that covers all of the inner surface of the eye except for the front, where light enters. Oddly enough, the pigmented cells are located at the back of the retina and to get to them, the light must first pass through two other layers of cells which are involved in communicating signals to the brain.

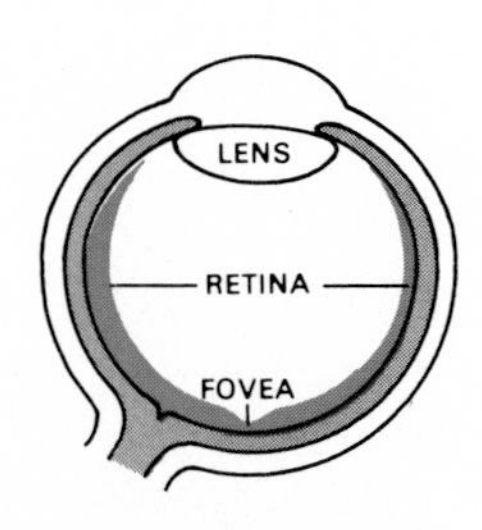

THE EYE'S GREATEST ACUITY occurs in bright light when an image falls on the fovea, a tiny dimple in the retina *(above)*. There are two reasons for this: first, there is a great concentration of cones in the fovea and, second, these cones usually have a one-for-one connection *(below, right)* with bipolar and ganglion nerve cells, the first links in the transmission lines to the brain. Thus, each foveal cone can send a direct signal uncomplicated by impulses from other photoreceptors. On the periphery of the retina, where there is a mixture of rods and cones *(below, left)*, this direct linkage does not exist. Several rods and cones may connect with the same bipolar cell, and several bipolar cells with a single ganglion cell. Because each nerve fiber carries many signals, interpretation by the brain is less specific, thus reducing acuity.

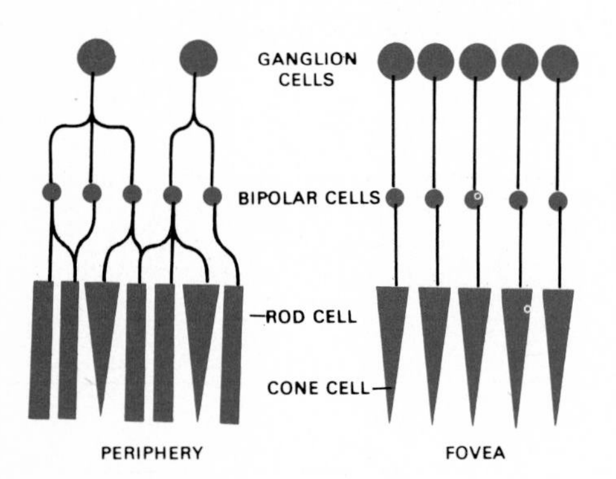

Vision for two kinds of worlds

Human photoreceptors are of two kinds: rods and cones. The rods are straight and thin, the cones more bulbous. They lie packed together on the back of the retina—about 130 million of them in an area the size of a postage stamp. Man has these two kinds because, like many other animals, he lives in two kinds of visual worlds: day and night. The plump cones, some seven million of them, are for detailed examination in bright light; the slender rods, almost 18 times as numerous, are for dim light.

The two types of photoreceptors differ in much the same way that color film differs from black-and-white. In the daytime a photographer can capture all the color in a scene with color film. But in extremely dim light, his color film will not work well; it is simply not sensitive enough for the job. If he wants to record the scene, he must give up the idea of getting a color picture and settle for one in black-and-white—which he *can* get because black-and-white film is much more sensitive, and will respond in dimmer light. The human eye is like a camera with two kinds of film in it at all times. The cones come into play when the light is strong, and give man color vision. But at night, only the rods will work, and they give only black-and-white responses. This explains why colors disappear at night and all things appear to be different shades of gray.

The rods and cones are mixed together in the retina so that the eye can switch from one type to the other with relative ease. However, their distribution is not even, and this produces some interesting results in the way man sees. In the center of the retina, for example, is a small dimple called the fovea. It contains only cones, and this concentration makes the fovea the most accurate place for vision in bright light, and man uses it constantly to look at whatever is of immediate interest to him. However, the fovea is small, and therefore has a limited field of view—about four square inches at eight feet. To compensate for this limitation, the eyeball moves almost continuously to keep the image on this concentration of cones. There are, of course, cones on the periphery of the retina, but there are not enough of them to give man sharp, clear vision. The periphery serves primarily as a warning system. When man sees something in this area that alerts him, he shifts his eyeball so that the image falls on the fovea, where he has maximum acuity. But because the fovea contains only cones, it is useless in dim light. To see an object in semidarkness, a man must look not directly at it, but just to one side, so that the light entering the eye will fall not on the fovea but on the periphery of the retina, where there is a concentration of rods.

The amount of light is not the only factor that determines how well man sees a given object. Its color is also important. Cones are most responsive to the yellowish-green part of the spectrum, whereas rods, although still giving only black-and-white vision, respond best to the blue-green wavelengths. As a result of this, a red flower and a blue one may look equally bright in daylight but not at night. Then the blue one, to which the dim-light rods respond, will seem much brighter than the red one, which will look almost black. The cones, which normally respond to red, are not functioning properly in the dark, and the rods are relatively insensitive to red.

Before anything at all can be seen in the dark, the eyes must have time to adjust. This adjustment to changing light conditions, known as dark and light adaptation, is a far more intricate process than it might seem. The study of this process has revealed much about the mechanism by which the pigments in the photoreceptors convert light into signals for the brain.

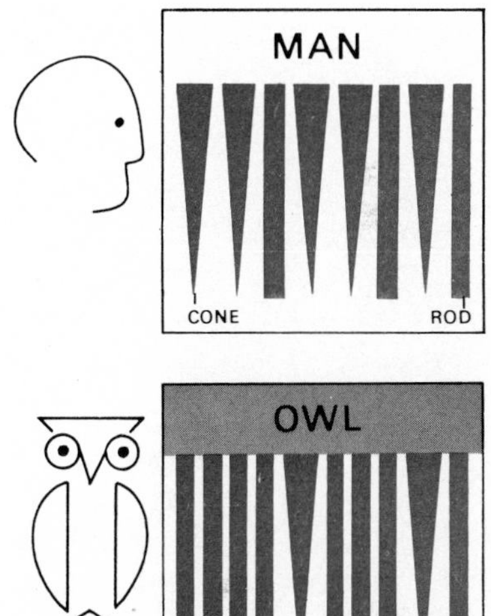

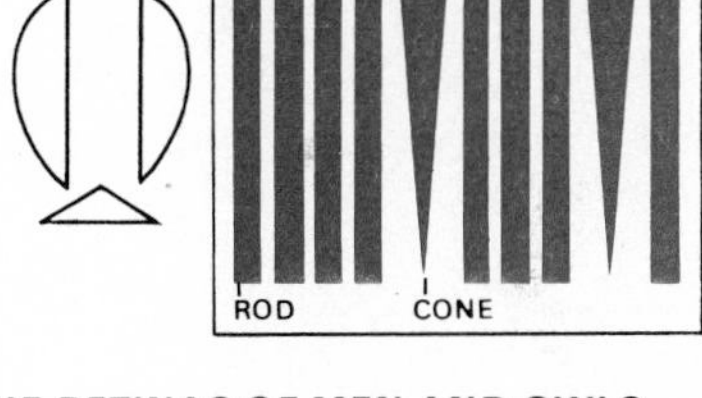

THE RETINAS OF MEN AND OWLS, diagramed above, have developed strikingly different proportions of rods and cones to meet different needs. Man, who is primarily a daytime creature, has a high proportion of cones, the color-sensitive receptor cells, which form their sharpest images in bright light. The owl, on the other hand, is a predator that hunts by night; it requires a far greater proportion of rods, which are much more sensitive, in order to see well in dim light. Because of its small number of cones, the owl is almost completely color-blind.

Problems of twilight

Normally, the transition from day to night vision takes place slowly as the light itself diminishes. There are periods and levels of illumination just before the shift is completed when both rods and cones are functioning simultaneously, but neither with full effectiveness. This explains why motorists find that the hardest time to drive is just about twilight. The image is not clear either when one is looking directly at an object (relying on the cones) or using peripheral (rod) vision.

But the natural form of transition is still much easier than the abrupt shifts made necessary by artificial light. One person may sit outdoors reading and still find the page legible as the light slowly becomes dim, yet another person, coming out of a lighted house at that time, may find the outdoors so dark he can hardly see the reader, much less the book. When the shift is from one extreme to another, a lag occurs. It takes several minutes for the eye to become adapted to the shift from dim light to bright, and considerably longer to adapt from bright light to darkness. This accounts for the awkward problem of finding a seat in a darkened movie theater after entering from a brightly lit lobby.

Dark and light adaptation involves a major change in the size of the pupil, which in semidarkness opens wider to admit as much light as possible and on a bright day closes down to prevent excessive sunlight from entering. But the most important part of adaptation takes place in the retina. The process entails the depletion and restoration of the photoreceptors' supply of visual pigment, a reaction known as bleaching and regeneration. The effect is much like wearing down a car battery by leaving the lights on when the engine is not running, then recharging the battery by driving for a while. In the battery, prolonged drain produces a chemical change which reduces the amount of current that can be produced. In the retina, exposure to bright light causes a molecular change in the pigment, bleaching it and diminishing the responsiveness of the visual system to light. Like the battery, it runs down, and the signals it produces become weaker. Darkness reverses the molecular change and regenerates the pigment.

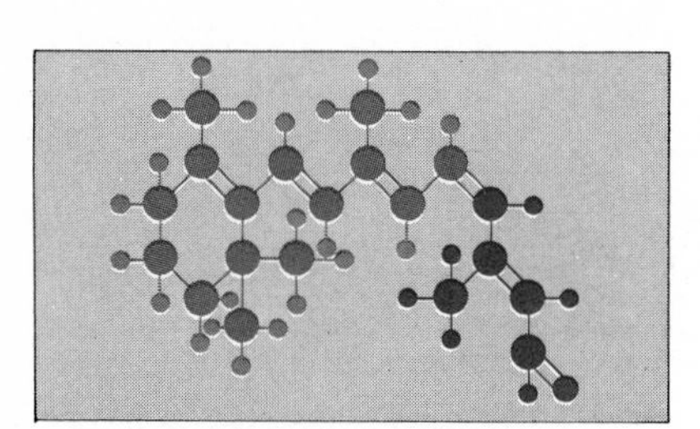

RETINENE IN DARKNESS

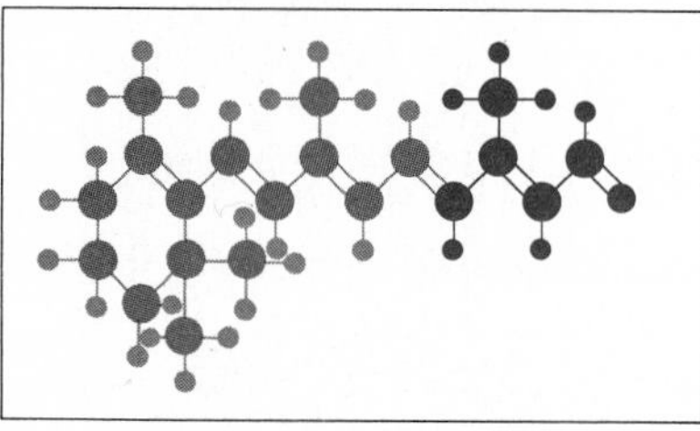

RETINENE IN LIGHT

MOLECULAR STRUCTURE, diagramed above, is changed and visual signals created when light hits the rod's rhodopsin pigment and affects its retinene group. Before light hits, the retinene structure *(top)* is twisted; note the position of the dark-colored atoms at lower right in the illustration. When light hits, the structure is "straightened out" *(bottom)*—the dark-colored group of atoms moves in line with other clusters. By some means not fully understood, this simple change sets off electrochemical impulses in the retina's nerve cells. The light, having transferred its energy, ceases to exist. The rest of the visual process occurs in darkness.

Learning from a frog's eye

Discovering the molecular change that "bleaches" visual pigment was the essential first step in understanding the chemical reactions that convert light into signals of sight. The key was Boll's realization that the rod pigment in a frog's eye could be temporarily destroyed by light. Soon after Boll had seen the pigment in action, Wilhelm Kühne managed to extract some from frog rods. (Discovery of cone pigment did not come until much later.) The rod pigment was a colored substance that he called *sehpurpur,* a German word that means "visual scarlet" but was translated into English as "visual purple." The English misnomer continues to be used although Kühne and other scientists knew that the pigment may range from rose-colored in land animals to deep violet in freshwater fishes. Today most scientists prefer the term "rhodopsin" for the visual pigment of rods.

Although scientists were certain that there was pigment in cones as well as in rods, there was no laboratory evidence of its existence until nearly a century after Kühne had extracted rhodopsin. When cone pigment was finally discovered in the human eye, it turned out to be not one, but three kinds of pigment, differing in their response to colors. One is most sensitive to red, another to green and the third to blue. Only one kind of pigment exists in each cone, but none of them has yet been extracted as a chemical.

The rhodopsin pigment, experiments showed, includes a chemical relative of carotene, the vitamin A pigment of carrots—a discovery that had two quite dissimilar results. It suggested how the chemical transformation of light energy might operate. And it also threatened to set the population on a carrot binge. Researchers working with the retinas of rats that had been starved of vitamin A found that the rats' rhodopsin built up much more slowly in the dark than it did in normally fed animals. Both rod and cone vision in humans also is harmed by a vitamin A deficiency. To some persons this fact meant that eating quantities of carrots, which are the chief source of carotene, would improve their vision. It will—if they have poor sight because of a lack of vitamin A. However, if they are already on balanced diets with adequate vitamin A, they could eat carrots around the clock without the slightest improvement; the regeneration of both rod and cone pigments is already at its best, and the extra vitamin A would simply be discarded by the body.

The vital vitamin A

But the greater significance of the vitamin A discovery lay in the insight it gave into the fundamentals of vision. Vitamin A is a compound that can exist in any one of four molecular arrangements—but only one of these arrangements serves to regenerate visual pigments. This suggested that molecular rearrangement—a shifting about of molecular parts—was involved in bleaching and regeneration. There must, the investigators felt, be some kind of lock-and-key mechanism in pigment molecules that is operated by light.

At this point it is useful to remember the double nature of light. It acts as waves of energy with specific characteristics of waves such as length, frequency and velocity. But these waves also act like trains of individual particles of energy called photons. The latter aspect of the nature of light is of critical importance in understanding what goes on after a "light picture" has been absorbed by the visual pigment. The photon is not itself the key that unlocks sight; it uncovers the keyhole so that the key can enter the lock.

How this complex sequence of steps takes place can be seen in the pigment in the rods, rhodopsin. The molecule of rhodopsin consists of two parts. One is a protein, opsin, that serves as a base and provides the proper "environment" for the necessary chemical reactions. Fitted snugly on this base is the site of light absorption, a group of atoms that can be rearranged. This group, called retinene, is closely related to vitamin A. The retinene group fits over its opsin base like the cap that swings over the keyhole of a car door to keep out water that might freeze the turning mechanism. As long as the retinene is in its normal arrangement, it fits over the opsin keyhole and no key can be inserted. But the impact of a photon of light changes the shape of the retinene so that it "swings aside" like the keyhole cap, allowing crucial chemicals to slip into the keyhole. These chemicals increase the energy of the photoreceptors and send visual signals along them to the nerve cells. Thus begins the journey of sight to the brain.

However, this explanation cannot be the whole story. It assumes that a single photon of light is strong enough to power the chemical and electrical processes that actually produce the sensation of vision in the brain. But one photon could not do that. It is far too weak; just to provide the dim light from a small flashlight requires billions and billions of photons per second. Scientists are certain that the pigment reaction must be amplified for any perception of vision to occur. As yet, they do

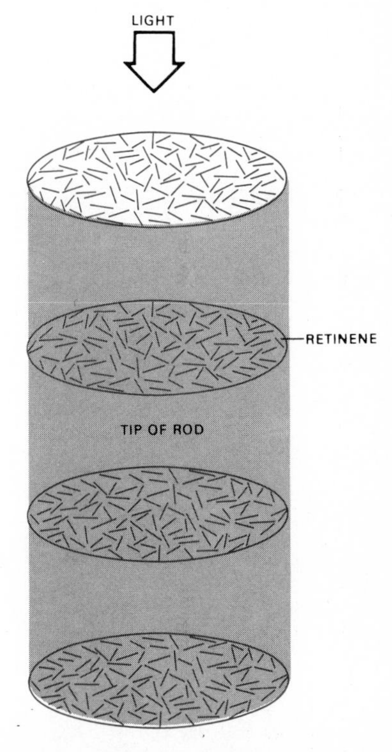

THE LIGHT-SENSITIVE MATERIAL of the eye is believed to be located in a series of rhodopsin-containing disks stacked, as illustrated here in simplified form, in great numbers in the tips of the rods. When individual photons of light enter a rod, they pass through the disks unless they hit one or another of the myriads of retinene groups *(small straight lines)* within the rhodopsin. Only a small percentage are actually absorbed as they streak through the disks. When a photon does collide with a molecule, however, it straightens out the retinene structure *(opposite)* and triggers the complex process whereby a signal is passed along to the brain.

not know how this amplification takes place in the eye. George Wald of Harvard's Biological Laboratories has suggested two possibilities. It may be that the absorption of a photon activates chemical boosters—enzymes—in the pigment. These enzymes may then be able to generate far greater amounts of energy than the original molecule could produce by itself. The other possibility is that when a photon of light hits the photoreceptor, it punches a one-molecule hole in the photoreceptor. If this second theory is correct, then electrically charged particles might be able to flow from the receptor into two other layers of the retina, where they may be processed and forwarded to the brain.

The eye-brain transmission system

The retinal nerve fibers that carry this visual message constitute an extremely complex interconnected network that fans out all over the forward-facing surface of the retina. One layer of the retina, lying between the photoreceptors and the transmission lines, is made up of bipolar cells, which pick up the electrical signals from the photoreceptors. The foremost layer contains the ganglion cells, which receive the signals from the bipolars and transmit the messages to the brain. All these nerve fibers constitute a data-collecting system. They come together at one spot on the retina; from this point, bunched together like a cable, they pass through the retina and out the back to become the optic nerve leading to the brain. At the place where the cable passes through the surface of the retina, there are no photoreceptor cells, and this produces a blind spot. Here the eye sees nothing.

Despite its size and importance, the blind spot was not discovered until the 17th Century. Then a French scientist, Edmé Mariotte, performed a revealing experiment with two small white disks and a dark screen. He placed the first disk about eye level on the screen, and the second slightly lower and to the right about two feet. He closed his left eye, stared at the first disk with his right and then slowly backed away from the screen. At about nine feet, the second disk disappeared from his view although the screen around it remained visible. Light from the second disk was falling squarely on the blind spot. When Mariotte slightly shifted his eye, he could again see the disk. In ordinary vision the blind spot causes no inconvenience, partly because of binocular vision and partly because of the rapidity and frequency of eye movements.

In binocular vision man's eyes must exchange information. Therefore, after leaving the eyes, the two nerve bundles, one from each eye, come together at an intersection called the optic chiasma. Here each bundle forms two branches. One branch, from the nasal side of the right eye, crosses over and joins the branch from the outer, or temporal, side of the left eye. The other two branches—from the nasal side of the left eye and the temporal side of the right—combine on the right. After this regrouping, the two newly formed bundles go respectively to the left and right lateral geniculate bodies, way stations that are located just back of the brain's midsection.

Each lateral geniculate body is a laminated material and its layers are organized to receive signals from only one of the two eyes. However, because of the close proximity of the layers, there is some form of interaction between signals. This interaction, along with such features of human vision as the placement of the eyes and the overlap of the visual fields, may be among the reasons man has stereoscopic vision.

The original fibers end at the lateral geniculate bodies. There, new nerve fibers continue to the visual cortex, where the actual phenomenon of "seeing" takes place. The cortex is a mass of gray matter, a pair of hemispheres that curve to form a shell around the very back of the brain. If the cortex were unfolded and spread out, it would be about a tenth of an inch thick and some 20 square feet—the area of a four-by-five-foot rug. The section devoted to vision is only a tiny portion of the entire cortex. The billions of cells in the visual cortex are arranged in a number of layers, and the millions of fibers that enter it from the lateral geniculate bodies connect with the fourth layer from the top. From here they disseminate to all layers of the cortex. The cells of some of the layers—particularly the ones just above and below the fourth layer—send out projections to other areas deep in the brain. Because vision involves memory and association, it may be that these outside lines connect with the parts of the brain that store up the data of experience.

At this point, scientists face a fundamental and appallingly difficult question: How does the brain use these signals to produce a visual image?

With the aid of sensitive electrodes it is now possible to locate exactly what area of the cortex is activated by a stimulus from a specific part of the retina. One section of the cortex receives the signals from the fovea, and another part responds to the periphery of the retina. Not unexpectedly, researchers have found that the larger region of the visual cortex serves the central portion of the retina, where cones predominate and man has greatest acuity.

Measuring signals in a single cell

In recent years, this mapping of the cortex has become so refined that scientists can monitor a single nerve cell in the brain. The work of Hubel and Wiesel, the men who wired a cat's brain for sound, has been of special significance. By means of their microscopic electrodes, they have been able to measure the responsiveness of individual brain cells to various kinds of stimuli. Different nerve cells, they found, reacted to different sets of signals from the retina. For instance, one cell reacts vigorously if the stimulus is a slender upright rectangle that moves horizontally, but shows no response at all to the same rectangle when it moves up and down. Such experiments have shown that the interpretive function of vision involves not only areas of the cortex but also the reaction of highly specialized, individual cells in the cortex.

Somehow, in a manner yet to be discovered, all of these specialized cells add up, combine and exchange visual data and thereby create perception—a picture in the mind.

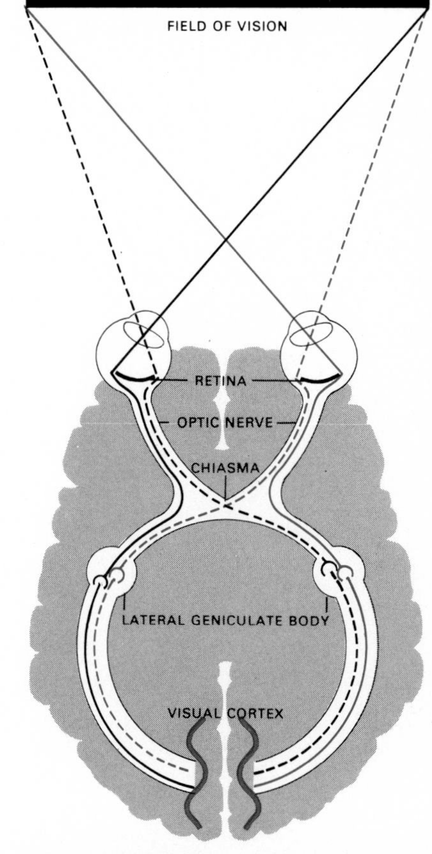

THE CROSSOVER of visual nerve fibers results in the left part of the brain "seeing" only the right half of the field of vision, while the right part "sees" only the left half. The retina of each eye receives the entire image of an object, as shown by the solid and dotted lines passing through the lenses *(colored for the right eye and black for the left)*. Impulses generated by the images on the retinas are carried from the eyes by the optic nerves. However, at the chiasma, the fibers in each optic nerve divide into two bundles. The inner branch from the right eye *(dotted colored line)* crosses over and joins with the outer branch from the left eye *(solid black line)* before continuing to the left lateral geniculate body. The other branches are routed to the right lateral geniculate body. Both sets of fibers are then relayed in newly formed nerve bundles to terminals on either side of the visual cortex.

How Vision Begins in the Eye

"If an optician wanted to sell me an instrument which had all these defects, I should think myself quite justified in blaming his carelessness in the strongest terms." Thus wrote Hermann von Helmholtz, the 19th Century's greatest authority on the nature of vision, about the human eye. Although Helmholtz had a point, he was being unnecessarily harsh. The eye is in fact an extremely versatile instrument. It can discern a golf ball at more than 300 yards and then change focus in a twinkling to read a score card held a few inches away. It can adjust rapidly to variations in the intensity of light and distinguish thousands of color variations.

But compared with a modern camera or telescope, the eye does suffer from optical limitations. Though its overall visual horizon is broad, it sees sharply only in good light and then only in a small central area. In dim light, the eye sees poorly and loses all color perception. Each eye also has a built-in blind spot, a hole in its field of vision where no image registers. All sorts of ailments can affect the eye's function. Imperfections in the eyeball's shape produce astigmatism, farsightedness or nearsightedness—conditions which cause more than 75 million adults in the United States to wear eyeglasses.

GLINTS IN A GOLDEN EYE

Light reflections sparkle from the entrance to the eye, revealing its structure. The pupil shows up as a dark hole in the fawn-colored iris; the bright gleam inside it is only a reflection from the lens. The lids help to wash the eye. They open and close about 25 times a minute, carrying lubricating tears across its surface. The lashes protect the eye from dust.

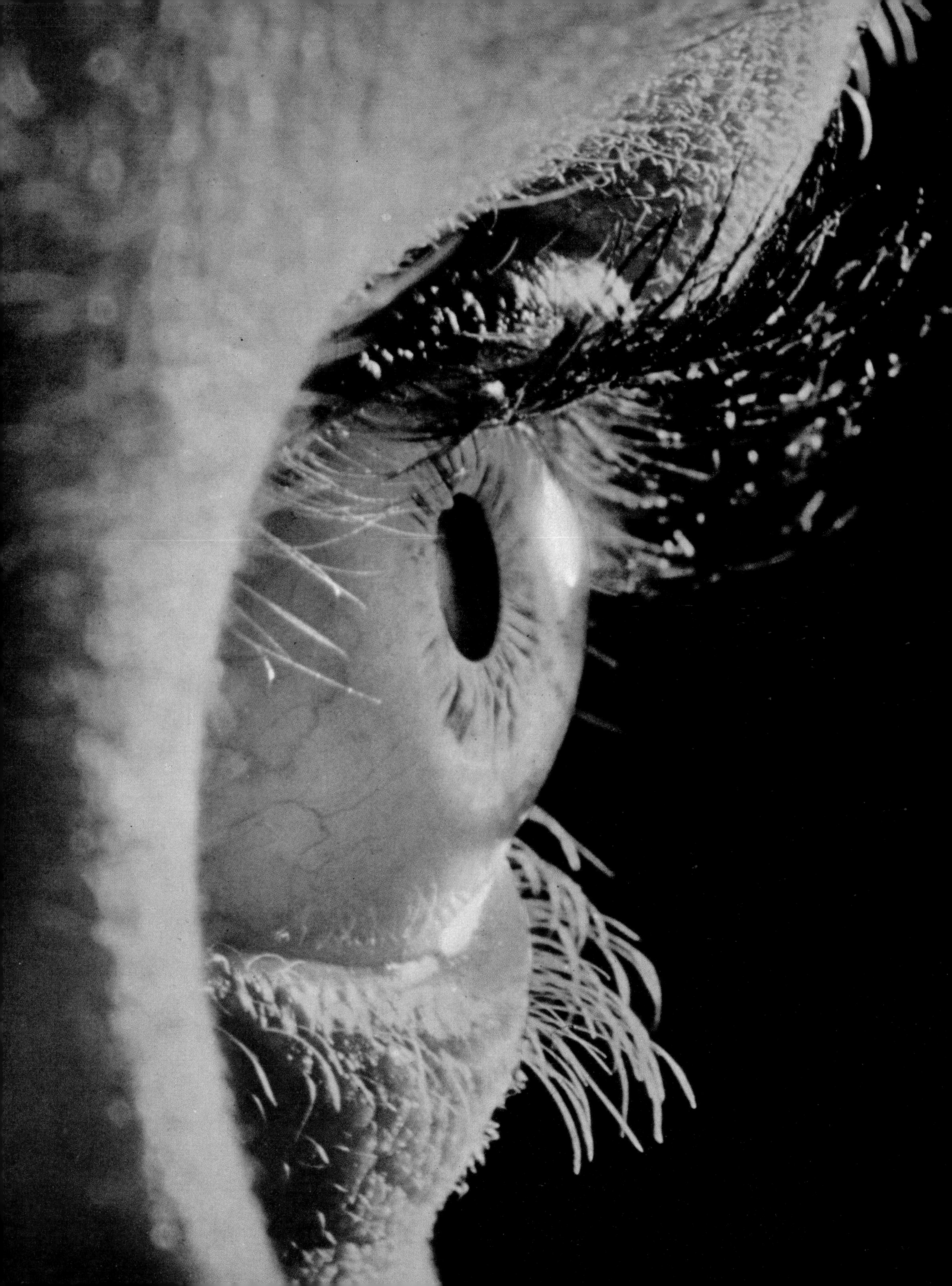

An Inside Look at Eye Structure

Mechanically, the eye is an instrument which collects light rays and focuses them into an image registered on its rear surface.

Light enters through the cornea, a tough, transparent membrane at the front of the eye. Because of its rounded shape, the cornea acts like the convex lens of a camera, bending light rays together. Behind the cornea, a colored circular curtain—the iris—opens and contracts like a camera's diaphragm to regulate the amount of light which enters the eye. The small round hole in the center of the iris is the pupil. Light passes through it and into a transparent body—the lens—whose shape can be changed by the ciliary muscle connected to the capsule of the lens by a network of tiny fibers.

Control of the lens by its muscle is for the purpose of focusing the light precisely on the retina, a light-sensitive layer at the back of the eye and covering about 65 per cent of its interior surface. Photosensitive cells in the retina convert the light energy into signals that are carried to the brain by the optic nerve. In the middle of the retina is a small dimple called the fovea; it is the center of the eye's sharpest vision.

The choroid and iris, which are richly supplied with blood vessels, nourish a portion of the eye, as does the aqueous humor, a watery fluid which washes through the front of the eye between the cornea and lens. The vitreous humor, a transparent jelly which fills the interior of the eye much as air fills a balloon, helps the eye hold its shape.

Muscles for moving the eye spring from the sclera, the eye's tough outer coating; the conjunctiva—a supple protective membrane—joins the front of the eye to the inside of the eyelids.

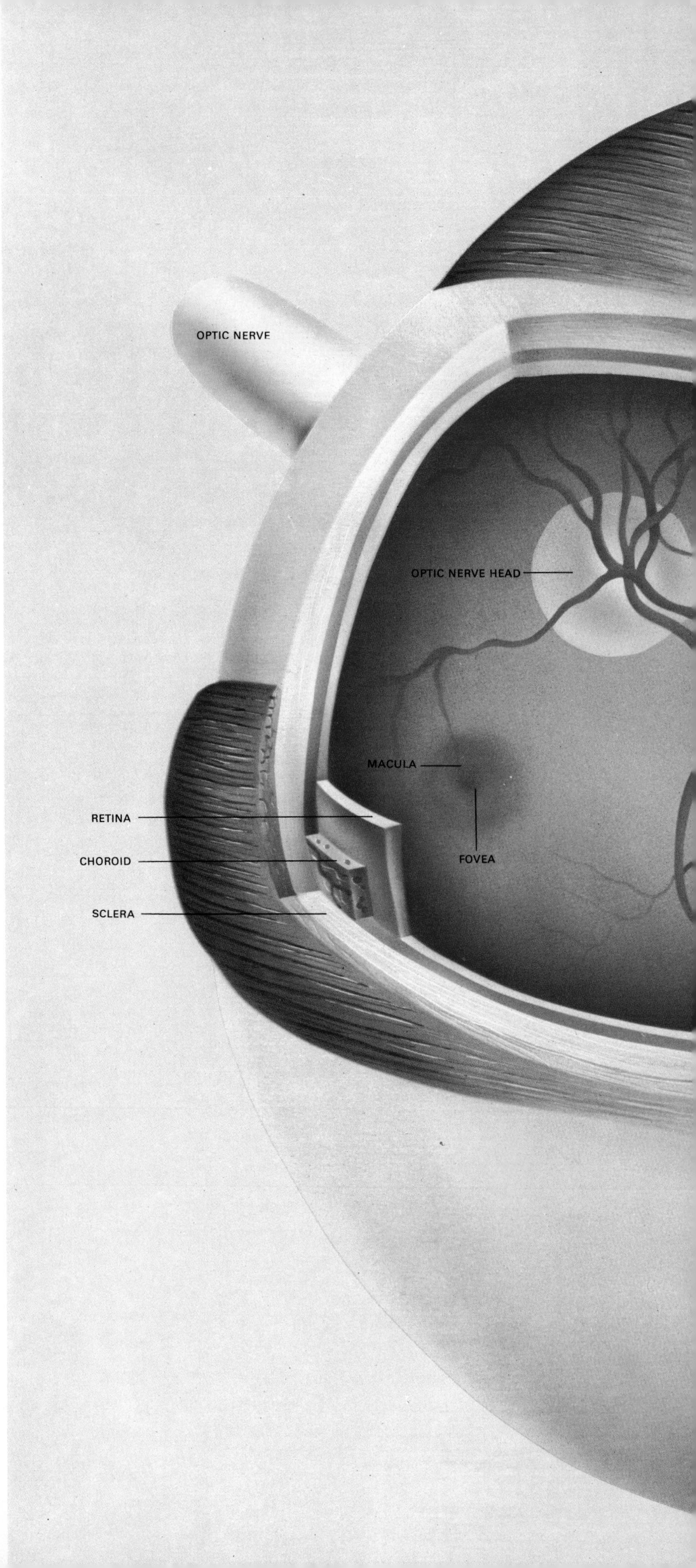

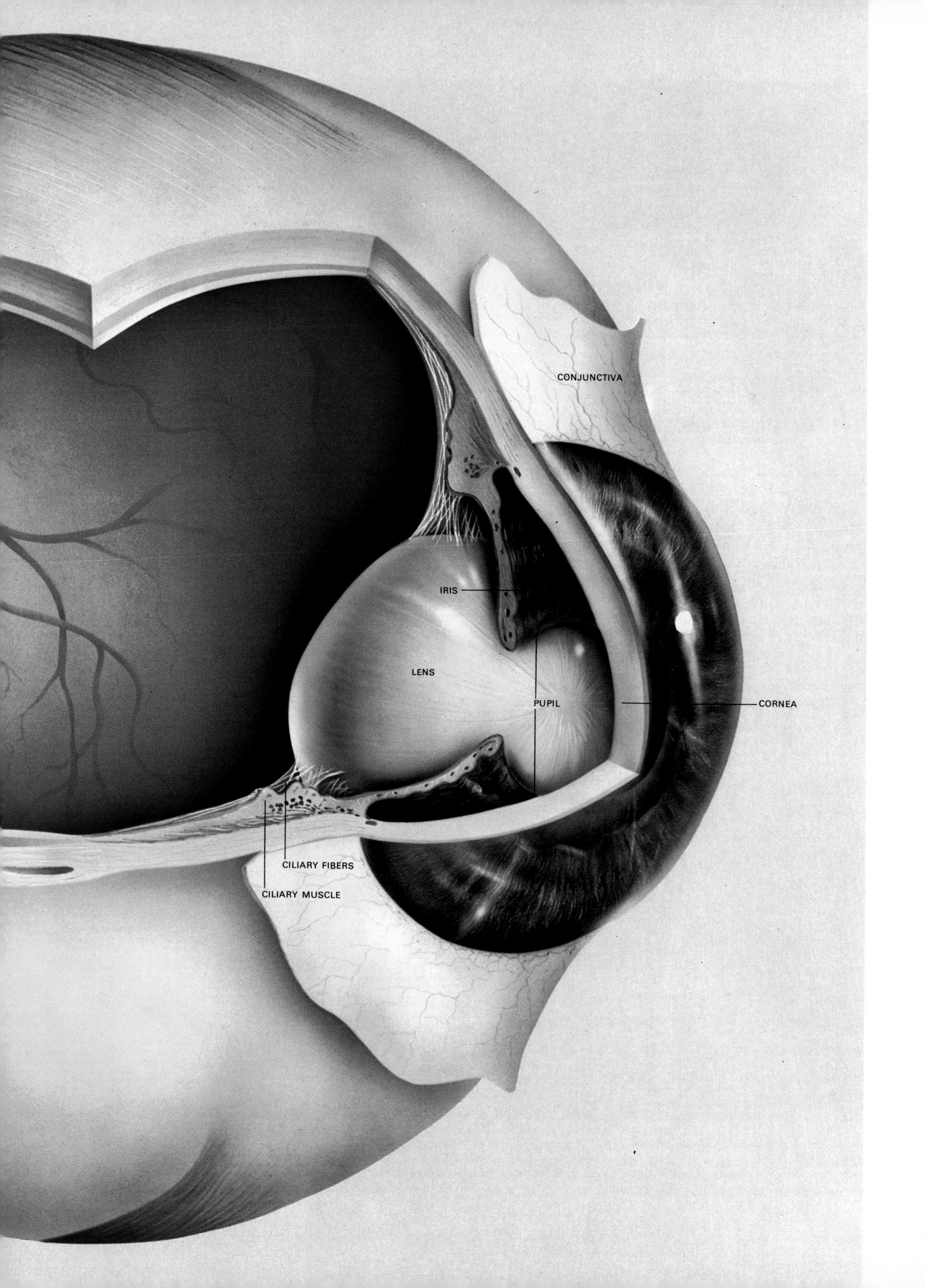
CONJUNCTIVA
IRIS
LENS
PUPIL
CORNEA
CILIARY FIBERS
CILIARY MUSCLE

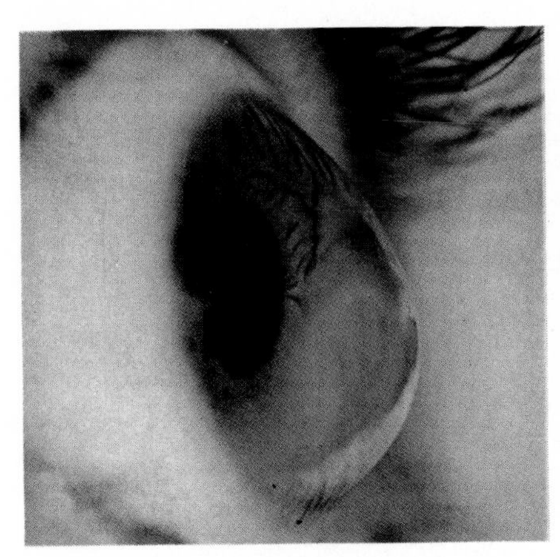

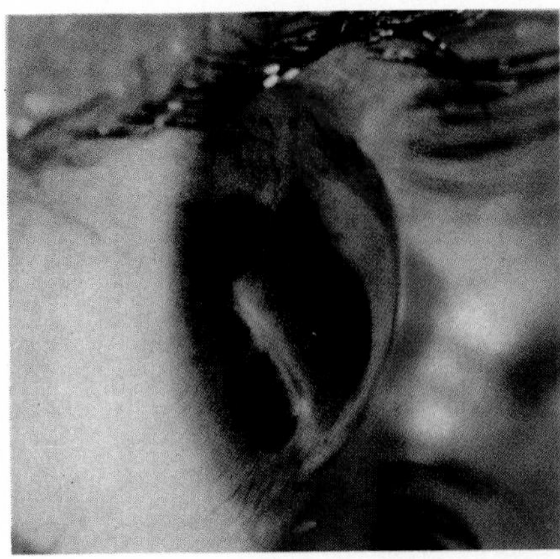

GRAFTING ON NEW SIGHT
Cornea damage, which causes blindness by fogging the eye's window, can be repaired by replacing the opaque section *(far left)* with tissue from a healthy cornea. This was first done successfully in the late 19th Century; today hundreds of corneas are transplanted annually.

A Transparent Window to the Eye

The profusion of light which hits the surface of the eye must be organized and directed inward to form a sharp image on the retina. About 70 per cent of the job is done by the cornea, an arced, glassy window at the entrance to the eye.

Because of its curved shape, the cornea bends light toward the retina in converging rays. When healthy, it is one of the most transparent tissues in the body. But disease or injury sometimes clouds over the cornea, and this may result in blindness. Eye surgeons have learned how to overcome this by replacing damaged corneas with clear ones from human donors. Also, imperfections in the shape of the cornea may cause distortion. This condition—called astigmatism—affects almost all people to some degree.

The iris, which adjusts the amount of light entering the eye, sits behind the cornea like a shade behind a window. The pigmentation which renders the iris opaque also gives the eye its color. All irises have the same dark pigment. But brown and hazel eyes have more of it than blue ones.

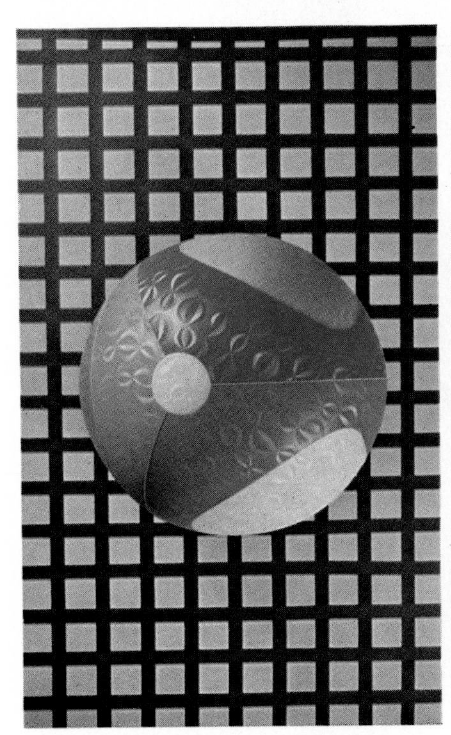

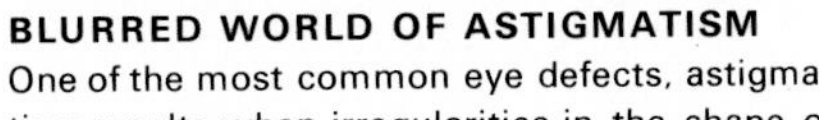

BLURRED WORLD OF ASTIGMATISM
One of the most common eye defects, astigmatism results when irregularities in the shape of the cornea distort the eye's focusing ability. The first photograph shows a nonastigmatic view of a multicolored beach ball on a symmetrical grid. In the next two pictures, an astigmatic lens, ground to duplicate the effect of a deformed cornea, sends the focus askew, warping the image of ball and grid vertically and then obliquely.

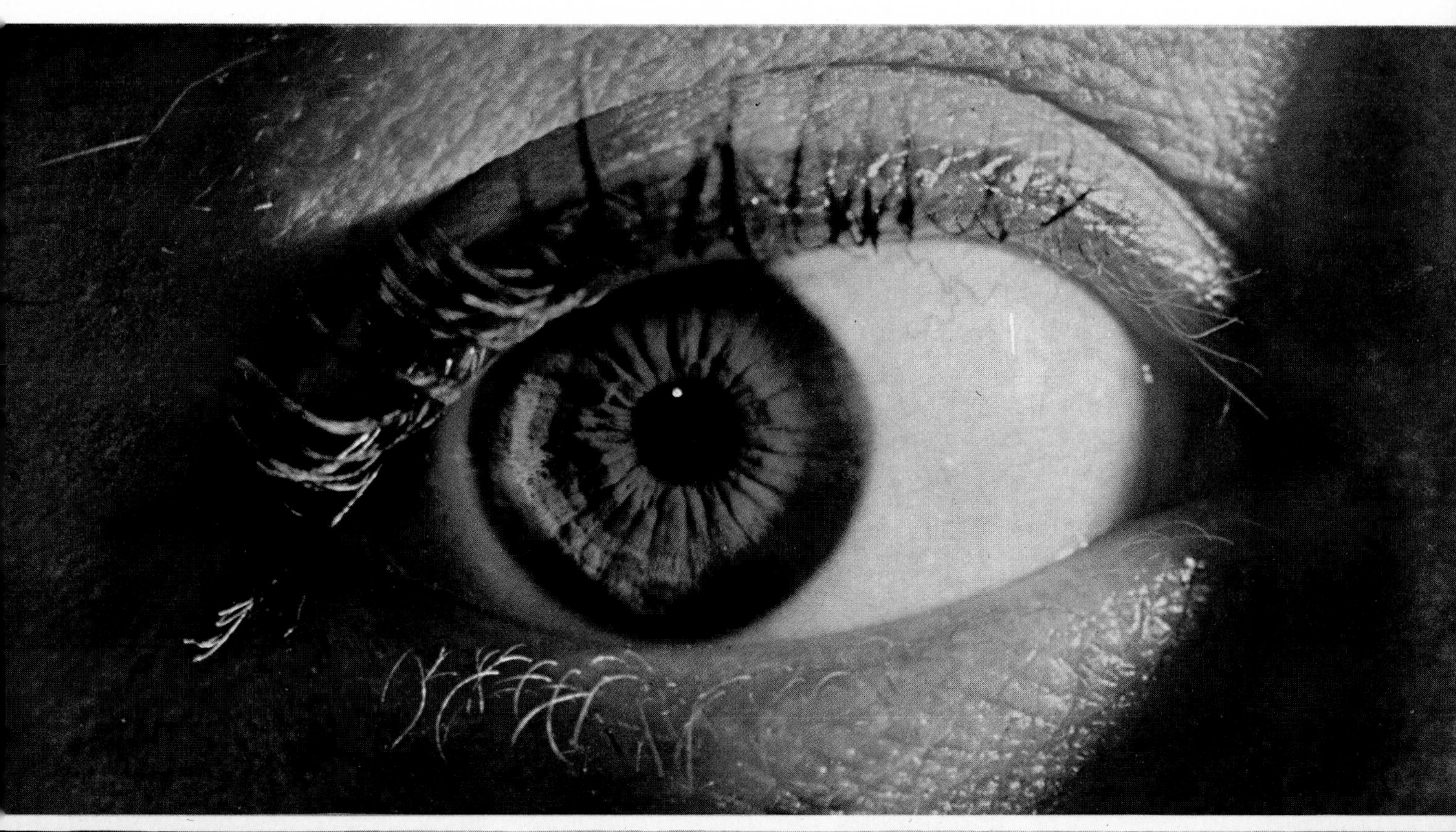

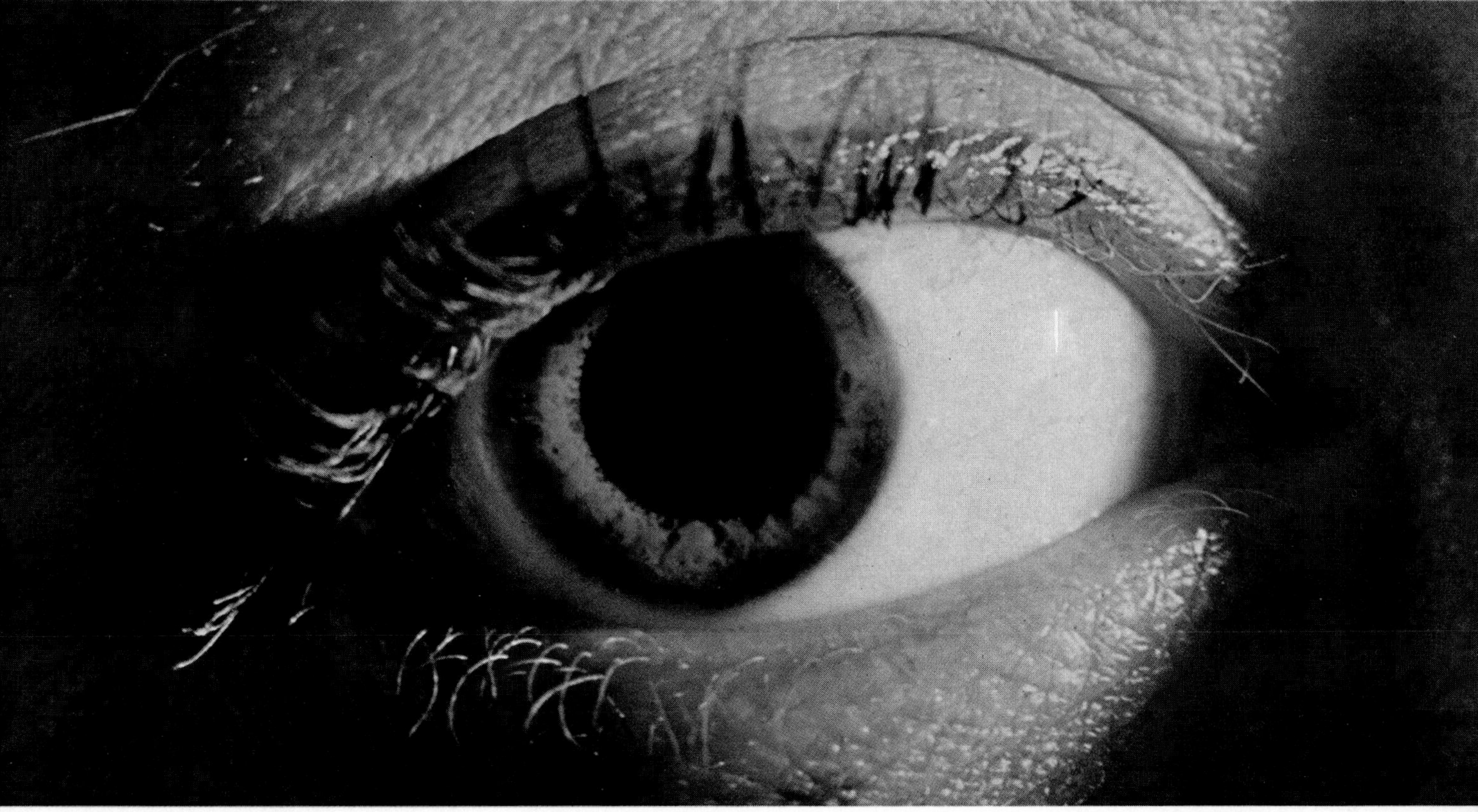

AN ADJUSTABLE SHADE

Flecked with pigment to screen out light rays, a fawn-colored iris closes down in bright light *(top photo),* cutting the amount of light entering the eye through the pupil. In dim light *(bottom)* the iris opens up, allowing more light to pass. When an overdose of light strikes the sensitive cells at the rear of the eye, nerve impulses are relayed back to the muscles of the iris, which cause it to shut down automatically.

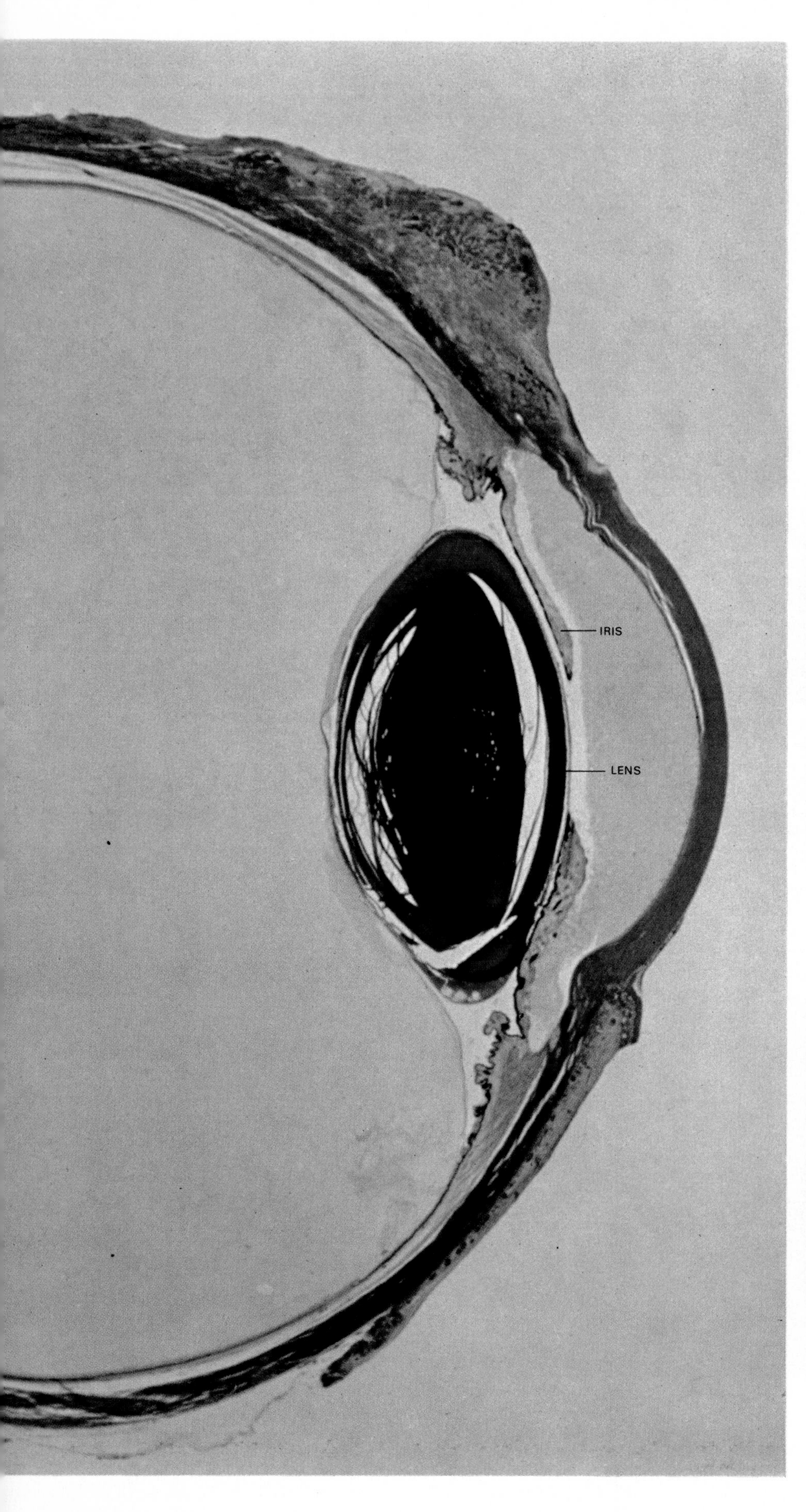

THE LENS IN PROFILE
The transparent structures of the eye's focusing apparatus have been magnified about nine times in this unusual cross-section photograph. Long fibers, arranged like the whorls in a fingerprint, are packed together to form the body of the lens, here dyed a rich plum color. They are sheathed in a transparent, rubbery envelope, which gives the entire structure the elasticity it needs in order to change shape for focusing.

A DISTANCE VIEW
Like the camera that snapped this photograph, the eye may focus on objects in the distance; but this makes foreground objects indistinct.

OR A CLOSE-UP
When adjusting for near-vision, both the eye and the camera throw distant objects out of focus, like the buildings behind this traffic sign.

A Pliable Lens for Changing Focus

Like the fine adjustment on a microscope, the flexible lens allows the eye to change focus. It can adjust for either long-distance vision or for close-ups, but not both at once.

Most of the eye's focusing ability is supplied by the cornea. But when nearby objects are sighted, additional refraction is needed to produce sharp images on the retina. For this the eye must rely on the lens. The lens adjusts by changing shape. The thicker it becomes, the greater its ability to converge light rays for close vision. This ability of the lens to vary its shape is called accommodation.

A pliable body smaller than a lima bean, the lens is suspended behind the iris at the threshold of the eye's inner chamber. A network of slender fibers connects it with the surrounding ciliary body. The tension of the fibers holds the lens flat. The ancient Greeks likened the arrangement to a spider crouched in the center of its web.

To accommodate for nearby vision, the muscles in the ciliary body contract, like a drawstring closing a duffel bag. This eases some of the tension in the fibers. No longer pulled flat, the flexible lens bulges thicker, so that its focusing power increases. Since accommodation means work for the ciliary muscle, long periods of close vision can result in eyestrain.

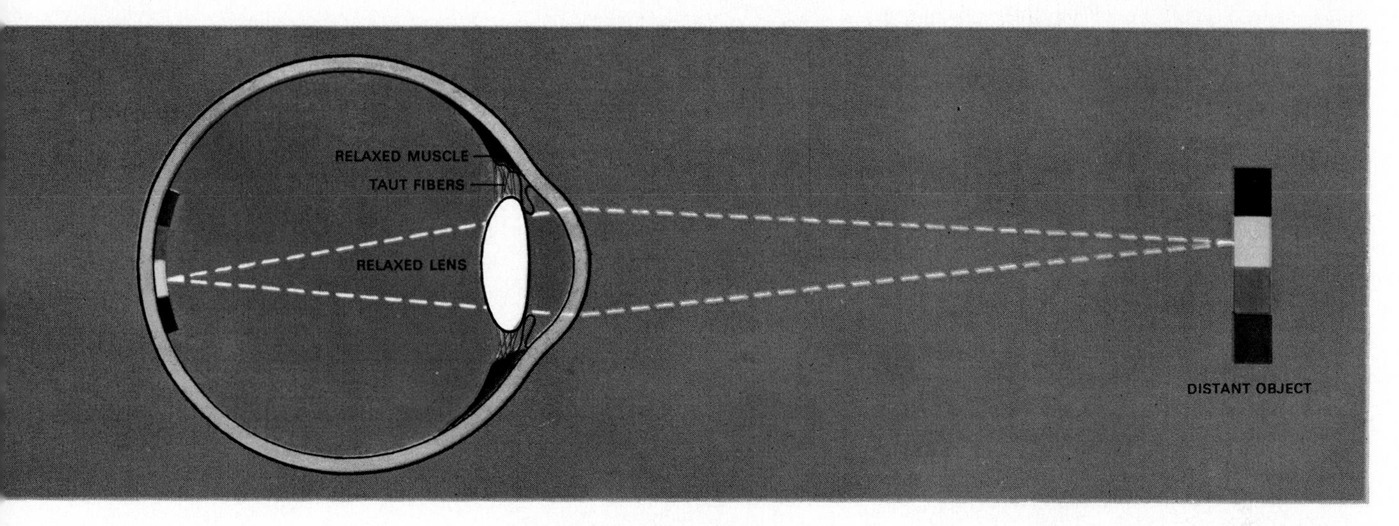

THE LENS: LONG RANGE
Diverging light rays from a point on a distant object are focused by the cornea and lens into a corresponding point on the retina to form part of the retinal image. The lens, stretched thin by the taut fibers which hold it, adds only the minimum amount of its focusing power.

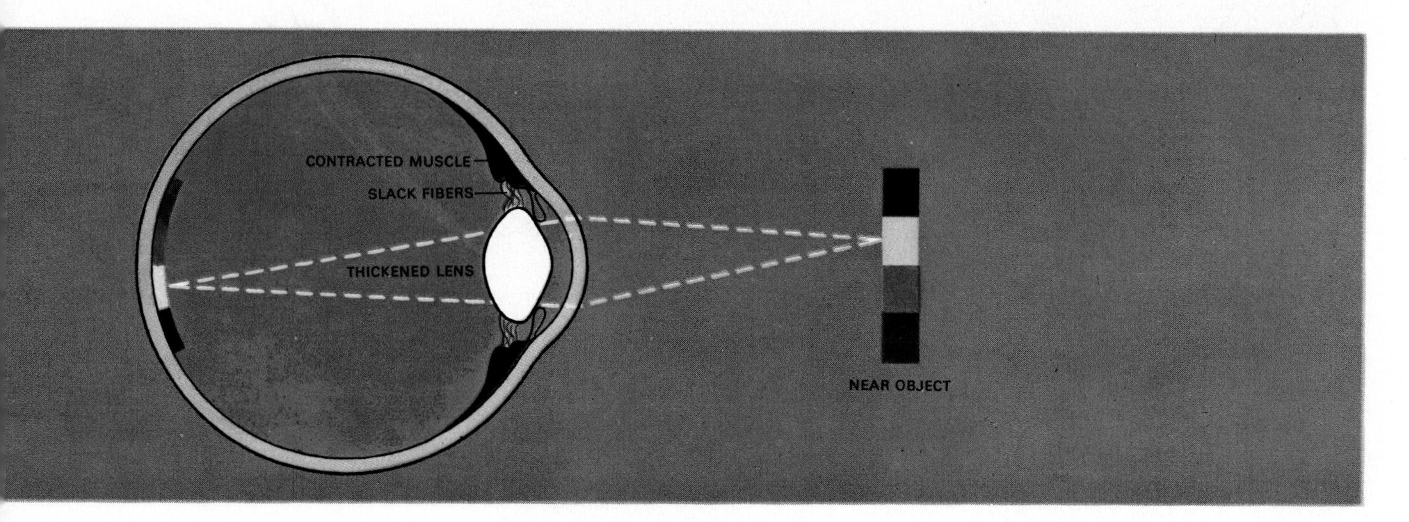

THE LENS: CLOSE-UP
Light rays from a near object hit the eye at a relatively wider angle, and the lens thickens to provide the greater focusing powers needed to converge them. Retinal images are inverted, but the brain has learned how to compensate for this, so that the world appears right side up.

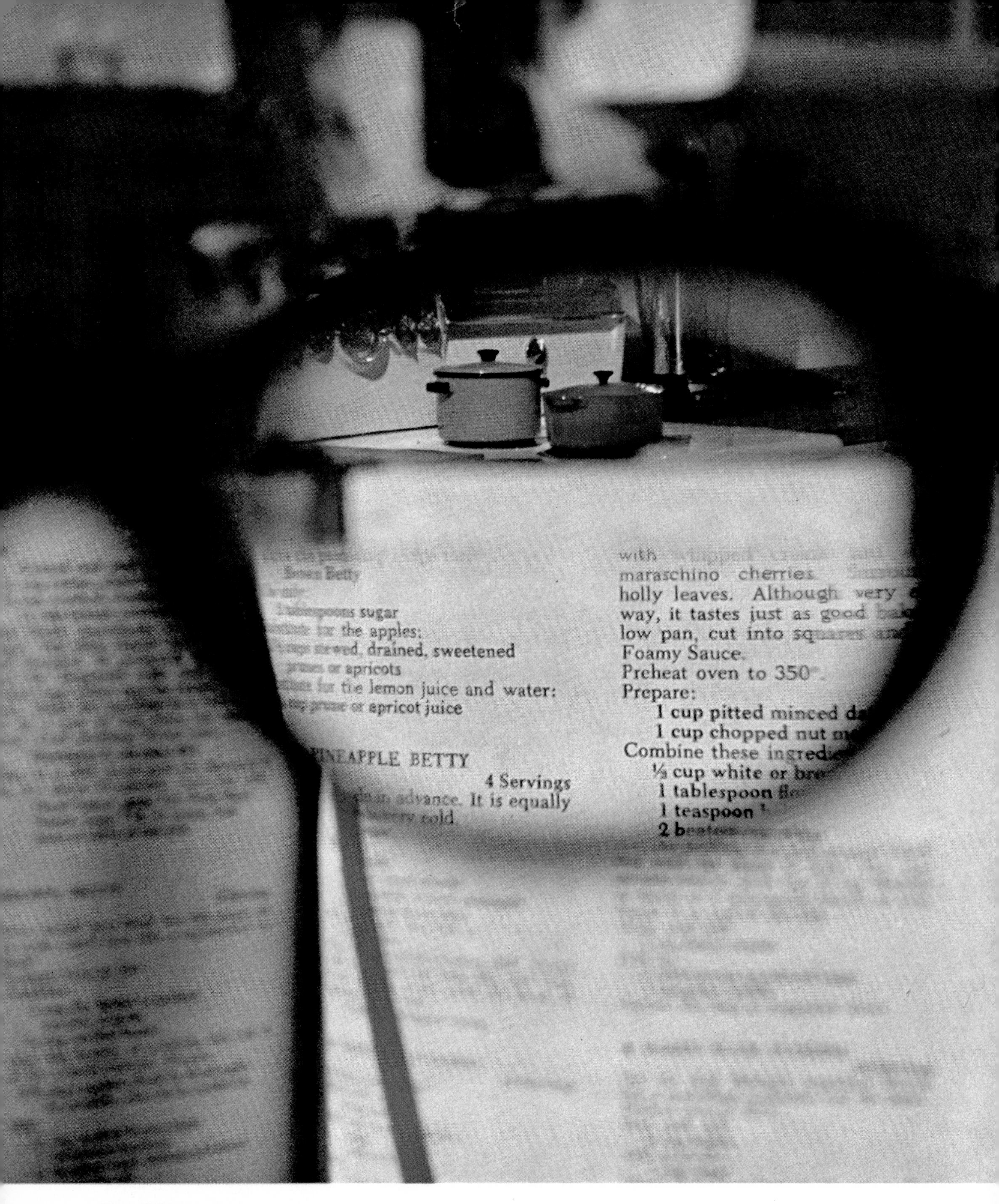

TWO LENSES IN ONE

Bifocals—introduced to America in the 18th Century by Benjamin Franklin—help older people with rigid lens structure to focus at both near and far distances. The upper half of the spectacle lens gives slight correction for distant viewing. The lower half is for closeup work; it provides the increased refraction needed to compensate for the increasing rigidity—and the inability to focus—of the aging lens.

Extra Lenses for Oddly Shaped Eyes

Unlike telescopes, built with scientific precision, eyes vary in shape, which may hinder their focusing ability. But ever since the 13th Century, people have used eyeglasses to correct faulty focus.

If the eye is too long, distant images fall in front of the retina. The result is myopia, or nearsightedness. Hyperopia, or farsightedness, occurs when the eye is too short—the lens and cornea are not powerful enough to converge light rays from close objects onto the retina. Even when looking into the distance, a farsighted person not wearing glasses must make a constant effort to focus.

Aging also affects focus. Each year, the lens grows less pliable and loses some of its ability to adjust. This phenomenon—called presbyopia—can be corrected with bifocal eyeglasses.

THE NEARSIGHTED EYE

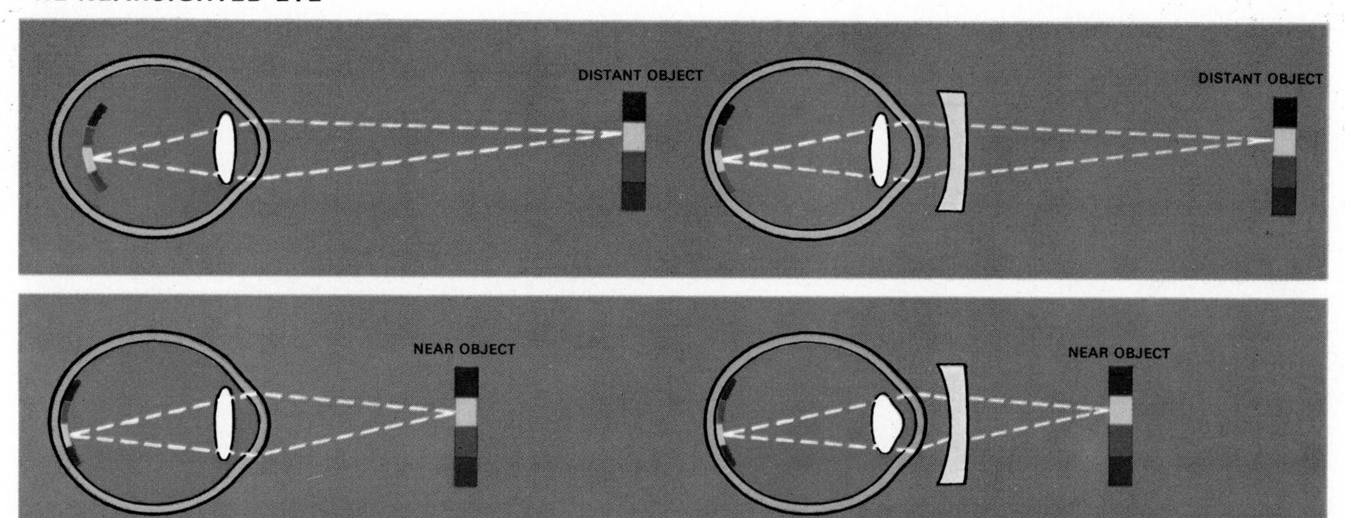

CORRECTING NEARSIGHTEDNESS

In nearsightedness, the eyeball is actually too long for the normal focusing power of the lens and cornea. Light rays from a distant object converge in front of the retina. A concave glass, however, diverges light rays slightly, and the image is moved back onto the retina *(top right)*. For nearby objects the image falls on the retina *(bottom left)* without accommodation; but with glasses, the lens accommodates for near vision.

THE FARSIGHTED EYE

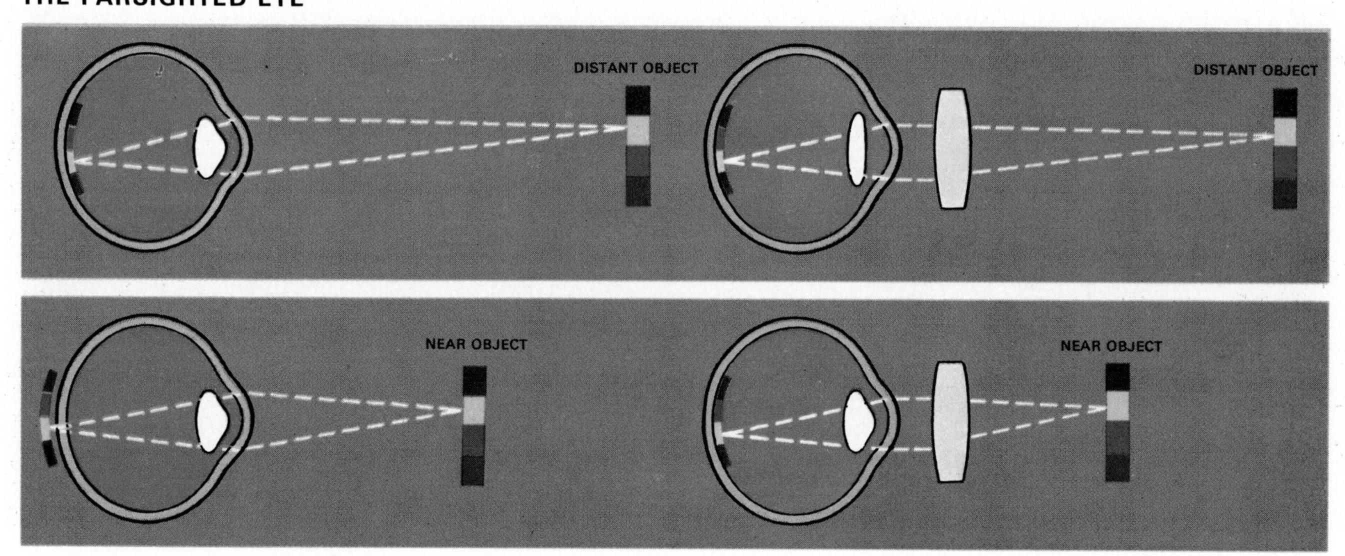

CORRECTING FARSIGHTEDNESS

The farsighted eye is too short; thus its lens must accommodate to focus images even of distant objects *(top left)*. For nearby objects the lens cannot accommodate enough to keep images from falling beyond the retina *(lower left)*. A convex glass lens, by converging the light rays, helps to compensate for the short distance between the lens and the retina, and enables the eye's lens to focus in a normal manner.

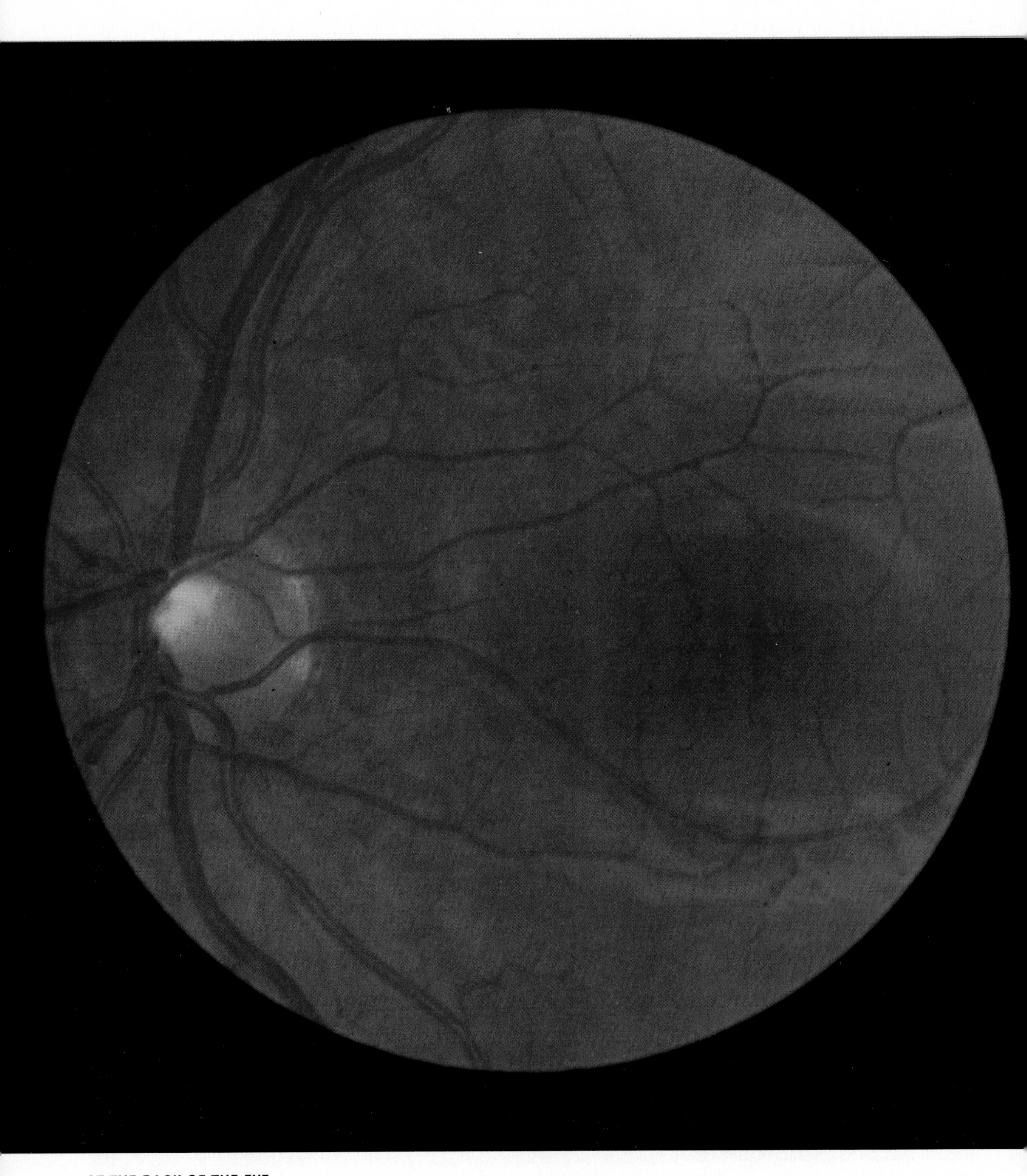

AT THE BACK OF THE EYE

Like a strange planet, the retina reflects a weird reddish orange from a shaft of light beamed in through the pupil in this photograph of the back surface of the eye. The dark area to the right is the macula region, with the fovea, the seat of sharpest vision, located at its center. To the left, the pale-yellow optic nerve head is the only point at the back of the eye not sensitive to light. A network of arteries and darker, larger veins streams across the retina; it bypasses the fovea, however, where it would obstruct the tiny area of the eye's most acute perception.

A Screen for Viewing Images

The business end of the eye is the retina, a paper-thin membrane which lines the inside of the eyeball like a miniature curved movie screen. Here light rays, focused mechanically by the cornea and lens, are transformed into electrical signals and sent to the brain. But unlike a movie screen, with its unmarred surface, the retina is rivered with veins and arteries, and marked with areas of greater or lesser sensitivity. Acute vision takes place only for objects seen straight on; their images fall on the fovea, a tiny pit in the center of a slight depression called the macula. Another spot, about the size of a pinhead, is blind because it has no light-responsive cells. This is the point where the optic nerve fibers leave the eye. These fibers carry the signals collected from the nerve cells of the retina to the brain for translation into eyesight.

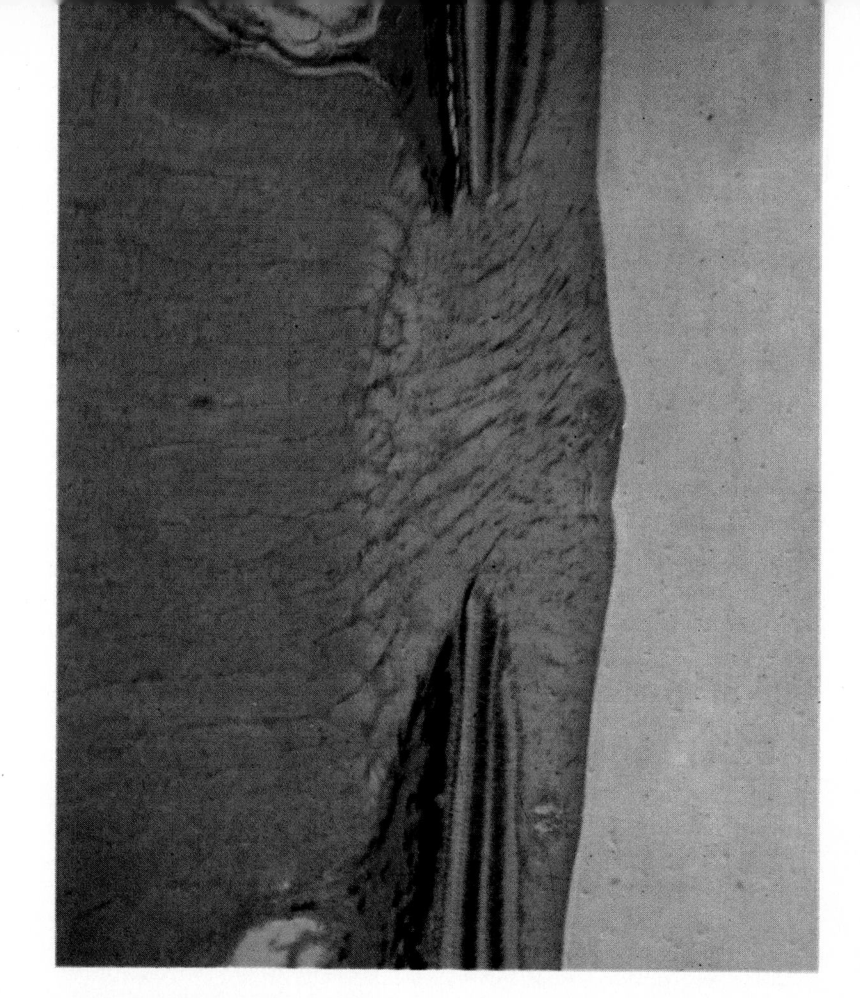

THE EYE'S BLIND SPOT
Shown in cross section, magnified 270 times, is the place in the retina where the light-sensitive cells are interrupted by the presence of the optic nerve head. This accounts for the blind spot. Here nerve fibers from the retina converge to form the optic nerve, which transmits the nerve signals to the brain for decoding into visual images.

LOCATING THE BLIND SPOT
To "see" your blind spot, hold the book at comfortable arm's length. Cover your left eye and focus the right eye on the apple. By adjusting the distance from the book to your eye, you can make the orange vanish, indicating that its image has fallen on the optic nerve head of your right eye. The blind spot, outside the area of normal visual attention, is hardly ever noticed.

Rods and Cones for Sensing Light

The final destination of the light rays focused by cornea and lens is a battery of light-sensitive cells at the back of the retina. There are two types of cells: rods and cones, so named because of their shapes. Both contain chemicals which, when excited by light, are altered. This marks the transition from light to nerve signals.

Some 130 million rods and cones line the retina. The cones are used for daylight vision, and are capable of producing the clearest signals to the brain, which interprets them into keen perception. They also contain light-sensitive pigments which make it possible for them to distinguish color. The highest concentration of cones is in the fovea, the spot where the eye obtains its sharpest images.

Outside the fovea, rod cells predominate. Rod cells, used in night vision, cannot detect color, but register only in black and white, and the images which are formed from them seem fuzzy. That is why night and twilight scenes appear less distinct and seem to be made up of various shades of gray—the sharp-vision, color-detecting cones are not functioning, and the whole job must be taken over by the rods. Because the rods are located outside the fovea, it is possible to see an object in the dark only by looking at it slightly off center rather than gazing straight at it.

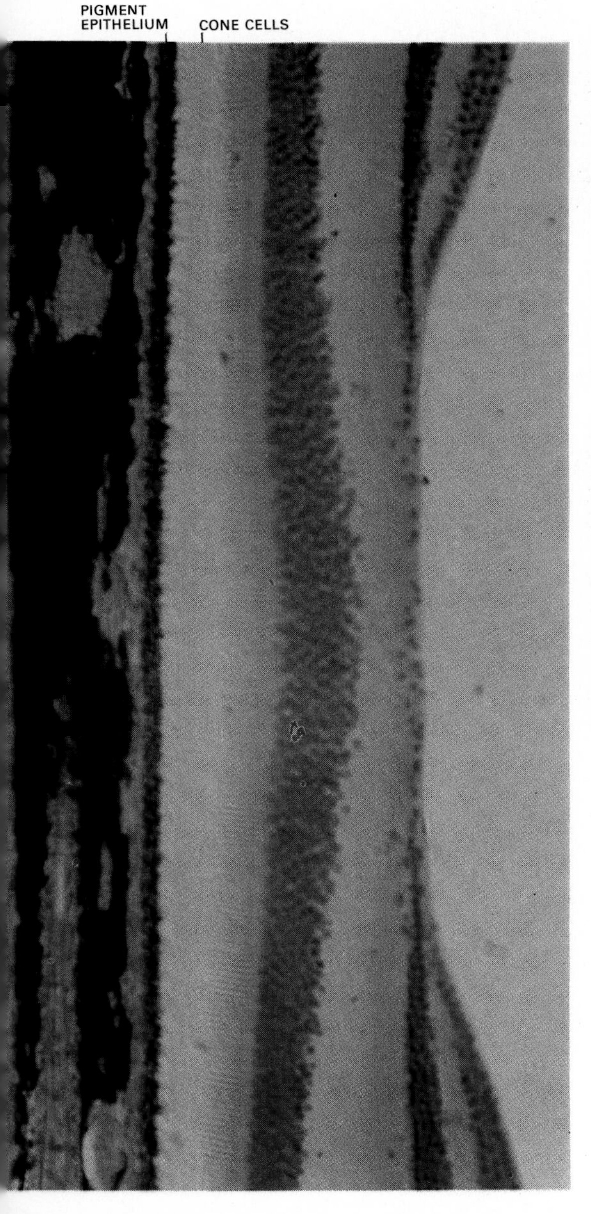

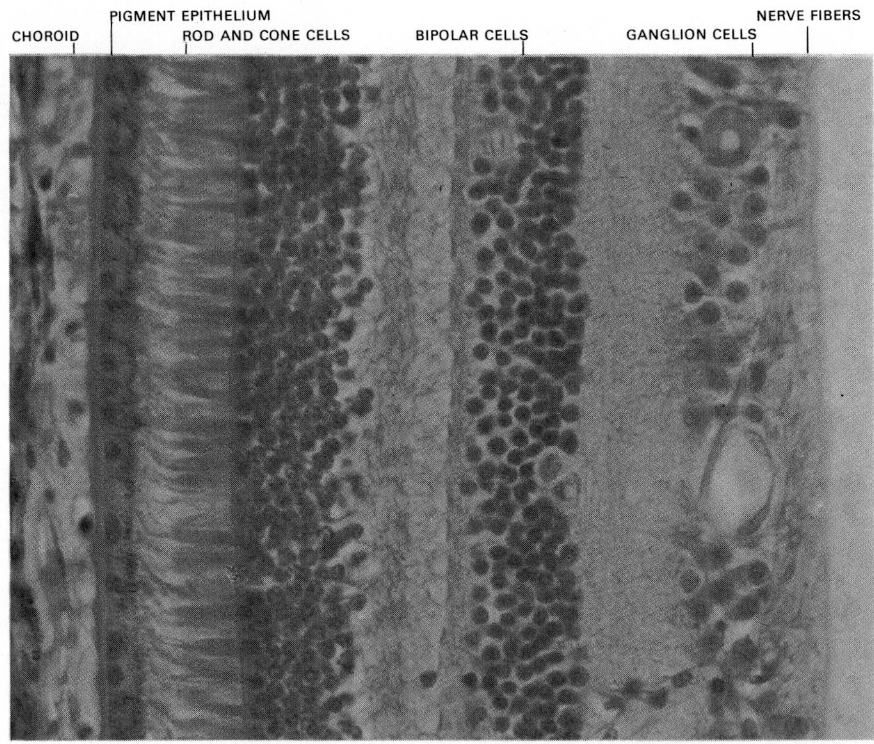

VALLEY OF KEENEST SIGHT
The fovea, a dimple on the retina where the eye sees sharpest, is shown at left in enlarged cross section. A slight depression occurs where layers of nerve cells have spread aside. Some 10,000 cones in the light-colored band give the fovea its remarkable perceptive ability.

THE RETINA IN PROFILE
Layers of cells are sandwiched together to form the retina, shown above in magnified cross section. Light entering from the right pierces several rows of nerve cells before registering on the layer of rods and cones. The cone cells can be differentiated by their slightly darker stain.

SIGHT BY DAY AND NIGHT
The photographs of the French château opposite indicate how the eye registers color and sharp detail in daylight *(top picture)*, and fuzzy monochrome at dusk *(bottom)*. The black spot in the center of the bottom picture denotes the failure of the fovea to function in dim light.

5

Exploring the Spectrum

The great ball of sun setting over the desert appears yellow because some of its rays have been scattered. At this time of day, the longer, yellow wavelengths predominate. At sunset the longest wavelengths turn the sun deep red.

LIGHT IS THE ONLY SOURCE OF COLOR in the world. The ripest tomato, the most spectacular peacock, the gaudiest clown's costume—all are merely reflectors, absorbers and transmitters of one or more of the colors that make up light. Without it, not even the faintest color exists.

This is not an easy concept to accept because color seems an inherent part of everything man sees. He lives in a world of bright spring and summer flowers and breathtaking fall foliage, of blue seas and red-gold sunsets, of rich canvases painted by master artists. If light is the only source of color, how does nature achieve its endlessly diverse palette, and how does man get the remarkable effects he does with color? The answers to these questions lie in the nature and interrelationship of three elements: light, the source of color; the material and its response to color; and the eye, the perceiver of color.

Man's entire concept of color was thrown into turmoil by Isaac Newton's epochal discovery that sunlight is a mixture of colors. Others had, of course, noticed the pretty colors that dappled the wall when sunlight passed through a prism, but they had assumed that something in the glass changed the properties of light and gave it color. Newton believed that the prism merely separated the light into its components—the colors of the spectrum—and proved his view by passing the separated rays through a second prism and reuniting them into white light.

Newton's discovery was enormously disturbing because it called for a major unlearning process. Until then, most of the commonly accepted concepts about color had been advanced by artist-scientists like Leonardo da Vinci, who based their theories on their experiences with pigment mixtures. The old and the new ideas were often in direct conflict.

Inevitably, Newton's revolutionary doctrine met with violent opposition. Not only did scientists battle over the validity of Newton's findings, but prominent literary figures of the day entered the lists. Johann Wolfgang von Goethe, the German poet, philosopher and student of light and vision, was so outraged by the new concept that he devoted many years to bitter denunciations of the theory and its author. On the other hand, the great French satirist François Voltaire, wrote: "There is in this world a devil of a Newton who has found out how much the sun weighs, and of what color the rays are that compose light. This strange man has turned my head." Newton was, Voltaire said, "the greatest man that ever lived."

It is easy to see why Newton was unsettling to orthodox views. Even modern man is likely to share the confusion because he usually gains his first knowledge of colors from the paint box, and lessons learned in mixing pigments can rarely be applied to the mixing of the colors of light. The reason for this is not difficult to understand if one keeps in mind the fact that the two are fundamentally different: light is the source of all color, and pigments are simply reflectors, absorbers and transmitters of colors.

If an artist is asked to name the primary colors—those which, if mixed in proper proportions, will produce any other color—he will probably answer: blue, yellow and red or, if he is somewhat more sophisticated in his field, cyan (blue-green), yellow and magenta (blue-red). If a scientist is asked the same question about spectral colors, he will respond: red, green and blue. No yellow? Certainly no pigment combination of those colors will produce yellow. Yet strangely enough, if a beam of red light and another of green are overlapped, the result is yellow.

Mathematics by the eye

Exactly why beams of red and green light combine to produce yellow is not fully understood. One explanation proceeds from the wavelengths of the different colors that make up light and the way the human eye averages a mixture. In the wide band of electromagnetic waves that range from the very short gamma rays to the miles-long radio waves, the only wavelengths visible to man occupy a narrow span from about 400 to 700 millimicrons (a millimicron is about 1/25,000,000 of an inch). Green is moderately short, about 500 millimicrons; red is extremely long, about 700 millimicrons. The eye averages these two wavelengths and sees one of 600 millimicrons, which is in the yellow sector of the spectrum.

Despite this explanation, it is difficult for anyone who has ever played or worked with paints to comprehend immediately how yellow can result from a mixture of red and green light. For if red and green paint are put together, the result is a dirty black.

The answer to the riddle lies primarily in the totally different ways colors are achieved with light and pigments. The differences are analogous to addition and subtraction in mathematics. All spectral colors can be created by *adding,* in varying degrees of intensity, different amounts of three primary components of light. Pigment colors, on the other hand, are arrived at by *subtraction.* (Although it is now evident that, strictly speaking, the word "colors" in connection with pigments is erroneous, it is used as a matter of convenience.) Pigments achieve their color by absorbing, or subtracting, certain parts of the spectrum and reflecting or transmitting the parts that remain.

The subtraction is done by the pigment molecules present in flowers, trees and animals, in paints, dyes and inks—in fact in almost every object created by nature or man. Although most pigment molecules are comprised of a small number of atoms—40 or 50 at most—they can take a wide variety of structural forms. And each of these forms has its own characteristic way of subtracting, or absorbing, certain wavelengths of light and reflecting others. Each pigment of a given structure may be said to have a resonance for a certain color wavelength—just as a radio may be tuned to pick up one certain station broadcasting on a specific frequency—and this resonant frequency represents the color or colors most strongly absorbed by the pigment molecule.

For example, the particular arrangement of the pigment molecules in chlorophyll accounts for the greenness of most plants and trees. When white light falls on such a plant or tree, the chlorophyll absorbs most of the deep purple and blue, and most of the long waves at the red end of

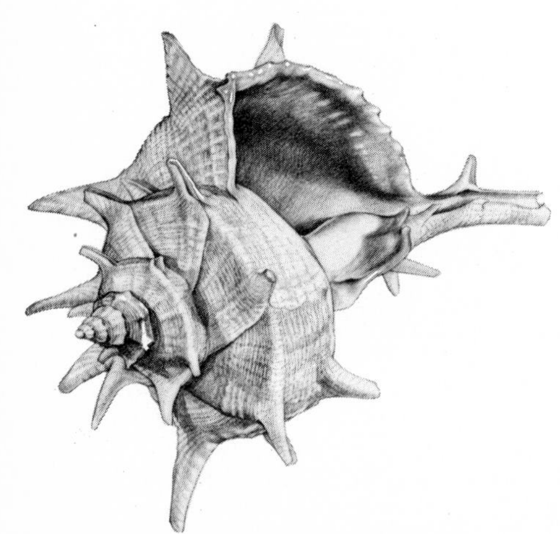

THE MUREX BRANDARIS SNAIL, whose shell is shown above, secretes a yellowish fluid which, when boiled and treated, becomes a permanent purple dye. This pigment provided the ancient Phoenicians, Greeks and Romans with the rich color called Tyrian purple.

the spectrum. What remains, then, is green and a little red, which are reflected back to the eye. The same process takes place in the pigment molecules of carotene, found in carrots, daffodils, dandelions and other plants. The difference is that carotene reflects the yellow-orange wavelengths and absorbs all others.

The same law applies to man-made colors. A red dress is red because the dye subtracts all the other wavelengths of the visual spectrum and reflects only red. A blue package absorbs all the long-wave colors and the eye sees only the short-wave blue. Black absorbs all wavelengths and reflects no color at all. On the other hand, white gives back equally all the colors of light, which together comprise white.

Not all light is as white as sunlight, of course. Man-made light in particular usually has a dominant color, and these variations from white greatly alter the reflected light the eye receives from a given pigment. The old practice of taking a suit outside a store to see the fabric in daylight is well grounded in the differences between natural and artificial light. For instance, fluorescent lights, because they have relatively little red, make skin tones unhealthily blue; candlelight, on the other hand, has long been the favorite illumination of women because it gives a warm rosy-yellow tone to the most pallid complexion. Regardless of the color of the light, it is worth repeating that all that pigments can do is reflect, absorb or selectively transmit light.

Mother-of-pearl rainbows

But the color of some objects depends not so much upon the internal molecular arrangement of the pigment molecules nor the dominant color in the light as upon the surface structure of the object. This surface texture can have a remarkable effect upon the light which strikes it. For instance, mother-of-pearl, a lustrous material that appears to glow with muted rainbow hues, gets its color because the layers of which it is composed are subjected to a slicing process that exposes hundreds of tiny parallel ridges. The ridges break up the wave front of white light into many smaller waves that cross and recross and, by combining or interfering, spread out into the various spectral colors.

POMPEIAN DYERS, in this adaptation of a mural painted about 70 A.D., take cloth from a heated vat and wring out excess dye over trays that funnel the liquid back into the drum. At that time, all dyes came from nature; artificial dyes were still centuries away.

Some rather curious phenomena of a different kind result from the selective reflection of certain surfaces. Gold leaf, for example, absorbs only blue light. However, its textured surface strongly reflects only yellow and red. What, then, happens to the green part of the spectrum if it is neither absorbed nor reflected strongly? Simple enough: it comes out on the other side. If light is shone through a thin piece of gold leaf onto a white screen, the color that appears on the screen will be green. This is an example of transmission of color.

Regardless of such variations in the usual subtraction process, an object is still dependent for color upon the kind of light that strikes it. Primarily, all objects except light sources are reflectors. A surface that is normally white in daylight becomes red when lit by a red light, green in a green light, and so on. An article that is red in daylight appears black when illuminated by a green light because such a light does not contain the one color, red, that can be reflected. Thus, no color is reflected. The same effect would be achieved if the article were green and the light red.

A special kind of reflection phenomenon, called scattering, underlies the great expanses of color in the sky and clouds, and in the often spectacularly hued sunrises and sunsets. If there were nothing in the heavens at all, no dust or gases, the sky would appear black. In fact that is the way it does look, beginning at a point about 10 miles above the earth's surface, where the atmosphere thins out almost to the vanishing point. There the sky is always dark and stars may be seen at any hour of the day or night. However, when sunlight passes through the earth's atmosphere, molecules of gases of various densities scatter the light. But because they scatter the short wavelengths—the blue end of the spectrum—more than they do the longer wavelengths, the sky takes on a blue hue. But when there is considerable dust or moisture in the air, these layers of particles do scatter the longer waves, causing the blue of the sky to become whiter. Thus the sky is deepest blue when the air is clean and dry, palest when the atmosphere is dust-laden or humid.

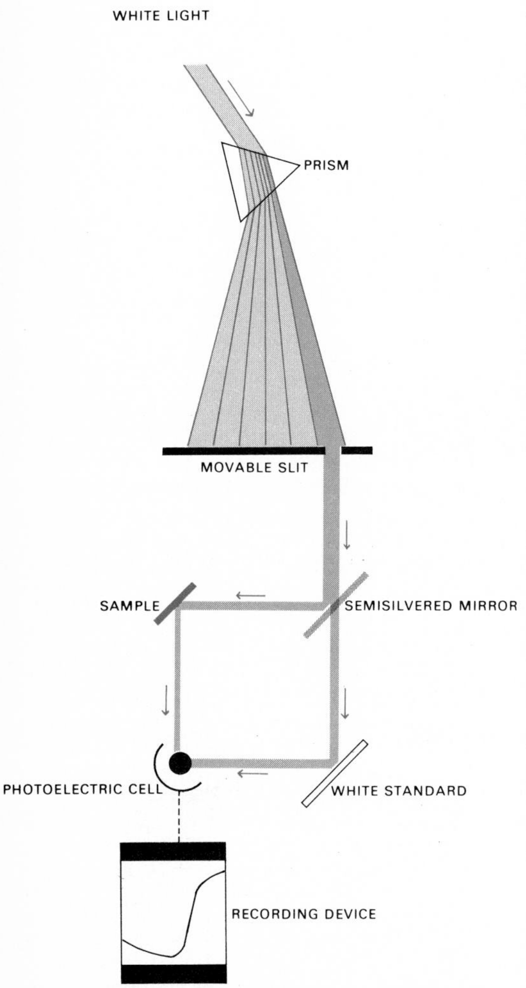

Colors from dust

Increase the amount of dust or water vapor, and still other colors are produced. The daily variation in the sun's appearance is an excellent example of how these changes occur. When the sun is high in an atmosphere that is relatively clean and dry, it looks almost white, riding in a deep blue sky. But later in the day, as it sinks toward the horizon, its light comes to earth at an increasingly sharp angle. Instead of shining straight down, it now has to pierce miles and miles of dusty, occasionally vapor-filled air close to the surface of the earth, and more blue light is removed and other colors come into play. The lower the sun gets the more its color changes. First it is yellow, then a deep orange, and finally, just before it drops below the horizon, it glows a deep red.

The innumerable changes, large and small, in the conditions of the atmosphere create a wide range of differences in the colors of the sun, the sky and objects on earth. In the summer, after a long drought, particles of sand and dust blown up by the wind scatter more and more of the red in the sunlight. The resulting mixture of red and blue light makes the sky whiter. Heavy showers, breaking the drought, wash away the dust, and the sky becomes brighter and a more deeply saturated blue. At the tops of high mountains and at airplane flight levels, where the atmosphere is free of the concentrated layer of dust and moisture that rarely rises more than a few thousand feet above the earth, the sky is a much deeper blue than at sea level. At different latitudes, too, the quality of sky coloring varies. In the northerly countries, there is generally more moisture in the air and the blue is paler; the drier air of southern countries gives their skies a far richer hue, for fewer dust or vapor particles means less scattering of the longer waves. One result: the intensely blue skies of Italy that have inspired poets and painters for centuries.

COLOR "FINGERPRINTS" are made by the spectrophotometer, which measures intensities of various colors reflected by a sample like a paint chip. The process starts with a prism splitting white light into a spectrum of colors. A movable opaque sheet with a narrow slit releases a beam containing a small band of wavelengths of a given color *(far right)*. Half the beam is reflected off a partly silvered glass to the sample; half passes through to a "white standard," which reflects all colors equally. The two halves are then reflected to a photoelectric cell, which measures and compares their reflected light. As each color band is successively tested on the sample, a recording device produces an exact analysis *(opposite)* of the sample's color.

The effect of particle size on sunset and sunrise colors is so direct that they have, for centuries, been used for weather prophecy. The mariner's rule of thumb, "Red sky at night, sailors' delight; red sky at morning, sailors take warning," has its origin back in the Biblical passage from Matthew: "When it is evening, ye say, it will be fair weather: for the sky is red. And in the morning, It will be foul weather today: for the sky is red and lowring." There is a perfectly logical explanation for the fact that these prophecies are often correct: the sky is red only when the air contains dust or water droplets, and since this is not usually the case in the morning, a deviation from the normal usually indicates a worsening of weather. At night a red sky—or more exactly, a purplish red—results from the expected presence of moisture and high pressure, and therefore portends a clear day.

Strange color effects may result from unusual and specific events that alter the ordinary atmosphere. In late September of 1950, the sun hanging low above the horizon appeared indigo blue in many places in Europe. An Edinburgh scientist, R. R. Wilson, noting the curious hue of the sun over Scotland, made a study of the event and attributed it to an outbreak of forest fires that had raged in Canada three days before. The scattering effect was most probably caused by oil droplets released from burning wood which, by the combined effect of wind and gravity, sorted themselves into a remarkable uniformity of size as they crossed the ocean. In 1883 the world witnessed a series of remarkably beautiful sunrises and sunsets caused by the eruption of Krakatoa in the Dutch East Indies, which for many months afterwards spread a layer of fine volcanic dust through the earth's atmosphere. Similarly, within a week or so after any eruption of Mount Vesuvius or Mount Etna, people living in the Western Hemisphere see exceptional twilights. And in the spring of 1910, the earth passed through the tail of Halley's comet, apparently picking up particles of the comet's dust; for two nights the twilights were described as "magnificent."

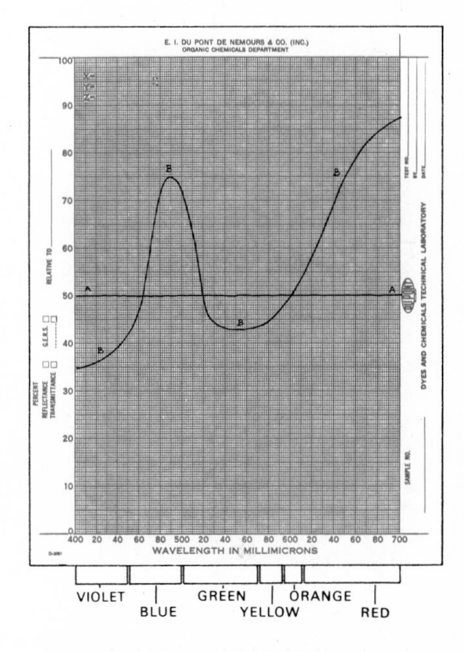

TWO SHADES OF GRAY may look alike to the eye, but their differences become readily evident when recorded by a spectrophotometer *(opposite page)*. Line A represents a shade of gray that is halfway between black (0 on the light-reflectivity scale) and white (100 on the scale). Because it reflects equally all the wavelengths of visible light *(bottom)*, it appears as a straight line. The gray of line B, however, reflects colors unevenly, as indicated by the dips and peaks of its graph pattern: low in violet, high in blue-green, low in green, high in red. By daylight, when the various colors are neutralized, only gray can be seen. But under incandescent light, which enhances the red component, the gray takes on a reddish tone.

Weeds in a "wine-dark sea"

The effects of scattering, however, are not restricted to the atmosphere. The sea may receive its color partly from reflection from the sky—on gray days it looks leaden—but it probably gets most of its color from scattering by the molecules of the water itself and of microscopic materials in it. Near the shore the water often looks pale green because of fine sand in suspension which scatters the somewhat-longer-than-blue light waves; when sunlight hits these sand particles it adds yellow to the blue that is already being scattered by the water molecules. In areas where there is much seaweed, the blue of the sky combines with the red-brown reflection of the weed to make the sea purple or magenta—which may account for Homer's use of the peculiar term "wine-dark sea" that has puzzled literary scholars for many years. Some water contains so many fine particles that it looks green even when a small amount of it is put in a bucket. This has nothing to do with the colors of water in swimming pools; these take their color from chlorine or copper sulfate, used to purify the water, or from the paint on the sides and bottom of the pool.

There are a few rare and marvelous color phenomena in nature that are due neither to subtraction, addition nor selective scattering. Halos around the moon, multicolored raindrops or snow crystals, and the rainbow are some of nature's examples of spectrum effects, in which the light is split into its component colors in somewhat the way Newton's prism did it. Generally speaking, the rainbow is produced by the light-separating effect of each individual raindrop. The curvature of the drop refracts the various wavelengths to different degrees and spreads them out into a spectrum.

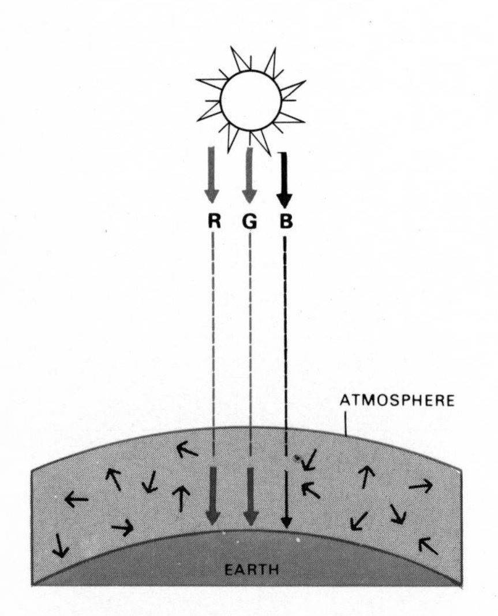

THE DISTANCE LIGHT TRAVELS through the atmosphere determines the changing colors of the sun, as seen at various times of day. When the sun is directly overhead *(above)*, its rays pierce the narrow band of atmosphere perpendicularly. The red and green wavelengths *(colored arrows and dotted lines)* pass through, but blue wavelengths *(black arrows and dotted line)* are scattered by particles in the air. This scattering makes the sky look blue and the sun yellowish. At sunset *(below)*, the light hits the same spot at a sharp angle, and passes through much more atmosphere. The additional particles scatter some of the longer wavelengths, and the sun changes from yellow to orange to a deep red.

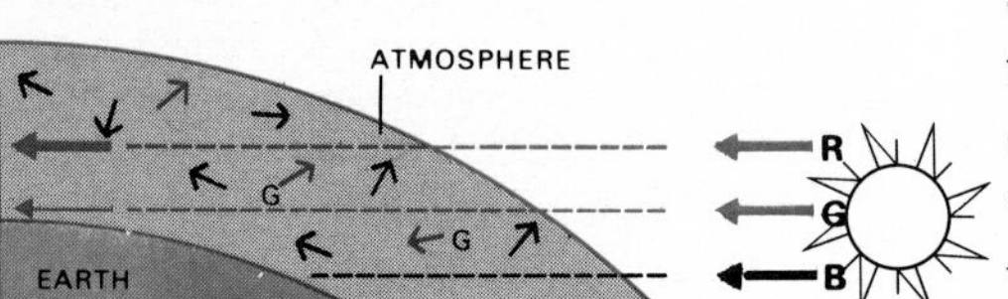

Reflection of the nonexistent

One feature of the rainbow that is particularly curious is that it can sometimes be seen reflected from a large body of water. Many experts once argued that the rainbow could not be reflected because it is not a thing; there is no object there to be reflected, since the rainbow consists of a complicated light sensation in the eye of the observer. In a curious little volume called *A Budget of Paradoxes* published in 1915, Augustus De Morgan wrote: "A few years ago an artist exhibited a picture with a rainbow and its apparent reflection. . . . Some started the idea that there could be no reflection of a rainbow; they were right; they inferred that the artist had made a mistake; they were wrong."

All that De Morgan, and the scientists who later agreed, mean is that "it" cannot be reflected because "it" is not a material object. But the rays of light that produce the rainbow in an observer's sight can in fact be reflected after leaving the drop but before reaching the eye.

As unique in its way as the rainbow is the color found in the swirling colors of soap bubbles and oil slick floating on water. The skin of a soap bubble consists of an outer and an inner surface. These two reflecting surfaces are separated by a thin layer—about 1/250,000 of an inch —of soapy water. Light hitting a soap bubble is partly reflected from the outer surface, but some is transmitted and then reflected—after a slight time lag—from the inner surface. This second reflected wave is therefore slightly behind the first. This means that it undergoes a shift of phase, rather like a company of soldiers getting out of step. Some of the irregularly phased waves reinforce each other while some cancel each other out. The result is a difference in the amplitude of various wavelengths. The irregularities of the thickness of the layer produce the variation in the dominant colors.

A related phenomenon accounts for the brilliant iridescent coloring of hummingbirds, of certain kinds of butterflies, and a variety of beetles and other insects whose wings have a metallic sheen. Like rainbows, soap bubbles and thin films, these strange color effects have occupied the scientific curiosity of many great men, from Baron John Rayleigh, an outstanding 19th Century physicist, to Albert A. Michelson, the first American to win a Nobel Prize in science and the man who—among many other things—was the first to determine the speed of light with accuracy. Michelson suspected that iridescence in certain insects was not because of scattering, absorption or pigment effects, so he looked for an explanation in the other possible phenomena: diffraction or interference. His studies indicated that in general the colors of insects, butterflies and certain brilliant hummingbird feathers are created by the special kind of selective reflection-transmission seen in gold leaf or other thin metallic films—with one remarkable exception. On the wings of the diamond beetle, Michelson found iridescent spots containing microscopic crisscrossed gratings with as many as 2,000 lines per inch. Michelson and other scientists were able to create even finer gratings in their laboratories by using delicate ruling equipment. Such gratings, by breaking up a uniform wave front of white light into a multitude of tiny individual wavelets, produce a whole new collection of waves that crisscross and recombine to produce again the variegated colors of the spectrum. The effect is much like that caused by the ridges in mother-of-pearl. Scientists are relying more and more on man-made diffraction gratings instead of prisms to analyze color.

The visual intermediary

The remarkable repertoire of color effects that gives man such delight is created with a handful of fundamental tools: the spectrum, the molecular structure of pigments, the behavior of waves. Subtraction, addition and what might sometimes be called multiplication fill the world with a dazzling range of lighting effects. But one more ingredient is required for any of this to be seen as color, the eye.

For 200 years after Isaac Newton opened the way to understanding how color is made in nature, few researchers took any interest in the analysis of the eye's contribution to color. Then, in the 19th Century, a scientist named Thomas Young offered a fresh look at the problem. James Clerk Maxwell, himself a contributor to visual science, said: "It seems almost a truism to say that color is a sensation; and yet Young, by honestly recognizing this elementary Truth, established the first consistent theory of colour. So far as I know, Thomas Young was the first who, starting from the well-known fact that there are three primary colours, sought for the explanation of this fact not in the nature of light but in the constitution of man."

With Thomas Young, the science of color vision picks up where the physics of color creation leaves off. With Young begins a whole new area of discovery that is concerned not with spectral light—which the eye rarely sees in isolated purity—nor with pigment colors—which the eye averages into a perceived color. What this part of color science deals with is how the eye builds colored worlds out of waves of energy, how it concentrates on what is essential and dismisses or subordinates what is transient or peripheral—how it recognizes and discriminates among colored objects in colored landscapes under the mixed and changing light of the sun and sky. This is the subject matter of the next chapter.

The Paradox of Color

Color is a paradox. It exists in light, which to human eyes seems colorless. It does not exist in soap bubbles, rainbows or paint, which appear colored. The symphony of varied hues we see around us does not mean that we live in a world of colored objects—it means only that the surfaces of those objects reflect back a particular portion of the light that is hitting them. Thus, an apple is red because it reflects red light, not because it is itself red. Green leaves are simply reflecting green light.

But that is only part of the story. What about an object that appears to be one color one moment and another color a moment later, or one that can flash a variety of tints, or two colors that can be put together to produce a third? Colors can play tricks like these because of variations in light sources and reflective surfaces. The tiny parallel ridges on a phonograph record will produce a rainbow effect if looked at from the proper angle, as will gasoline in a puddle—both reflecting different colors of the spectrum at various points on their surfaces. The colors in light can also be divided by rain droplets, added together in TV tubes, and absorbed by paints or natural pigments to create a host of new colors.

LET THERE BE COLOR

Without light, there can be no color, as is demonstrated by this glass tray filled with sourball candies. A beam of white light, concentrated at the tray's center, brings out the bright hues of the candies that are directly illuminated. But off to the sides, as the light fades, the sourballs lose their colors—and those at the edges appear dark gray or black.

Photographed in white light that contains equal amounts of all the colors of the spectrum, fried eggs have clearly defined whites and yolk

How Light Determines Color

With good reason, a woman buying a dress will often take it out into daylight to see the "true" colors. She usually finds that any red in the fabric is far more pronounced in sunlight than under the fluorescent lamps of a store. The reason is simple—fluorescent lamps concentrate much of their energy in the blue wavelengths of the spectrum, while the energy of sunlight is distributed evenly through the spectrum, thus giving the fabric sufficient red light to reflect.

A more exaggerated color change occurs on highways lit by sodium-vapor lamps. These lamps emit nearly all of their energy at two wavelengths in the yellow part of the spectrum: a yellow car glistens brilliantly yellow in sodium-vapor light, but blue or red cars—given little of their color to reflect—appear drab gray.

A white surface will reflect every visible wavelength. Under reddish yellow light, however, the white part of fried eggs *(opposite page)* becomes virtually indistinguishable from the yolk because it has only yolk-colored wavelengths to reflect. Because ordinary household light bulbs emit weak blue light and strong red light, they can produce a somewhat similar distorting effect. To register "true" colors, indoor color photography requires a special film that is extrasensitive to the spectrum's blue wavelengths.

But under red-yellow light, the white of the egg has nothing but red and yellow to reflect; hence it appears to be the same color as the yolks.

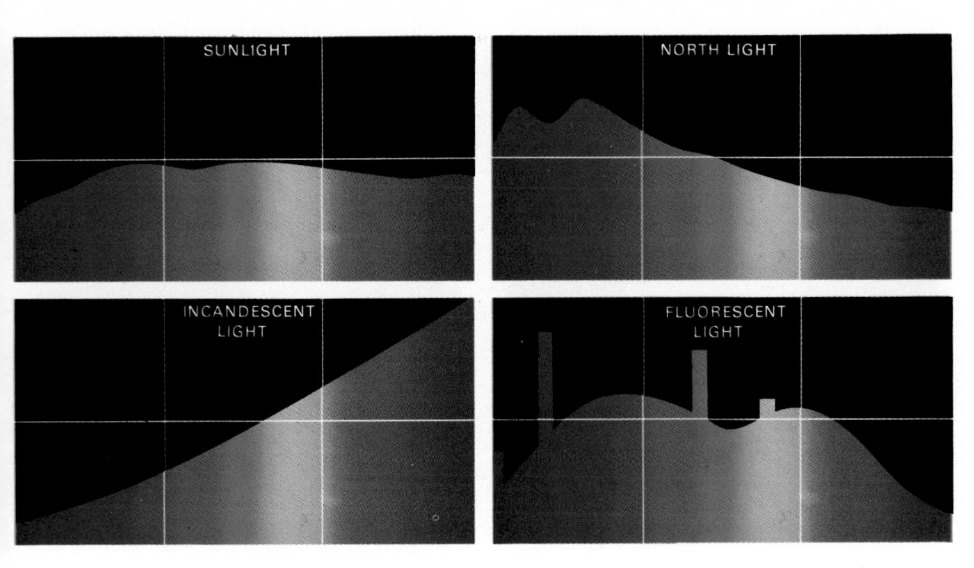

PORTRAITS OF FOUR LIGHT SOURCES
The graphs at left show the wavelengths of color emitted by different light sources. Though differing markedly from each other, all four still produce the general sensation of white in the human eye. Sunlight *(top, left)* spreads out its energy quite evenly, with a slight emphasis on the green wavelengths. Light from the northern sky *(top, right)*—the source favored by artists—is preponderantly blue, because molecules of air scatter short blue wavelengths through the atmosphere. Incandescent bulbs *(bottom, left)* radiate considerably more red than blue. Fluorescent lamps *(bottom, right)* emit high energy at only a few specific wavelengths due to excitation of mercury vapor—and this energy stimulates the white coating of the lamp to radiate the rest of the spectrum at weaker strength.

RAINBOWS IN MINIATURE

The four-and-a-half-carat diamond, flashing a host of tiny rainbows on a background paper, reveals the spectrum through the same effect as the glass laboratory prism below. In each, the light slows down as it enters a medium denser than air. This deceleration—more pronounced for the violet component of light than for yellow or red—is what fans out the wavelengths of the spectrum. Diamonds shed particularly dazzling color because they can bend light farther than any other transparent substance—thus producing more vivid rainbows. The diamond above, shaped with many facets in the so-called "brilliant" cut, releases a cascade of rainbows, because each facet acts as a separate prism.

Bursting Open White Light

The best color producers—prisms, thin films and finely ridged surfaces—use structure alone to open up the spectrum and put wavelengths on display. Diamonds and water droplets work like prisms to slow down wavelengths in varying degrees—violet most, red least—causing the colors to spread out in a rainbow pattern. The ridged surface of an LP record separates colors by a different process: diffraction. Depending on the angle from which the ridges are viewed, a particular wavelength—or color—will be reinforced, because the waves exactly coincide in their undulations as they reflect off groups of ridges. In soap and oily films, waves reflected from the inner and outer film surfaces undergo a similar reinforcement—and the colors that appear are determined by the thickness of the film.

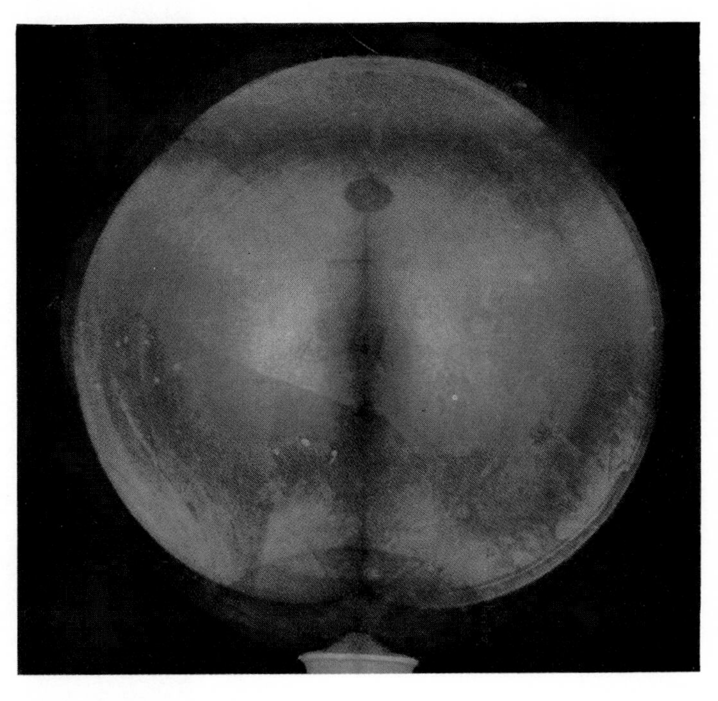

COLOR FROM BLACK RIDGES

The phonograph record above creates colors by reinforcing particular wavelengths at different points along the surface. The color is determined by the spacing of the ridges and the angle from which they are viewed. More orderly spectra are produced in the laboratory by transparent sheets *(below)* whose thousands of grooves are precisely spaced.

COLOR FROM THIN FILMS

The variations of color in the soap bubble above are produced by differing thicknesses of its fragile film. A change of only 12 millionths of an inch between the light-reflecting inner and outer surfaces of the film will cause red to appear instead of blue. The laboratory device below creates circles of colors with an air film sandwiched between glass disks.

Making Color by Taking Color Away

The green of leaves, red of roses, gray of rocks—and most other colors we see—are created by subtracting wavelengths from the spectrum. If all the keys of a piano were hit simultaneously, we would hear a chaos of sound—equivalent to white light, which contains wavelengths of all colors. But music results when only a few notes at a time are heard. Similarly, nature generates colors by filtering out some wavelengths and reflecting others alone or in combinations that the viewer interprets as color.

The series of filters at right schematically shows how selective absorption of wavelengths yields specific colors. In each of these nine pictures, daylight is represented as a white beam passing through the left side of the filters; this beam is the sum of the other three beams of red, green and blue—each from a primary section of the spectrum.

The filters in the first column of pictures demonstrate how two colors are absorbed to reveal a third. The filters in the second column subtract only one beam and pass two, successively yielding magenta (blue-red), cyan (blue-green) and yellow (red-green). The third column explains what happens when the colors on the opposite page are mixed together.

This process of wavelength-subtraction is accomplished in nature by molecules which absorb particular parts of the spectrum. Called pigments, these molecules are present almost everywhere—except in transparent substances such as water, air or pure diamonds. Blue-green paint consists of billions of red-absorbing particles suspended in a transparent medium, like linseed oil. Asphalt is made up of molecules "tuned" to absorb wavelengths throughout the spectrum; it looks black because very few wavelengths are being reflected. Although nature's pigments create color by the same technique as the filters shown here, they subtract the spectrum's wavelengths irregularly and incompletely. Since no wavelength is fully absorbed, the eye sees the everyday world in a jumble of colors.

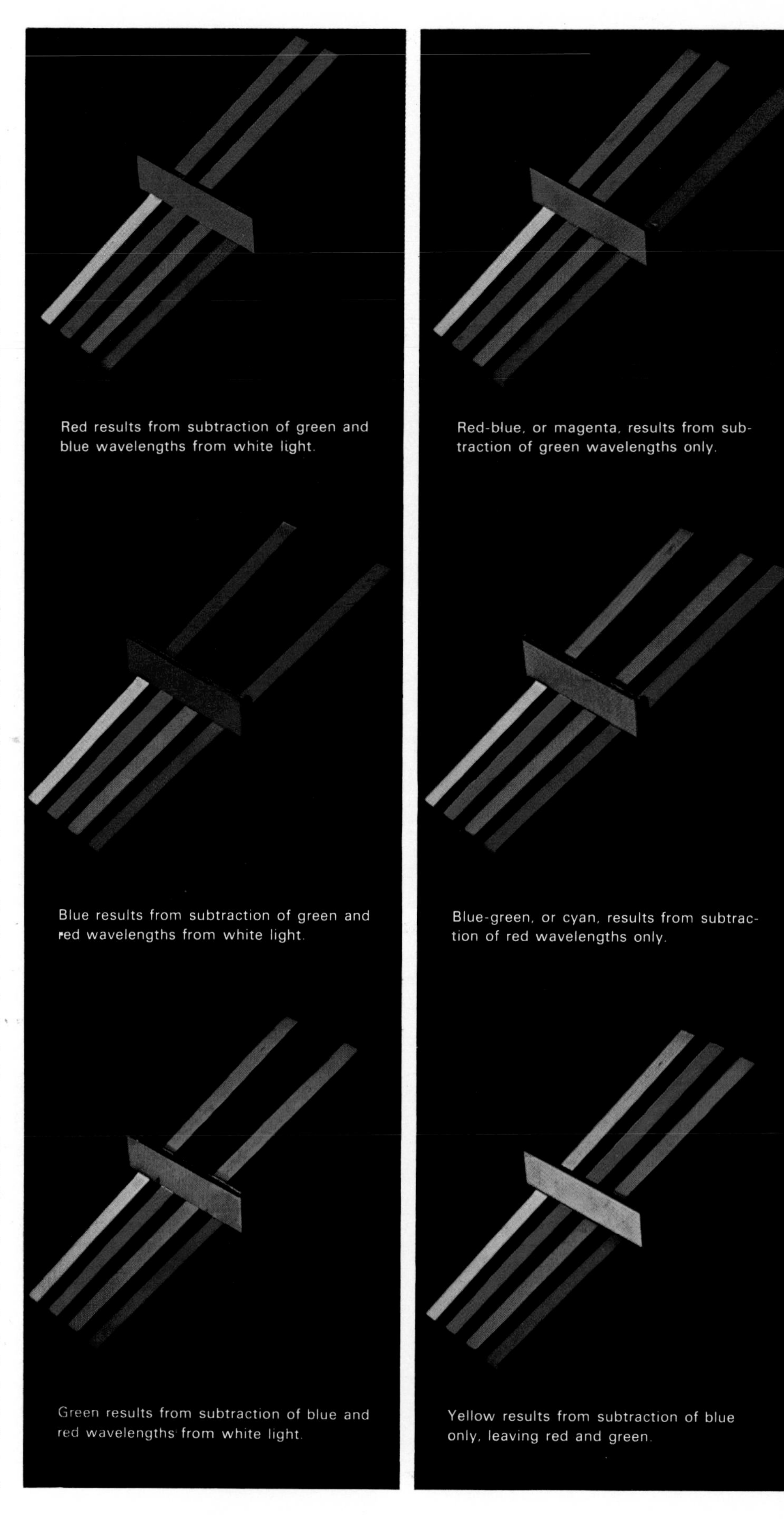

Red results from subtraction of green and blue wavelengths from white light.

Red-blue, or magenta, results from subtraction of green wavelengths only.

Blue results from subtraction of green and red wavelengths from white light.

Blue-green, or cyan, results from subtraction of red wavelengths only.

Green results from subtraction of blue and red wavelengths from white light.

Yellow results from subtraction of blue only, leaving red and green.

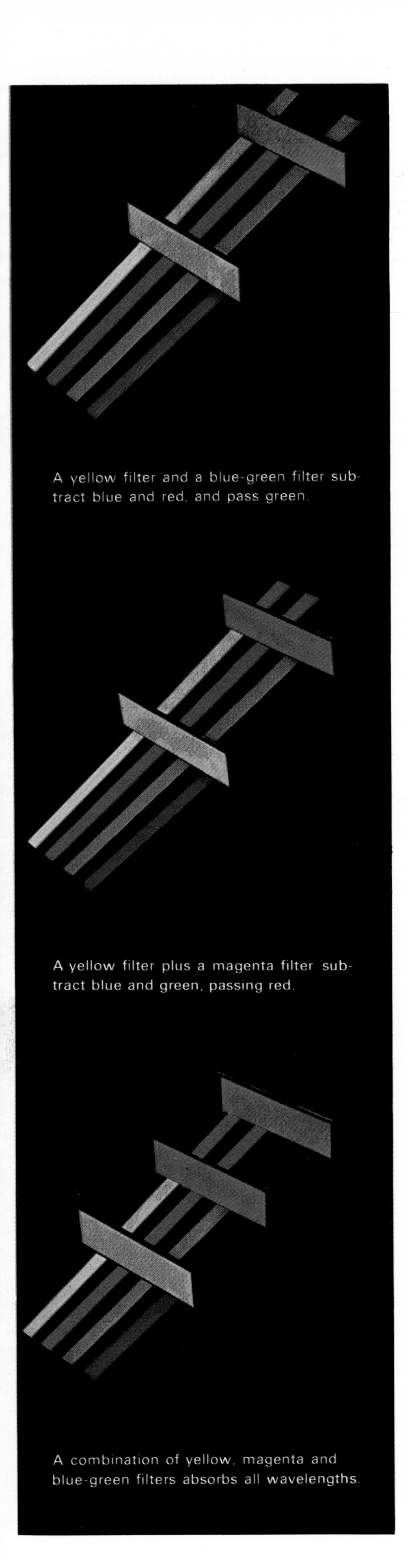

A yellow filter and a blue-green filter subtract blue and red, and pass green.

A yellow filter plus a magenta filter subtract blue and green, passing red.

A combination of yellow, magenta and blue-green filters absorbs all wavelengths.

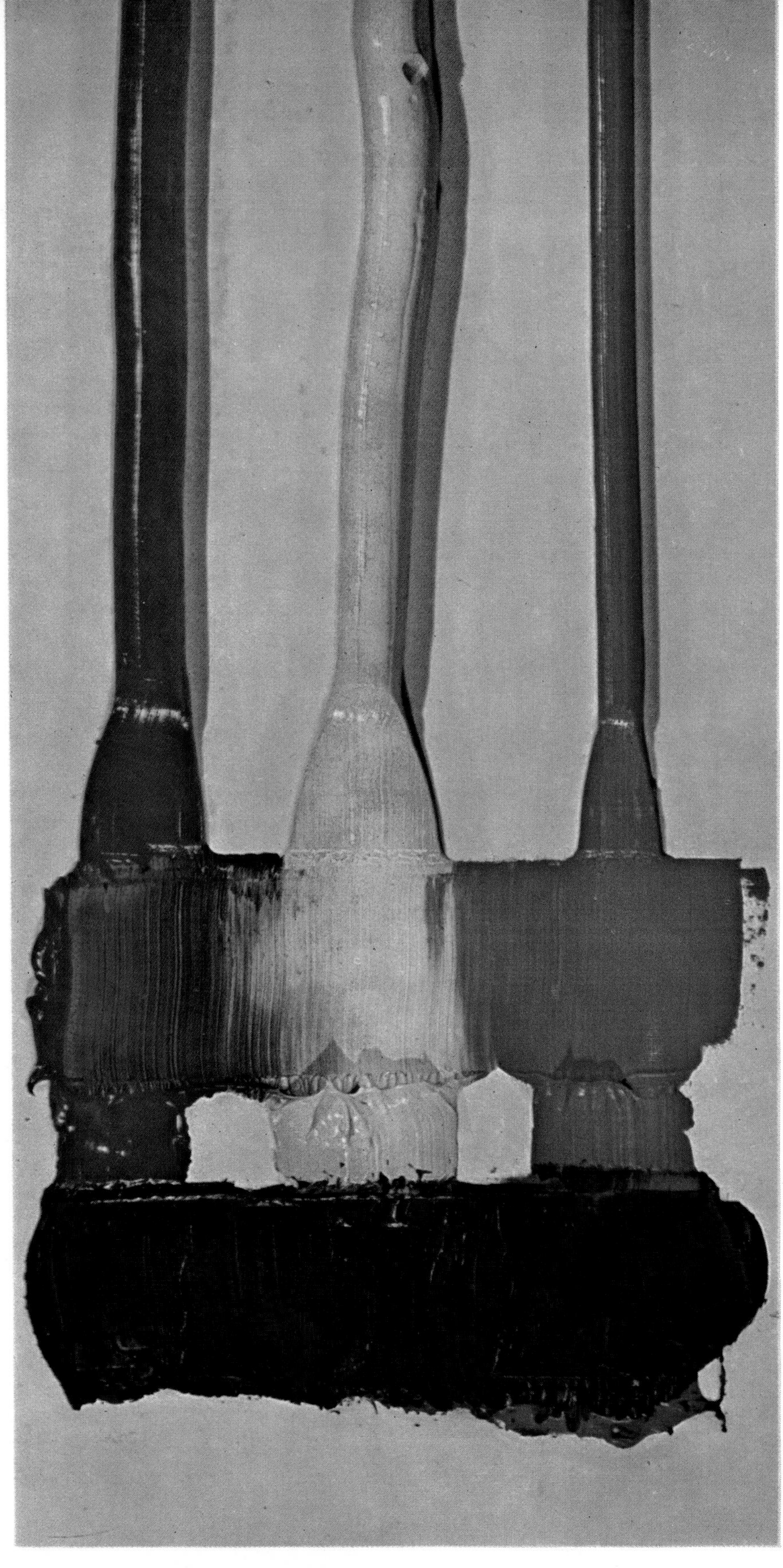

A SMALL BUT VERSATILE PALETTE
Most of the colors in nature can be reproduced by blending a small selection of pigments. The elementary mixtures of colors shown above are explained by the three sets of light filters to the left. A mixture of greenish blue (cyan) and yellow produces green, in the same manner as the filters at top. Yellow and magenta yield red, like the middle filters. And a blend of the three ribbons of pigment subtracts wavelengths throughout the visible spectrum, as the bottom filters do—resulting in a dark color that would be black if the absorption were perfect.

Mixing Colors by Addition

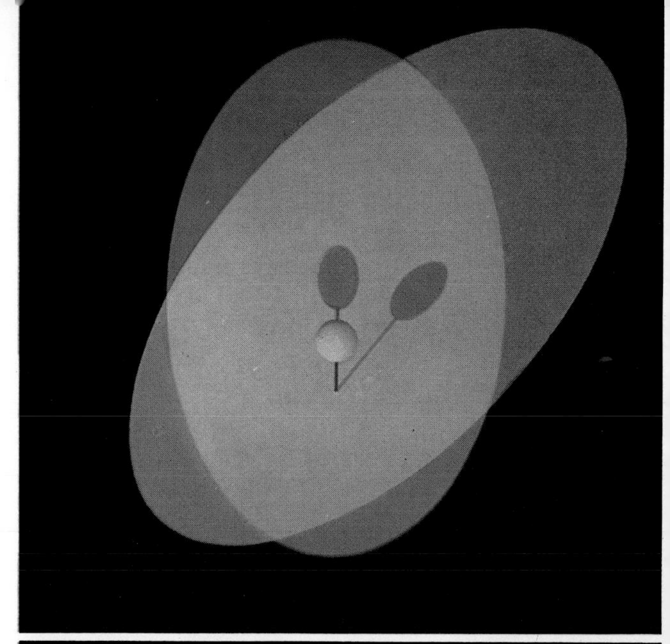

If the lighted screen of a color television tube were examined under a magnifying glass, it would be found to be covered with tiny phosphor dots arranged in groups of three—each group containing one red, one green and one blue dot. Without magnification, however, the dots are far too small to be distinguished, and the eye blends them together to see every conceivable color and shade.

This transformation of three colors into many more is called additive mixing. The same process is demonstrated at right with the light beams of three slide projectors equipped with red, green and blue filters. A mixture of any two beams *(small pictures)* will produce a new color: blue plus green makes cyan; red plus blue makes magenta; and red plus green makes yellow. Where all three beams overlap *(large picture)*, white appears. No matter how different from the component beams the mixtures seem, they are always combinations of red, green and blue—as is proved by the colored shadows cast by the white ball in each picture.

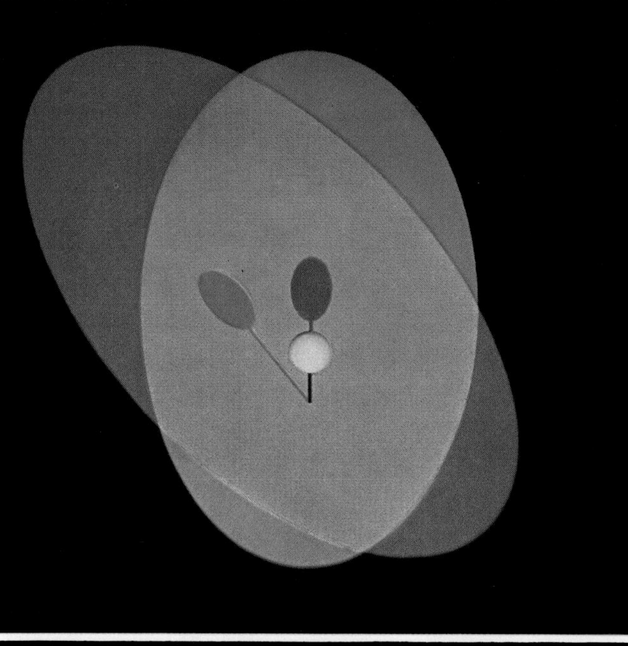

Other shades of color can be created by changing the intensity of the beams. Red and weak green light—with no blue at all—produces brown, since all browns in nature are simply low-intensity yellows (red plus green). To get pink, all three beams are used—with the red beam slightly stronger than the others.

Additive mixing can be based on any three colors, as long as each falls in a separate third of the spectrum. Television uses red, green and blue dots because these three can produce the widest range of colors. To create white in a color TV tube, electron beams stimulate the dots in each group equally; black is produced by not stimulating them at all. Thus, even the black-and-white programs seen on color tubes are in reality black-red-green-and-blue programs.

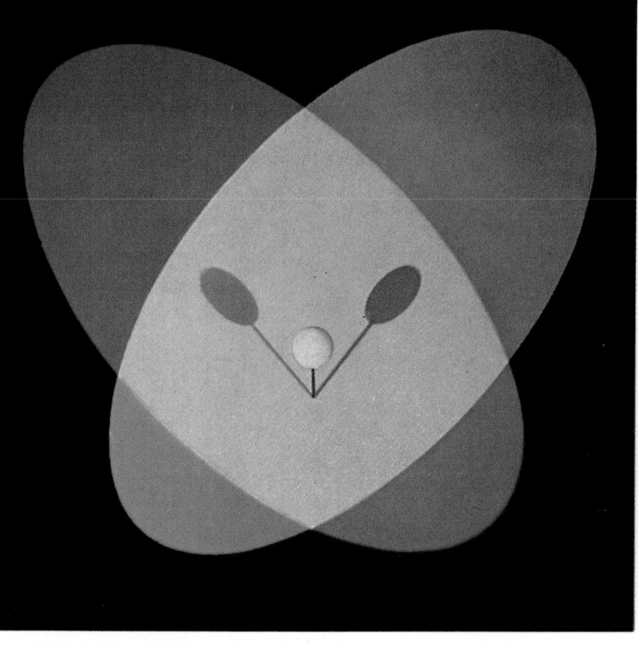

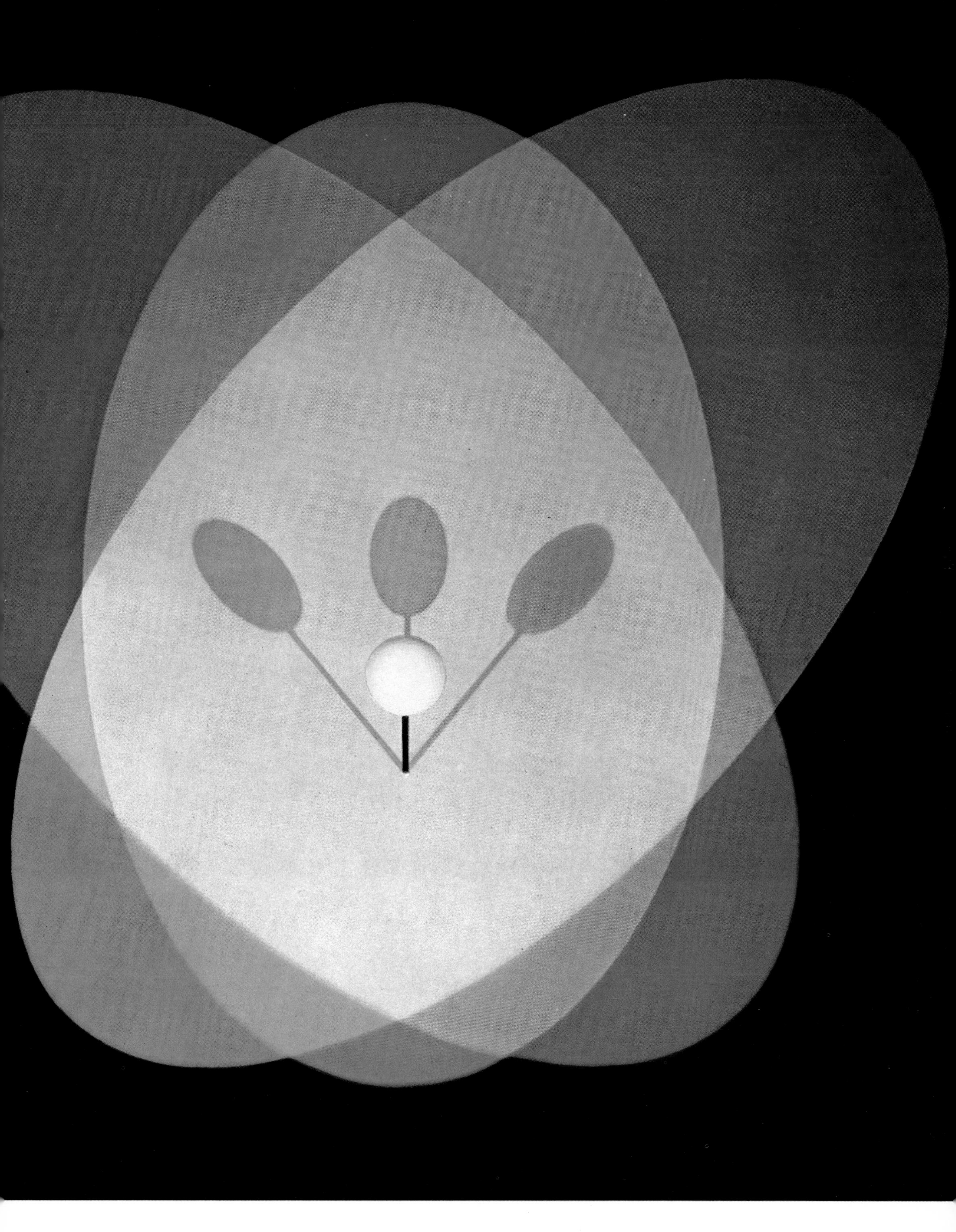

IT STARTS WITH YELLOW
As the paper rolls through the press, it receives an initial printing of yellow dots only. Each dot of ink is made up of pigments that absorb blue wavelengths and reflect back the red and green.

CYAN IS ADDED
A second plate *(top)* prints the cyan component of the picture. Where cyan and yellow dots overlap in the combined impression, green appears, because red and blue are being absorbed.

THEN COMES MAGENTA
The addition of the third primary, magenta, brings the color close to the original. In modern high-speed presses, the paper receives all of its impressions in about two and one half seconds.

Breaking Pictures into Color Bits

The television tube is neither the first nor the most familiar example of using tiny dots of primary colors to give an impression of many shades. All the color illustrations in this book—and in most modern books—are also made of dots, as a magnifying glass will quickly prove.

To reproduce a picture in color, an engraver starts by photographing it. He first puts a fine-mesh wire screen in front of his lens, along with a filter that blocks out all but the yellow parts of the picture. The result is a rather pale copy of the original, made up entirely of minute yellow dots—the dots representing the openings in the screen. An example of a "yellow plate" is shown at the far left of the opposite page. Next the engraver makes a cyan (or greenish blue) plate, getting a slightly different pattern of bluish dots. When the cyan and the yellow plate are printed together *(center bottom picture, opposite)*, the dots fall together in such a way as to build up other combinations of color which resemble the original more closely than either the cyan or the yellow plate alone could. And when a third magenta plate is added to the other two, the colors exactly match the original picture. The printing process is completed with a black plate that brings out depth and contrasts in the color reproduction.

AND FINALLY BLACK
Theoretically, overlapping yellow, cyan and magenta dots should absorb all color wavelengths and yield black. But since inks are imperfect filters, black must be added separately.

A CLOSE LOOK AT THE RESULT
An enlarged detail of the printed picture—a carnival dancer in Trinidad—clearly shows the different-sized dots of color. These dots are produced by photographing the original picture through a screen. The varying intensity of light passing through the screen's holes determines the size of the raised dots on the plates—which controls the amount of a given color printed.

A Language for Users of Color

The everyday names given to shades of a color—such as sky blue, aquamarine blue or turquoise blue—are hopelessly inadequate to the needs of industry and science. People rarely agree on the exact shade that a name describes.

One of the most determined attempts to formulate a precise nomenclature for color was made by the American portraitist Albert Munsell in 1915. He devised a three-dimensional color system, shown at right in the form of a tree, which classifies shades according to perceivable qualities: hue, value and chroma. Hue is what we generally interpret as color—meaning that an object is red, orange or blue; in this tree, 20 hues are represented by transparent plastic vanes, or branches. Value refers to the degree of brightness of a given color; the value of each of the square color samples is indicated by its vertical position on the hue vane. Chroma, or saturation, refers to the richness of the color sample—whether it is dull or vivid—and is indicated by how far the square is from the tree's center.

American industry began adopting the Munsell system as its standard of color in the 1930s. Today, if a fabric manufacturer orders a dye for the red stripes in the U.S. flag, he can describe it in Munsell shorthand as 5R 3/14—an intermediate red hue, with a moderately dark value of three, and a chroma 14 steps away from gray.

NATURAL COLORS
Nature mixes color with a flamboyant hand and little concern for order, as the varicolored assortment of flowers above shows. The number of shades that are created by natural pigments is virtually infinite—and a trained observer can distinguish thousands of such color variations.

MAN-MADE COLORS
A Munsell color tree at right, reflected from three sides by mirrors, contains 427 color samples arranged on 20 branches according to their hue, value and chroma. If the color tree were to include every man-made hue, however, it would have to carry some 200 branches.

6

Sensing Light's Many Shades

A colorful maze of crisscrossing cables links 20,000 switching points inside a typical telephone exchange. An elaborate system of color coding makes it possible to trace any of the 3,000 wires in a fraction of the time it would take if all were black.

WHEN A MUSEUM VISITOR looks at Georges Seurat's painting, *La Grande Jatte (pages 184-185)*, from a normal viewing distance of 20 or 30 feet, he sees well-dressed strollers and their children and dogs in an attractive, formalized park with brilliant sunlight, cool shade and a lake reflecting distant clouds and nearby trees—all of the many colors combining into a lovely, placid scene as refreshing as a glass of pure spring water on a summer day. However, if the viewer is not familiar with Seurat's work, he will receive quite a shock when he moves to within several feet of the canvas. He finds that all the hues he had seen from a greater distance are not there—individually. Instead, the painting is composed of tiny dots of color—a technique called pointillism or divisionism—and the mixing and blending of colors have actually taken place in his, the viewer's, eyes. What, he may wonder, has occurred in the visual process to account for this and other arresting phenomena of color perception?

The search for an explanation of how the human eye perceives color is a scientific detective story that spans centuries. Many substantial clues have been found and a number of theories have been advanced, but the mystery is still not fully solved. During most of the long period of investigation, the researchers themselves have been at acrimonious odds over the various hypotheses. At the present time, there are two major theories about color perception which still divide the scientific community. However, a number of men in the field now believe that *both* theories may turn out to be correct, just as both the wave and the corpuscular theories of light are correct.

The behavior of physical colors is now well understood. Scientists can, for example, measure the degree of refraction of any color moving through any transparent medium, determine with a spectrophotometer the exact color of any surface in terms of the wavelengths it reflects, and accurately calculate the intensity of any light source.

But color perception in the human eye cannot be categorized with the same neat precision that can be used to describe light. Human vision has its own, often baffling laws which may vary from person to person. Logical deductions made from the characteristics of physical colors frequently do not apply to color vision. The laws of physics do, of course, play a part in man's perception of color, and they are the foundation on which analysis of color vision is based, but they provide only the starting point for a process that is influenced by the physiology of the eye and the cortex, and by the psychology of man.

Subjective responses—man's description of what he is experiencing through his senses—inevitably pose a problem for science. Light waves, for example, can be precisely described through measurements of their wavelengths and their amplitude, separately or in combination. However, to describe what he *sees,* man resorts to three inexact words: hue, brightness and saturation.

Hue is used to give a name to a color—red, green, blue, yellow and so on, and therefore is related to wavelength. The degree of brightness is a convenient way of saying that a color is vivid or dim, and is a description of apparent strength. Yellow, for instance, seems a bright color, blue does not. Saturation refers to the purity or richness of a color, i.e., how much or little white seems to be in the mixture. Deep blue appears saturated, pink does not. Fortunately, there is a reasonably close correspondence between hue and wavelength, between brightness and intensity, and between saturation and the purity of wavelength of the light.

These relationships are, of course, the basis of color as man sees it, but they are not obvious, simple or direct. Each of the three attributes of perception can be changed by changing any one or more of the three physical measurements, not just the one primarily related to it. Hue, for example, can be changed not only by changing the wavelength, but also by altering the degree of saturation, or, in most instances, by increasing or decreasing the intensity of the light. Only three hues in the spectrum, those with wavelengths of about 475 (a blue), 505 (a green) and 570 millimicrons (a yellow), remain constant regardless of changes made in the intensity.

The simplest way to change brightness is to change the physical intensity of the light source, but it can also be changed by changing wavelength or the degree of saturation. Similarly, saturation can be changed, not only by altering the mixture of wavelengths, but also by increasing intensity or by changing the hue. These and other subjective responses are not in the province of the physicist; they fall instead into the realm of the physiologist and psychologist.

In broad terms, the physiology of the visual system has been understood for a long time. But it is only recently that a start has been made in actually identifying the substances in the cones which are specially sensitive to one or the other of the so-called primary colors, red, green and blue. And there are still knotty problems to be solved in tracing the color message from the photoreceptors, through the nerve cells in the retina, and along the pathway of the optic nerve to the lateral geniculate body, the visual cortex and the rest of the brain.

Psychological mysteries of vision

The psychological aspects of color vision pose even greater difficulties. For instance, if a color transparency of a girl in a blue dress is projected onto a yellow screen, a person with normal vision will see the dress as gray. So far, this follows the known laws governing light mixture and complementary colors: because blue and yellow are complementary, they neutralize each other and, in effect, produce no color. However, if the picture of the girl is first shown on a white screen and the viewer is thus able to see the "true" color of the dress, he will continue to see it as blue even if it is then projected on the yellow screen.

This particular experiment involves color constancy, one of the most remarkable and least understood phenomena of color vision. Man tends to see familiar things as the same color under a variety of lighting conditions. The owner of a blue automobile is likely to see it as blue whether it is in dim light, bright light, under a yellow streetlamp or bathed in the glow of a red sunset. However, someone who is not familiar with the car would probably have difficulty deciding what the "true" color is.

When the owner of the car sees it as blue under a variety of lighting conditions, he is relying on what is called "memory color," which is one facet of constancy. Throughout a lifetime, man sees familiar objects in many different kinds of lights, and eventually he learns to see them "correctly"—i.e., in terms of white light—regardless of the circumstances.

However, this generalization about memory color, as with many of the more complex aspects of color perception, must be approached cautiously, for color constancy is not a predictable reaction under all circumstances. Regardless of how many broiled steaks a man has eaten in his lifetime, he is likely to lose all appetite when he sees one under a blue light. His memory does not work; the meat looks putrid. Exactly why memory color works in some instances and not in other remains to be determined.

Clues for seeing color

There is another important aspect of constancy that has to do with the clues provided the viewer. Such clues include the physical nature of the object and its relation to other objects as well as the characteristics of the lighting, shadows and contrasting colors with which the object is surrounded. For instance, if a red box is partially lit by direct sunlight and partially obscured by shade, man tends to make an automatic adjustment and see the box as having a uniform color.

When the clues are removed, constancy diminishes or disappears. In laboratory experiments with "aperture colors," people look at variously colored objects through a narrow tube. The viewer has no way of knowing what the objects are, what the color of the light is or the direction from which it is coming. Under these circumstances, viewers report the color directly predictable from the wavelength of the light projected on the object. For instance, if a viewer looks at part of a ripe tomato through the tube, he will see it as green, brown or any one of a number of colors, depending upon the color of the light that is being shone on the section. In short, constancy must rely on clues to function—clues stemming from memory or clues concerning the nature of the illumination and the surrounding objects.

When Isaac Newton first publicly proposed his theory of light and color—in February 1672, within two months after his 29th birthday—he made no attempt to explain how the eye sees color, but in the years that followed he gave considerable thought to the subject. In 1704, when he published the first edition of his famous book, *Opticks,* he included some bold speculations about vision in the form of "Queries" for other researchers to follow up.

One "Query" was especially important and sounds prophetic of future color-vision theories: "May not the harmony and discord of Colours arise

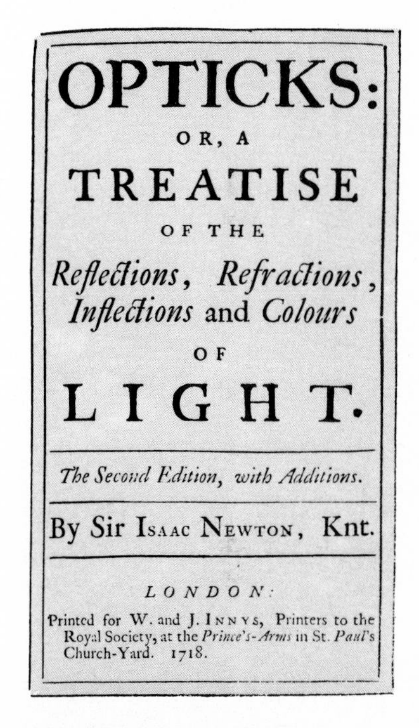
OPTICKS:
OR, A
TREATISE
OF THE
Reflections, Refractions, Inflections and *Colours*
OF
LIGHT.

The Second Edition, with Additions.

By Sir ISAAC NEWTON, Knt.

LONDON:
Printed for W. and J. INNYS, Printers to the Royal Society, at the *Prince's-Arms* in St. *Paul's* Church-Yard. 1718.

A MONUMENTAL TREATISE, Sir Isaac Newton's *Opticks* was first published in the early 18th Century and created a storm of controversy not only among scientists but among laymen as well. Along with descriptions of the discoveries he had made about the nature of light, Newton presented a series of "Queries" which were, in effect, a guide to exploration of new territory by other researchers. His purpose in writing *Opticks* was "to communicate what I have tried, and leave the rest to others for farther Enquiry."

from the proportions of the Vibrations propagated through the fibres of the optick Nerves into the Brain, as the harmony and discord of Sounds arise from the proportions of the Vibrations of the Air? For some Colours, if they be view'd together, are agreeable to one another, as those of Gold and Indigo, and others disagree."

It was almost a century before Newton's speculation was converted into a specific and generally consistent theory of color vision. The man who took this great step was Thomas Young, the English physician and physicist. Young addressed himself to the fundamental question of color vision: how is it possible for the photoreceptors to convey a different message for each of the numerous colors in the spectrum?

The average person can differentiate about 128 separate hues in the spectrum if he is permitted to make comparisons; for example, if a blue of 450 millimicrons is flashed on the screen and then a blue of 455 millimicrons is projected alongside it, he will be able to detect the variation. However, if the first color is shown and then removed before the second appears, he probably will not be able to notice the difference caused by that small change in wavelength.

A retinal palette

Young reasoned that the eye could not possibly have as many different types of photoreceptors as there are different colors, each receptor sensitive to a specific color, nor could the photoreceptors be so distributed on the retina that an appropriate color response would be generated regardless of where a part of an image might fall. Therefore, in 1801 he postulated that humans have only three types of color receptors, each of them sensitive to a specific color. He first designated those colors as red, yellow and blue, and later described them as red, green and violet. (Blue, instead of violet, is usually the third color used today.) To Young it seemed logical that if colored lights could be mixed on a screen, they could also be mixed on the retina.

Young's theory of color vision was first rejected and then ignored by his fellow scientists. But about a half century later, it was rediscovered almost simultaneously by James Clerk Maxwell, the Scottish physicist, and Hermann von Helmholtz, the German physicist and physiologist. Helmholtz's efforts in reviving and elaborating the trichromatic, or three-receptor, approach are recognized in the name it now bears, the Young-Helmholtz theory. One major modification by Helmholtz has to do with the way the cone receptors respond to the basic colors. A cone, he said, is not stimulated by only one color; it is stimulated most strongly by one, and to a lesser degree by the other two. Pure red light stimulates the red-sensitive receptors strongly and the other two feebly, thus giving the sensation of red. Pure yellow light activates the red and green receptors moderately and the violet slightly, thus producing the sensation of yellow. The extent to which all three receptors respond to every color stimulus explains why colors are "desaturated" and lose their richness; white is the result of just such a three-way response.

There are, however, certain shortcomings to the three-receptor theory that have not as yet been explained. One has to do with the identification of primary colors. According to one part of the theory, each of the three types of receptors has maximum sensitivity to a specific wavelength. But which three wavelengths produce the primary colors? Experiments have shown that if three wavelengths—one each from the red, green and blue sectors of the spectrum—are carefully chosen in relation to one another, they can be combined in an enormous number of variations to produce all the spectral colors in the retina. This poses the tough theoretical question, what are the "true" primaries?

Another problem is that some colors seem fundamental or unique, while others are obviously mixtures. Orange seems to be a mixture of red and yellow, purple of red and blue, and so on. But when people with normal vision are asked to pick the fundamental colors—those which seem to have no trace of other colors in them—they choose four: a blue of a wavelength of about 470 millimicrons, a green of approximately 500, a yellow of about 570, and a red mixed with a little violet.

This raises the question of why, if there are only three basic color receptors, four fundamental and unique colors are perceived. Ewald Hering, a German psychologist and physiologist, along with other scientists, felt that the Young-Helmholtz trichromatic theory directly contradicted actual visual experience in this and other aspects. In the 1870s, Hering finally formulated his own theory of color vision, which has ever since been the chief rival of the Young-Helmholtz theory.

Challenging the trichromatic theory

Hering's theory contradicts that of Young and Helmholtz on many important points, but they agree in accepting the fundamental concept that light of different colors can be mixed after entering the eye, and they both assume that the number of color receptors must be limited. Hering took as a starting point not only the perception of *four* colors that seem basic and unique—as opposed to the three primaries in the Young-Helmholtz theory—but also the interesting fact that the human visual system often appears to function in terms of pairs of colors, red-green and yellow-blue.

A major aspect of the pairing of colors is the way they both complement and oppose each other. Red and green seem to be antagonistic to each other; they do not blend. No one sees a color that could be called a reddish green in the way that one sees a reddish blue or a greenish yellow. And the same is true of yellow and blue; there is no color blend that could be described as yellowish blue.

But the partners in each pair also seem to demand each other, to call each other forth. Just as a sharply defined area of gray surrounded by white will look darker than it really is, and lighter if surrounded by black, the same neutral gray will look slightly red when surrounded by green, and slightly green when surrounded by red. It will also look blue when surrounded by yellow, and yellow when surrounded by blue.

JAMES CLERK MAXWELL, the great Scottish physicist of the 19th Century, is best known for his work in electricity and magnetism. However, he also made important contributions to the study of light and color perception. In addition, the principles of modern color photography were derived from an experiment made by Maxwell in 1860.

The same pairing also occurs in another phenomenon of color vision, the afterimage. When the eye has been fixed on a given color, and the color is then removed, the sensation of still seeing the original color may persist very briefly—if it is seen at all—in the so-called positive afterimage. But whether it occurs or not, what quickly follows the cessation of the colored light is a negative afterimage, which is always very close to the complement of the original color, red and green replacing each other as do yellow and blue.

Negative afterimages are explained in the Young-Helmholtz theory as temporary fatigue of the particular color receptors used in registering the original color. But Hering considered that the pairing of opposing colors and the fundamental and unique nature of yellow, ignored in the Young-Helmholtz theory, provided an important clue as to how color vision functions. Called the opponent-process theory, this approach stated that there are three pairs of unique sensory reactions—red-green, yellow-blue and black-white; no member of the red-green or blue-yellow combination can be active in the same receptor at the same time as its complement. However, black and white, in agreement with visual experience, can send a combined signal, producing intermediate shades of gray. Hering held that the mutually exclusive activity of each member of the two color pairs took place after the absorption of light by visual receptor substances. Hering also stressed that these responses were not isolated, but that the entire visual system was interrelated, that a response in one nerve fiber could antagonize a nearby fiber and prevent it from responding to a stimulus. Hering's explanation of negative afterimages was particularly simple. He said that when, for example, a red stimulus to the eye is withdrawn, the red process stops and automatically starts the opposing process, creating a green sensation.

Evidence from the color blind

Adherents of both major theories have utilized the study of color-blind persons to bolster their positions, but even here the results have not been conclusive for either theory. "Color blind" is a loose term because it implies a complete lack of ability to see color, and a total color blindness is extremely rare. However, some form of defective color vision is found in about 8 per cent of all men, though in less than 1 per cent of all women.

The two main defects are protanopia and deuteranopia. These are both forms of what has been called "red-green" color blindness, and the defects seem to be hereditary. Tritanopia (yellow-blue blindness) is most uncommon and is usually caused by disease. While people with normal color vision, according to the three-receptor theory, perceive three basic colors, the red-blind and the green-blind use only two, yellow and blue, to perceive all colors—which leads them to confuse red, blue-green and gray. The classic case was that of the great 19th Century English chemist John Dalton, who was red-blind himself and was the first researcher to study color blindness scientifically. He was also a Quaker, and is said to have gone to a prayer meeting one day wearing a pair of bright red stockings which a practical-joking colleague had switched for Dalton's own sober gray ones.

According to the Young-Helmholtz theory, the red-blind and green-blind suffer the loss of function of the red or green receptors in the cones of the retina. But, ask the critics, how do they both see yellow, which according to the three-receptor theory is mixed by the red and green receptors? According to Hering's theory, color blindness is not due to loss of function in the cones, but to a defect in the nerve structure farther along the visual pathway. But, ask the critics, if one half of the red-green opponent pair fails to function at whatever level, how does the other half operate? Later proponents of the two theories have answers to the questions, but none of the answers has been universally accepted.

New fuel for a heated debate

Thanks to the development of instruments so delicate they can measure activity of single nerve cells, a number of findings important to the debate have been made in recent years. Working with fish, cats and monkeys, light responses have been recorded in various nerve cells of the cortex, the lateral geniculate body and the retina (although not in the photoreceptors of the cones). These new data have provided strong physiological support for both the major theories. There have been responses to very narrow portions of the spectrum, indicating the operation of three specific color receptors; but there have also been responses indicating "on-off" processes involving red and green light on the one hand and yellow and blue light on the other, as would be expected if the opponent-process theory is correct.

In 1964, additional support for the Young-Helmholtz hypothesis came almost simultaneously from two teams of researchers, one at Johns Hopkins led by Edward F. MacNichol Jr. and William B. Marks, and the other at Harvard under George Wald and Paul K. Brown. Both teams have studied the absorption properties of individual cones from retinas of a number of vertebrates, including man. Three kinds of light-sensitive pigments have been identified in the receptor cells; one type is primarily sensitive in the blue band, one in the green, and the third in the red.

This is the way MacNichol has summed up what is known now: "Color vision is apparently at least a two-stage process, consistent with the Young-Helmholtz theory at the receptor level and with the Hering theory at the level of the optic nerve and beyond. Each receptor does not have its private route to the brain; three-color information is somehow processed in the retina and encoded into two-color on-off signals by each of the color-sensitive retinal ganglion cells for transmission to the higher visual centers."

The discussion is reminiscent of the old argument over whether light rays consisted of particles or waves. And it may be that it will be resolved as that fight was—by the synthesis of both ideas into a single theory.

The Mystery of Color Perception

Almost three centuries have passed since Isaac Newton first speculated on how colors are perceived, and yet the phenomenon of seeing in color—which man shares with a number of other animals, including apes, goldfish and bees—is only now beginning to be clearly understood.

The major problem has been that color vision involves a physiological process, whereby light energy is transformed into color signals to the brain, and a psychological process, by which the brain interprets the signals. An early theorist, Thomas Young, could present a satisfactory explanation of color vision as a purely physiological action, in which combinations of three primary colors are sufficient to create any hue. Later, however, Ewald Hering would set forth a more complex but equally plausible theory of four-color vision, based on human reaction to colors.

For many years the theories of color vision enunciated by Young and Hering were thought to be contradictory. But current research, conducted with sophisticated equipment and techniques, is finding validity in both viewpoints. A composite theory, now evolving, may provide the best explanation of how the human eye sees the world in cascades of color.

A TEST FOR COLOR BLINDNESS

Color blindness—defects in the color-vision system—can be detected by the Ishihara test *(opposite)*, one of many used for this purpose. Though the test is reproduced here in four colors rather than the usual 12, persons with normal color vision should have little trouble seeing the number 74 in the design; those with red-green blindness will see 21 instead.

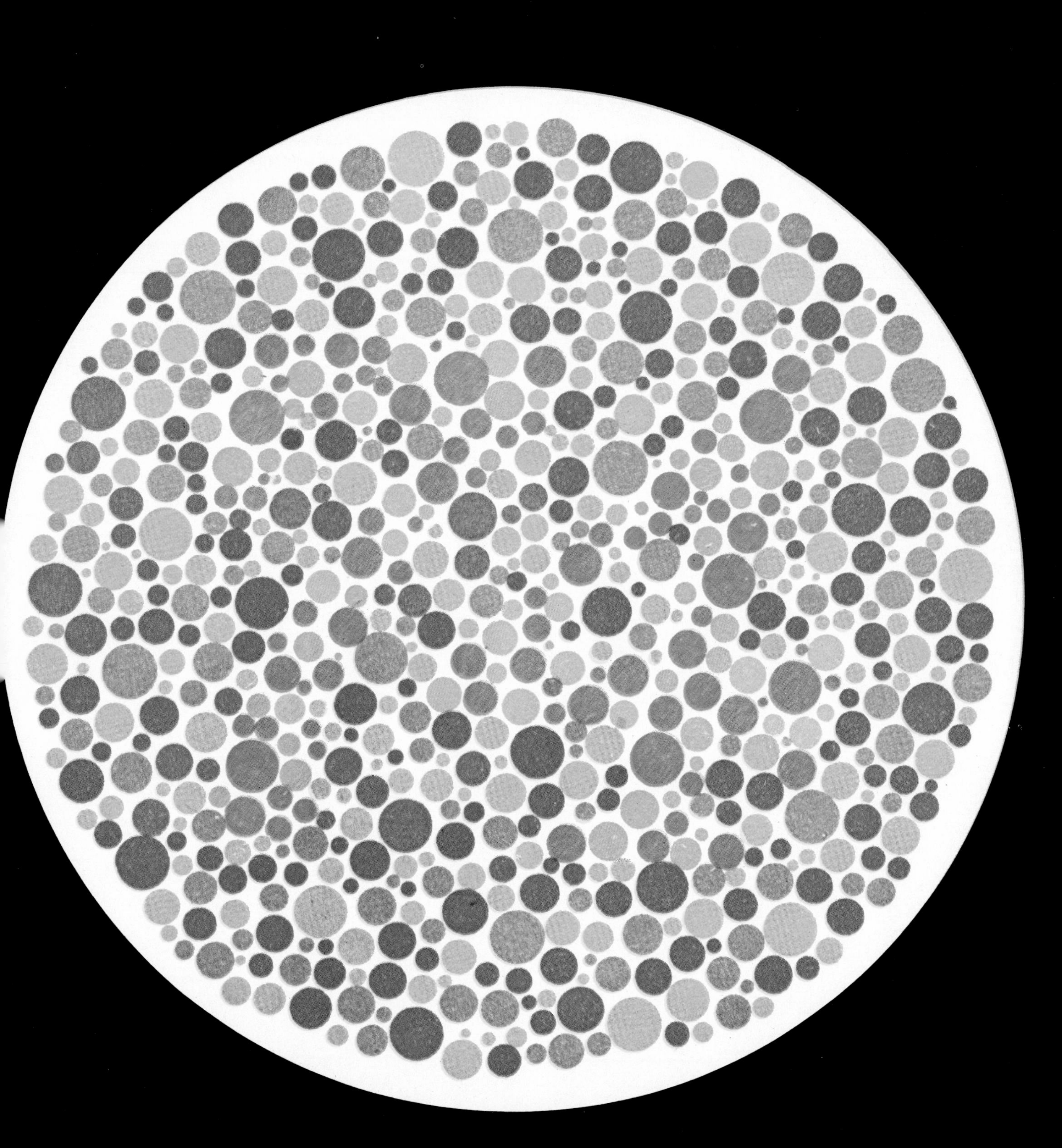

Isaac Newton: Pioneer of Color

The different theories of color vision have one thing in common: all are based on Isaac Newton's 1666 discovery that sunlight is white light that contains all of the colors in the spectrum. Newton was a 23-year-old instructor at Cambridge when he performed his famous spectrum experiments *(below)*, from which he was able to learn that an object assumes its color by absorbing some spectral colors and reflecting others. A lemon appears yellow because the yellow parts of the spectrum are the ones principally reflected.

Newton's work with light and color attracted little attention at first—he often lectured in almost-empty rooms—and he did not attempt to describe how the eye and brain per-

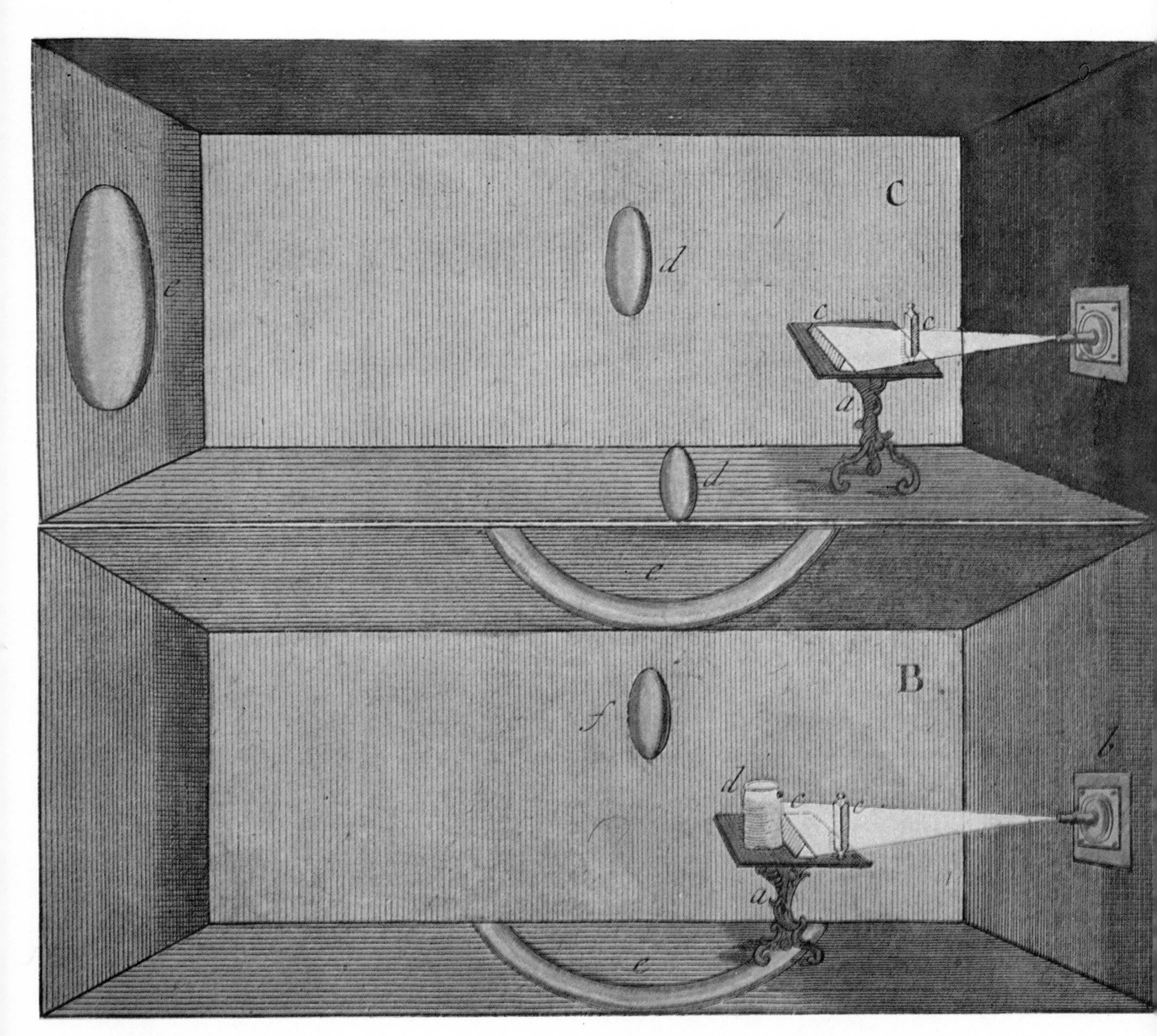

SPECTRA FROM SUNLIGHT

Newton's experiments with the spectrum were widely illustrated in the 18th Century, and two examples are shown here. In the upper drawing, two prisms are used to break down a beam of reflected sunlight into three oval spectra. The lower drawing shows how the addition of a water-filled jar bends light into rainbows. However, the artist has placed the spectra where he pleased, rather than in their correct positions.

ceive color until 1704. Even then, he confined himself to publishing a series of speculations in the form of unanswered "Queries." He implied that the retina of the eye might contain innumerable light receptors, each responding to a single color stimulus by transmitting an appropriate signal to the brain. Although Newton's queries were a cautious attempt to suggest a parallel between the way the eye sees color and the way the ear hears musical tones, such an analogy is obviously oversimplified and perhaps Newton himself realized this. By asking questions, he made it necessary for later investigators either to confirm his shrewd guesses —or come up with a more plausible explanation—before answering him.

ISAAC NEWTON

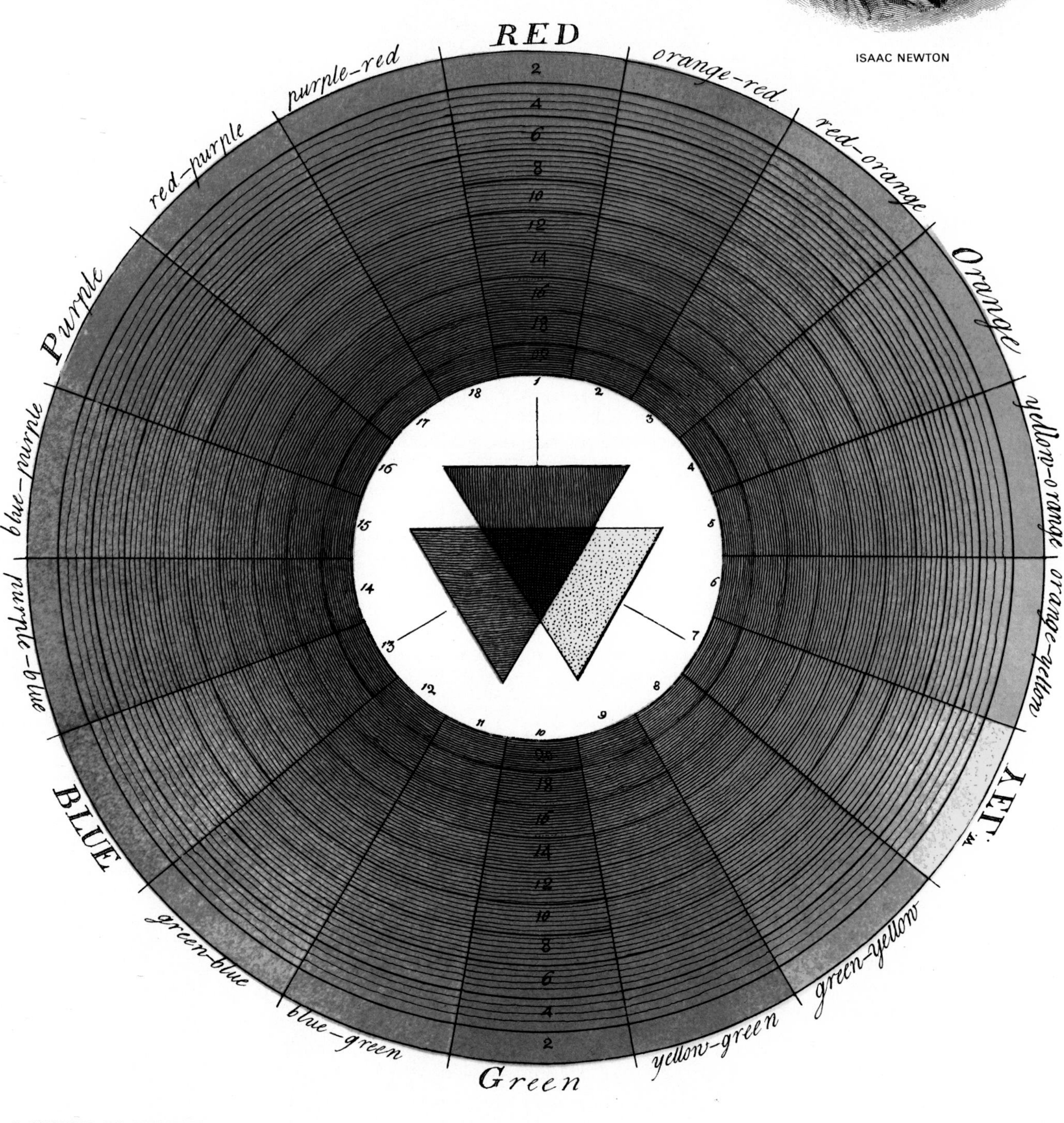

A SYSTEM OF COLORS

This 18th Century color wheel was an early attempt to illustrate the relationships among all visible colors. Moses Harris joined the ends of the spectrum to form a circle, a figure which Newton had only sketched in black and white. Each of Harris' 18 "prismatic" colors is shown in its various intensities, and the three triangles in the center support his belief that all other colors can be formed from red, blue and yellow.

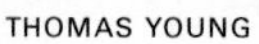

THOMAS YOUNG

HERMANN VON HELMHOLTZ

The Three-Color Theory of Vision

Thomas Young, who provided the first reasonable reply to Newton's queries on color vision, was a versatile scholar whose interests ranged from hieroglyphics to optics. In an 1801 hypothesis notable for its brevity—a scant 300 words—as well as its revolutionary concept, Young rejected Newton's notion that the eye held "an infinite number of particles," each capable of reacting only to a single color. Young theorized that there were three different kinds of receptors, each type responding to one of three principal colors. By combining these, all other colors, including white, could be produced. But Young did hardly any experimental work in color vision, preferring to concentrate on the physical nature of color. It remained for the German scientist Hermann von Helmholtz to revive and clarify Young's three-color, or trichromatic, theory in the mid-19th Century. Helmholtz explained that all three types of receptors reacted to all colors, but in varying degrees, and that it was the total "sensation" received by the brain that determined the colors actually seen.

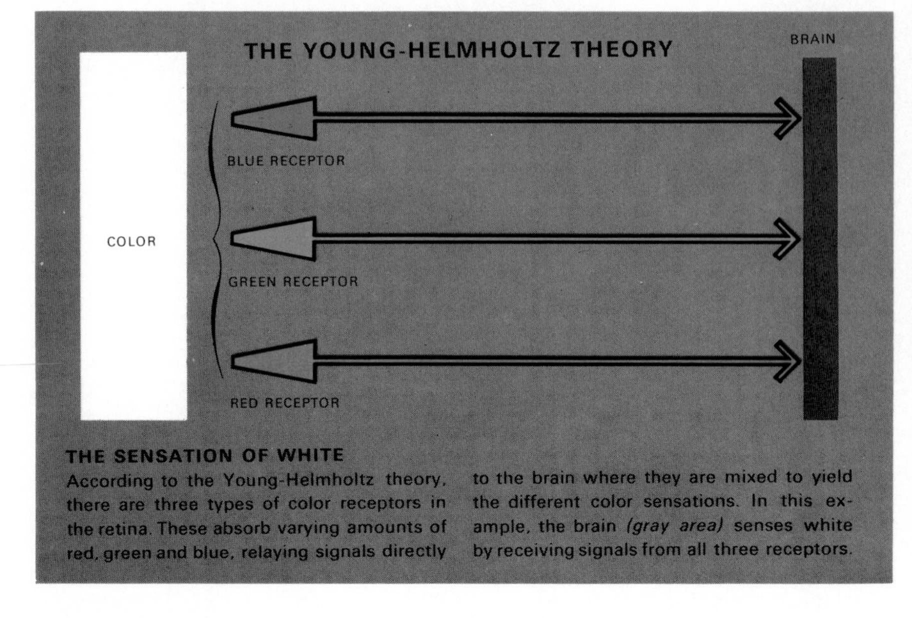

THE SENSATION OF WHITE
According to the Young-Helmholtz theory, there are three types of color receptors in the retina. These absorb varying amounts of red, green and blue, relaying signals directly to the brain where they are mixed to yield the different color sensations. In this example, the brain *(gray area)* senses white by receiving signals from all three receptors.

A COLORFUL DEMONSTRATION

Lectures on color, like the one shown in this engraving, were very popular in 19th Century England. The speaker here is aided by a lantern *(left)* that beams white light through a standing lens and into a spectroscope. The light is then projected onto a screen as a spectrum.

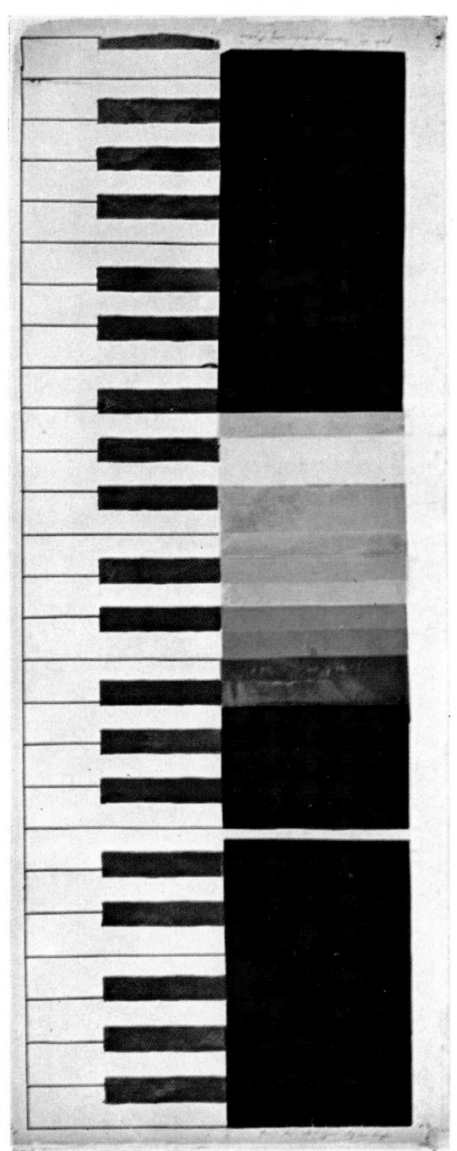

A MUSICAL COLOR SCALE

Using the device above, Helmholtz attempted to prove an analogy between the progression of colors in the spectrum and the progression of notes on a musical scale. Such detailed comparisons of sight and sound, common in the 19th Century, are no longer considered valid.

EWALD HERING

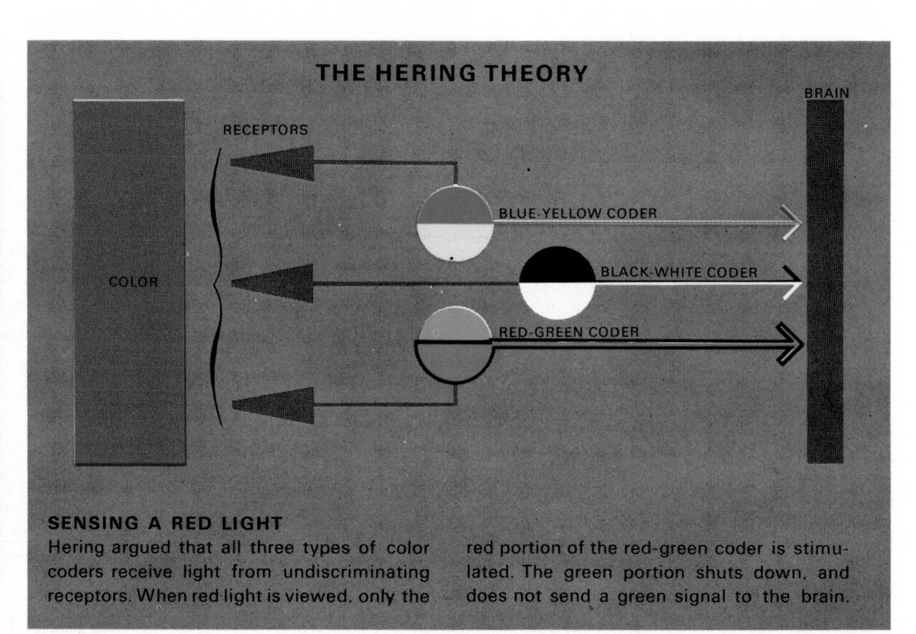

SENSING A RED LIGHT
Hering argued that all three types of color coders receive light from undiscriminating receptors. When red light is viewed, only the red portion of the red-green coder is stimulated. The green portion shuts down, and does not send a green signal to the brain.

A CHANGE OF HEART
Staring at the black dot in the center of the green heart for 20 seconds and then gazing directly at a white surface produces a remarkable visual phenomenon. A clear afterimage can be perceived of a red heart bordered in blue. The Hering theory explains this as a temporary switching of signals to the brain. Since red and green share a single coding mechanism, as do blue and yellow, withdrawal of the color stimulus shuts down one part of the mechanism and triggers the other part for a moment or two.

The Hering Theory: Color vs. Color

Even as Helmholtz was furthering Young's hypothesis of three-color vision, Ewald Hering was formulating an entirely different approach that stressed the psychology of color perception. Hering had done considerable research on color blindness and he could not harmonize the Young-Helmholtz theory with his findings, which seemed to indicate unusual relationships among four primary colors—red, green, blue and yellow. He theorized that the retina's receptors are mere absorbers of light—what he called "catching material"—and that color discrimination begins in the coding mechanisms located farther along the optic system. Most of these coders send only black or white signals to the brain, but two other types react to color in a peculiar way. One relays signals for either red or green; the other for either blue or yellow. But while the black-white coders can send a combined gray signal, the colors in the other coders oppose each other and will not mix. Thus, according to Hering, a red signal could be sent *(left, above)* only by "shutting off" green.

Hering also believed that the perception of brightness or darkness in colors depends on how "irritable" the coders are, and he even asserted that the manner in which a light mixture is received in the brain depends on the "mood of the organ of vision."

Even though the Young-Helmholtz and Hering theories seem to conflict, recent evidence suggests that it may be possible to combine them. The diagrams at right illustrate, in simplified form, such a compromise theory.

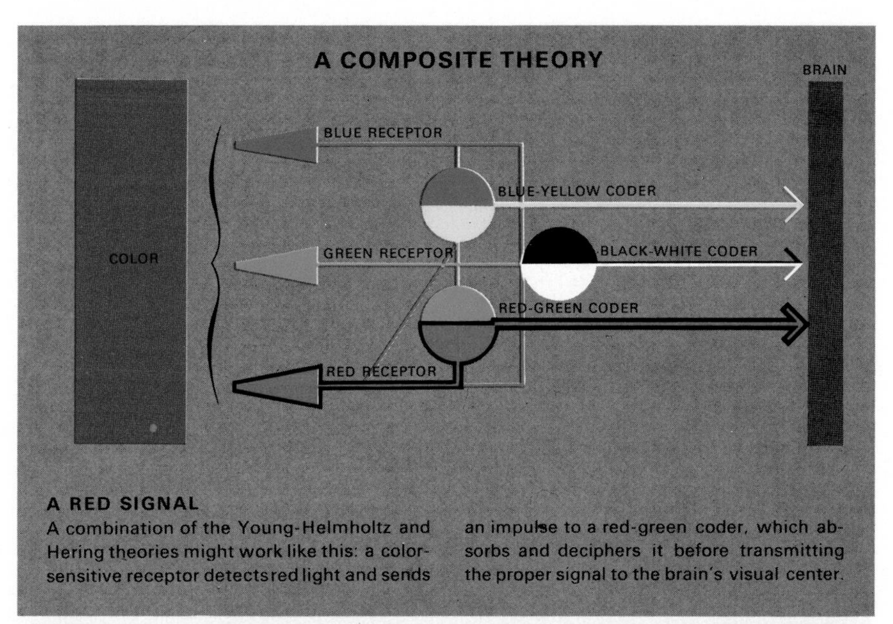

A RED SIGNAL
A combination of the Young-Helmholtz and Hering theories might work like this: a color-sensitive receptor detects red light and sends an impulse to a red-green coder, which absorbs and deciphers it before transmitting the proper signal to the brain's visual center.

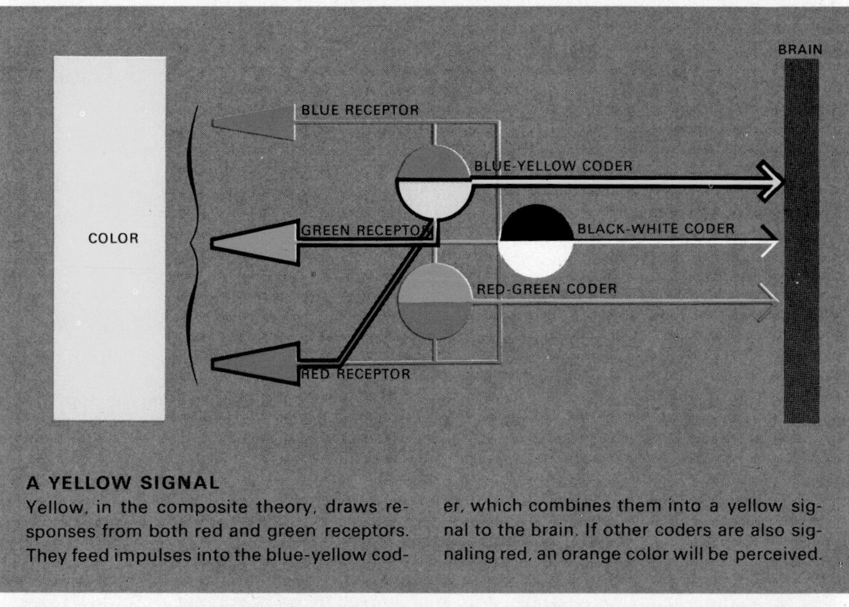

A YELLOW SIGNAL
Yellow, in the composite theory, draws responses from both red and green receptors. They feed impulses into the blue-yellow coder, which combines them into a yellow signal to the brain. If other coders are also signaling red, an orange color will be perceived.

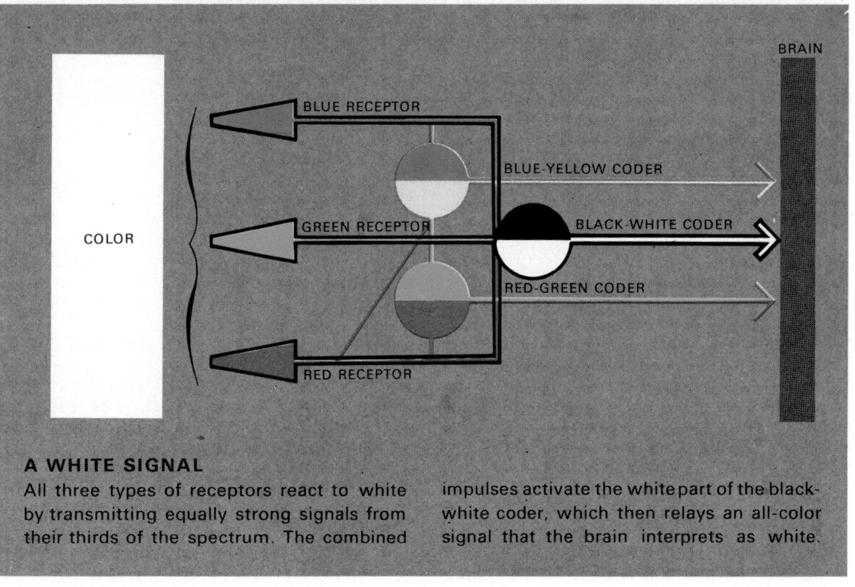

A WHITE SIGNAL
All three types of receptors react to white by transmitting equally strong signals from their thirds of the spectrum. The combined impulses activate the white part of the black-white coder, which then relays an all-color signal that the brain interprets as white.

Testing the Eye's Color Receptors

Only in recent years, with the refinement of scientific technology, have scientists been able to make direct studies of the eye's color-vision system. The retinal cones—so small that they can be seen only with powerful microscopes—that are the eye's color receptors can now be isolated and subjected to a variety of tests. In one such project, directed by Edward F. MacNichol Jr. of The Johns Hopkins University, light from different parts of the spectrum is directed through these cones, and the energy transmitted by them is analyzed by a computer. The data seem to confirm at least one aspect of the Young-Helmholtz theory: there are three types of cones, each particularly sensitive to a different range of the spectrum.

However, there appears to be no evidence that the cones send color signals directly to the brain, and MacNichol believes that color vision may be at least a two-stage process, with the cone signals passing through a coding mechanism like that which Hering linked to the nerve fibers. But much more research remains to be done before the color signals' path to the brain can be traced and the response measured. Not until then can Isaac Newton's queries on how the eye perceives color be answered.

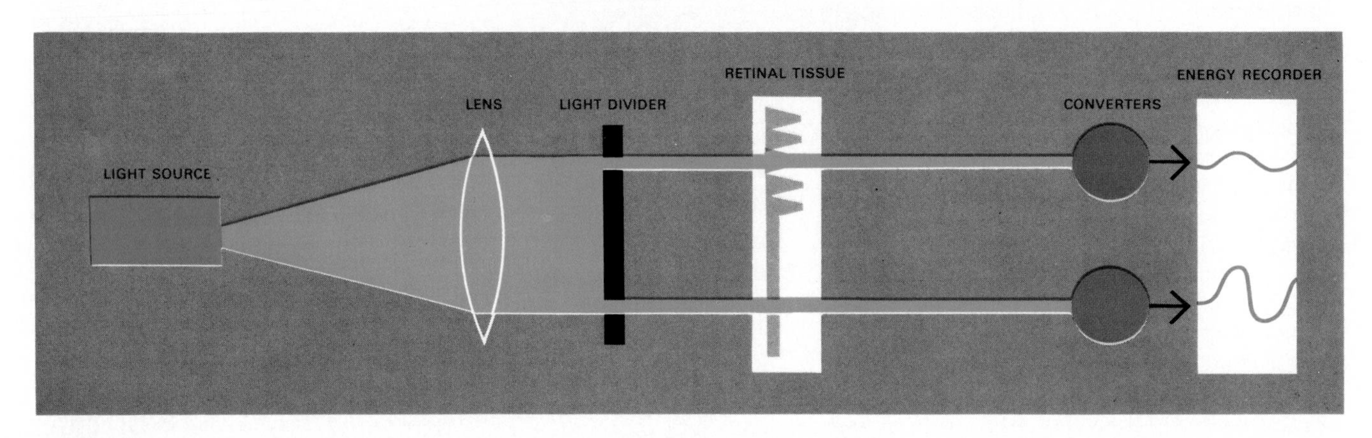

MAKING A CONE "SEE" AGAIN

In the MacNichol test, diagramed above, a focused beam of light is divided into two channels before passing through a section of retinal tissue. The tissue portion facing the top channel contains cones; the other portion has none. Converters at the end of each channel change light into measured electrical energy, and the readings are later compared by a computer. The apparatus used in the laboratory is seen below.

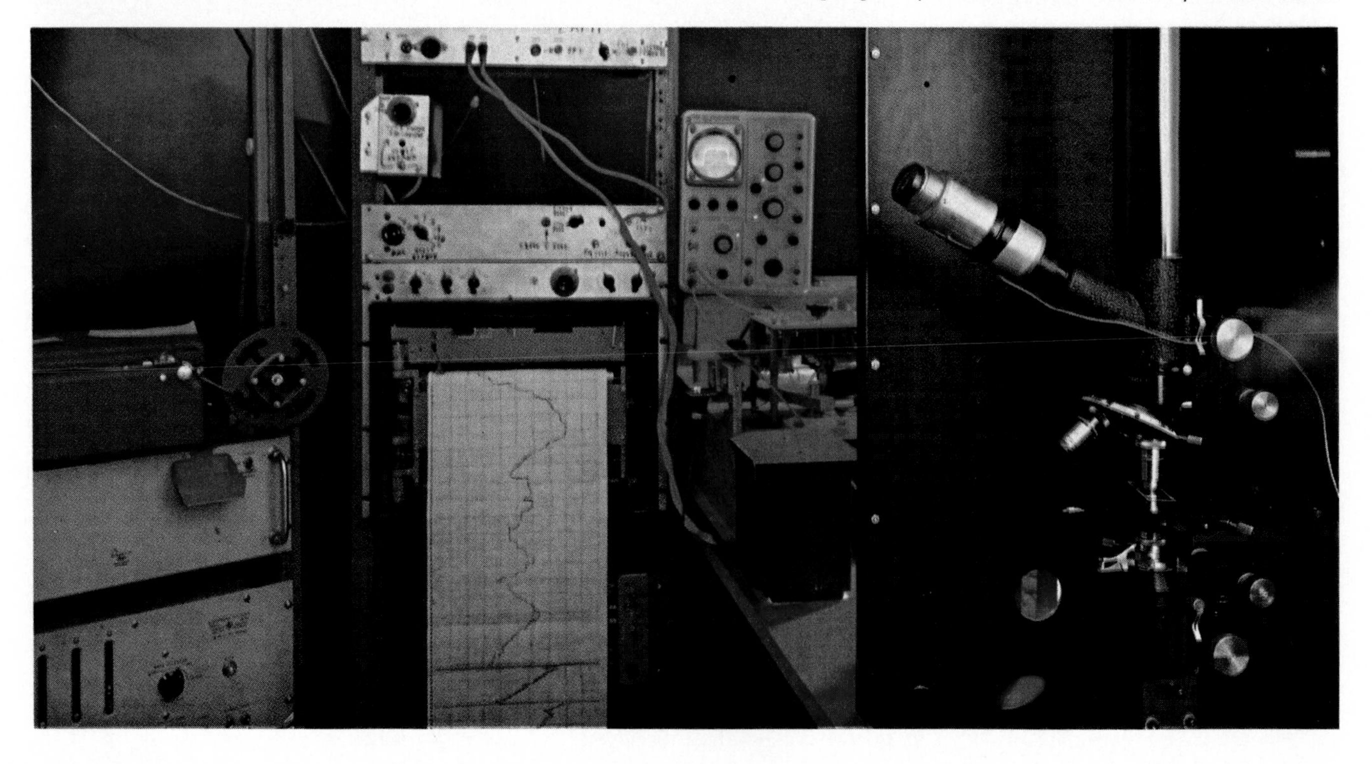

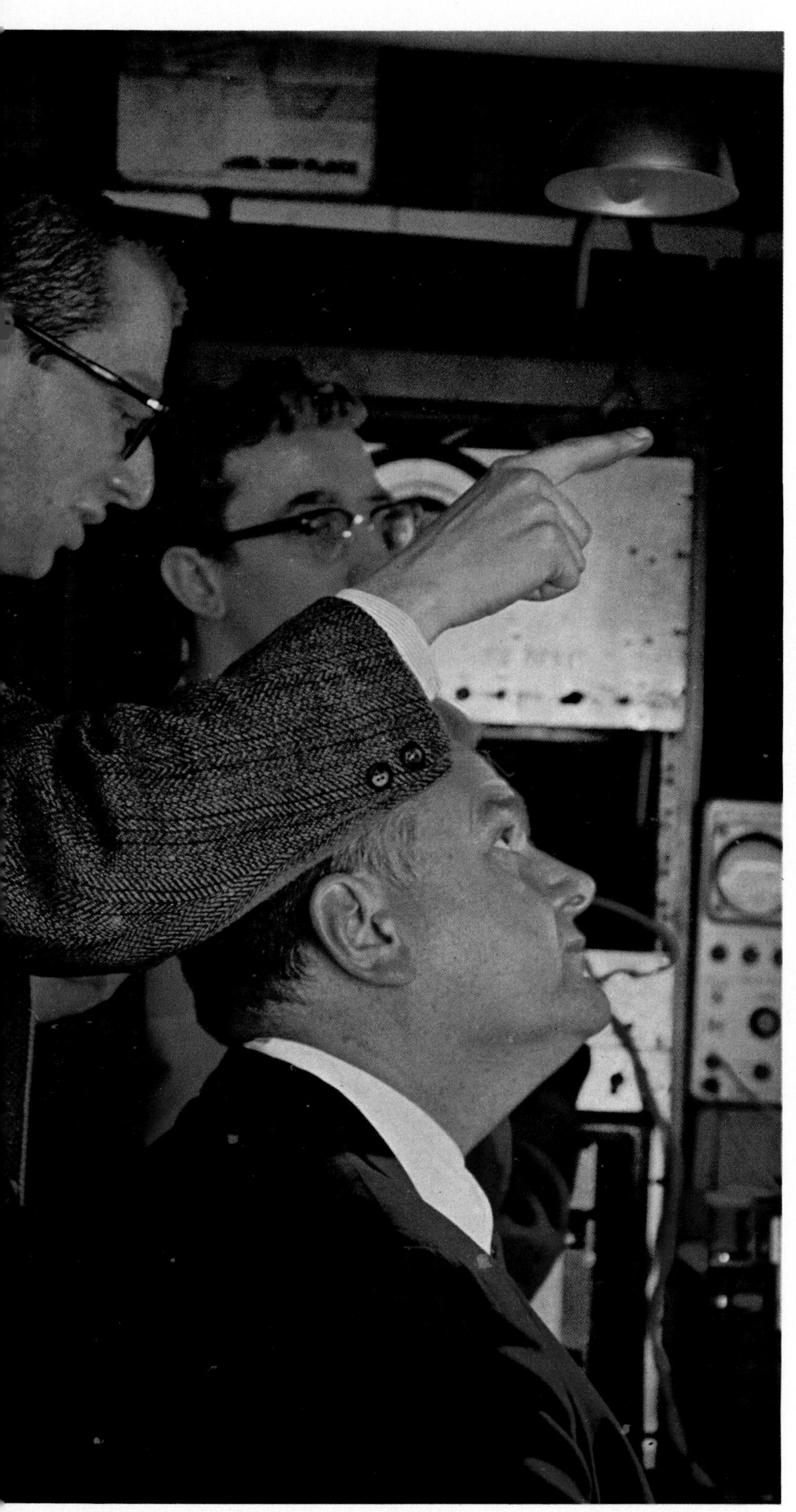

READING THE RESULTS
MacNichol *(seated)* and his research team observe the results of one of their cone experiments. Precise measurements of light energy passing through the cones have shown that individual cones vary from one to the other in their ability to absorb different wavelengths of the spectrum. This is the first direct evidence confirming Young's belief that there are three types of color receptors within the human eye.

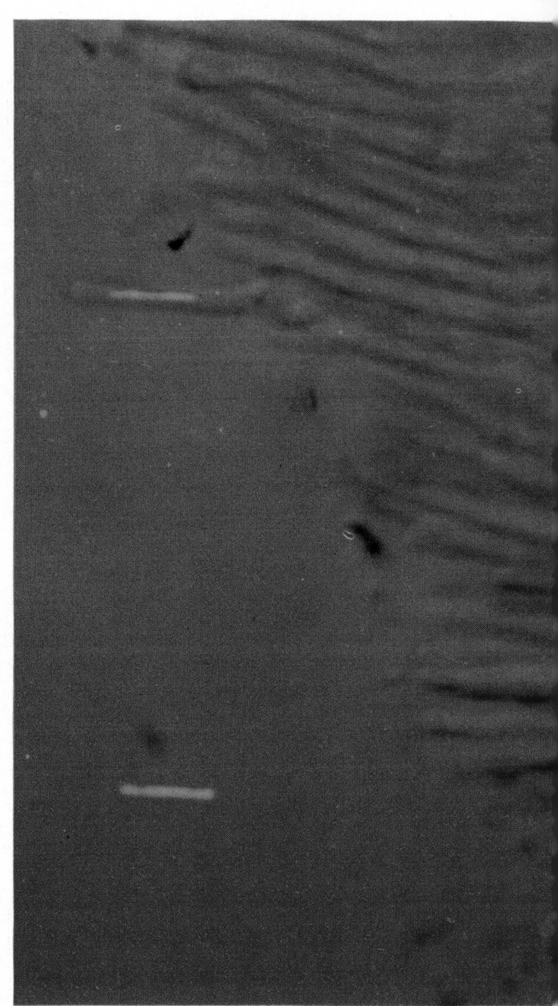

A CLOSE-UP OF A CONE
In the greatly enlarged photomicrograph above, two beams of green light are seen head on as they penetrate a section of tissue from the fovea of a human retina. The bottom beam is passing through a cone whose diameter is only about 1 / 100 that of a human hair. The other beam, a control, bypasses the massed cones, resembling a logjam at the right of the picture.

The Brain's Response to Color

Although no one knows exactly how the eye's color signals reach the brain, research in color perception by scientists like Dr. and Mrs. Leo Hurvich at the University of Pennsylvania *(right)* is producing a wealth of information on how people react to colors.

The Hurviches have helped to revive interest in the Hering theory by proving that many of Hering's ideas —notably the linkage between the perception of red and green on the one hand, and yellow and blue on the other—can be systematized into a clear and precise approach to color perception.

This type of approach has proved that red and green can be identified in poor light more easily than yellow or blue, although the opposite is true in bright light. Steady exposure to any color, however, tends to weaken the brain's response; a "bleaching" effect makes the color fade or turn neutral gray. Such investigations of the psychophysical aspect of color vision —i.e., the effect of a physical stimulus on a mental process—have also turned up some interesting information about the absence of color. In complete darkness, the eye sees dark gray, but not black. For black does not exist except as a sensation that accompanies or follows other colors; the lighter those colors are, the deeper the black that will appear. Black is "blackest" in contrast to white.

TESTING FOR COLOR VISION
To test color perception in different parts of the visual field, Dr. and Mrs. Hurvich place a subject before a screen so that his eyes are fixed at a point straight ahead as a small circle of red light slowly passes before them. The circle, perceived as bright when directly in front, fades to gray and then disappears as it nears the limits of peripheral vision. The black spot on the screen is an observation peephole. This test is normally conducted in complete darkness.

7
Three Dimensions of Vision

This two-dimensional photograph of Nevada's Great Basin achieves an illusion of depth from a variety of perception cues: the converging railroad tracks, shrinking telegraph poles, and the blue haze across the distant mountains.

ALMOST EVERY PERSON CAN REMEMBER, as a child, lying in the grass on a summer day, gazing at the great dome of the sky, pondering infinity—and wondering about the relationships of things. That speck in the air overhead, for example—is it a gnat two feet away or an eagle a mile high? For an instant there may be bafflement, but if one moves one's head a bit and tries to relate the speck to other things in the scene, like clouds or trees, it quickly takes its proper place in its surroundings; its size and its distance from the eye are no longer a mystery. What remains is wonder at the speed—literally the blink of an eye—with which these intricate adjustments are made, considering the problems that must be solved.

The physical world, from which visual experience is derived, has dimensions—depth, breadth and height. It extends beyond and around, above and below the observer. The seeing man is in the middle—the visual scene stretches out before him in various sectors, with large distinct objects making up the foreground and with innumerable surfaces and contours arranged at various distances beyond. Though he does not have eyes in the back of his head, man is aware that his world also stretches back behind him and is visually available with a turn of the head. But the receptive surface of the eye, the retina, on which this image of the world falls, has only two dimensions. Although the retina is curved around the inside of the eyeball, the retina is a two-dimensional surface, like a sheet of photographic film or a pane of transparent glass, on the surface of which the objects beyond the glass are drawn. Yet man does not see the world as a flat photograph or an etched windowpane: he sees it in all its dimensions, and is able to make judgments about the position, distance, shape and size of objects with security and exactness. This ability, as Hermann von Helmholtz pointed out, "is the necessary foundation for all our actions, from threading a needle through a tangled skein of silk to leaping from cliff to cliff when life itself depends on the right measurement of the distance." And, as a 20th Century scientist adds, it even allows the pilot to land a jet plane "very fast and possibly in a cold sweat."

Here, then, is a paradox: the world has depth, the visual image is flat, our visual experience has depth. Somehow, somewhere in the visual system, the dimensions must be reconstructed. But how? By what devices does man manage to see a three-dimensional world in all its solidity, with objects in certain places at distances he can estimate with remarkable accuracy and speed?

The problem has occupied wondering men for centuries, capturing the imaginations of men so distant in time and disparate in interest as Euclid in the Fourth Century B.C., Leonardo da Vinci in the Renaissance, Bishop George Berkeley in the Age of Enlightenment, Oliver Wendell Holmes in the 19th Century. The approach to the problem has ranged from the mystical and philosophical to the experimental, but scientists today tend to think of spatial vision "not as a paradox of philosophy but a fact of stimulation." It can be approached not as a mystery but as a physical event that begins when something in the environment reaches the eye, there to be handled in specific ways by the visual apparatus.

For example, one of the most noticeable things about the three-dimensional world is that it is upright and man is upright in it. This is quite remarkable, for the image on the retina is actually upside down as a result of the way light rays pass through the cornea and lens. Nevertheless, man sees ceilings above him and floors below; the sky is up, the earth down. Early thinkers assumed that there was a physical structure inside the eyeball that reinverted the image; when this was disproved, it was suggested that the brain somehow mysteriously turns the picture upright. Today scientists do not even think of this as a problem. They agree that the upside-down image on the retina is not transmitted, like a picture postcard, to a little man who sits in the head and turns the card over before he reads it; it is, instead, sent as a series of electrochemical signals, and these signals are properly analyzed by the brain, partly through our inherited ability to do so, partly by experience.

Living in an upside-down world

From the beginning of life man feels his feet on the floor, feels the pull of gravity from below, reaches up with his hands to gather fruit or down to pick a flower. So "upness" and "downness" are part of him. They are with him from the first breath he draws, constantly shaping his learning process. They were with his ancestors for millons of years, shaping and refining the organs he now uses. This concept has been dramatized by a series of experiments with eyeglasses that turn everything upside down. At first the volunteers who wear them are completely disoriented; they reach up to tie their shoelaces and step down on the up staircase. Their movements are so uncoordinated that some volunteers have to crawl to get safely across the room; yet after a while they are able to ride bicycles and even ski. Upside-downness eventually seems right to them and they can live comfortably with it. And when the glasses are taken off after several weeks, the volunteers have to reverse the process of adjustment and go through another period of disorientation before things are normal again. However, the artificial adjustment has never proved as complete or as stable as the ordinary, right-side-up integration of visual experience with bodily sensations. The brain is so powerfully organized to experience the world in its "real" position that it has not been able to readapt fully to a different arrangement.

Right-side-upness is only one of several fundamental factors that help man in his visualization of space and dimension. In addition to being upright, to the viewer the visual world also is bounded. The sky seems to be a limited dome—vastly distant, but still limited. The field of vision is limited in more intimate ways—by the positioning of the eyes in the skull and their limited ability to move. These visual limitations give

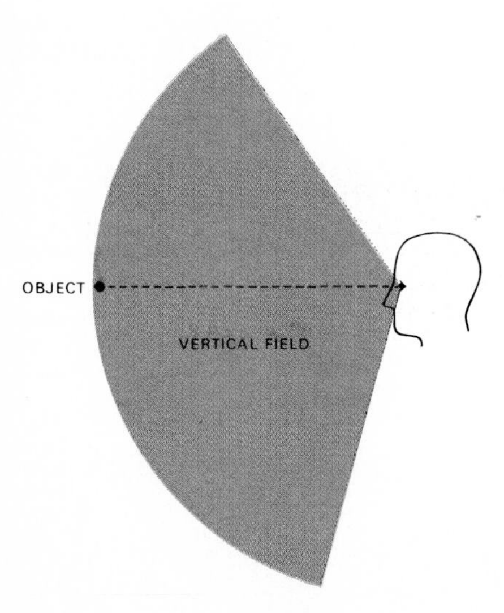

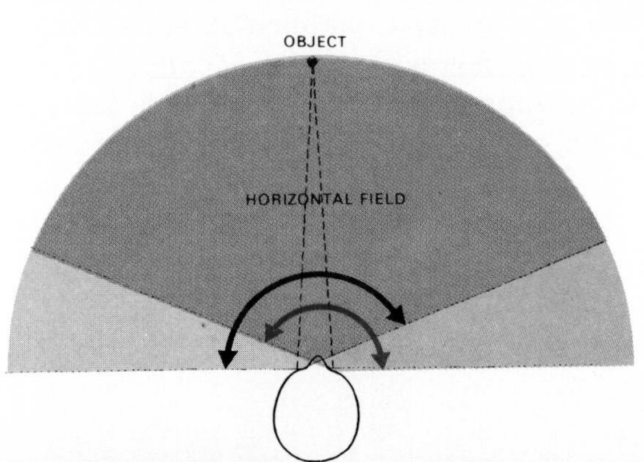

THE SWEEP OF HUMAN VISION is shown in these two diagrams. The vertical range of the eyes *(above)* is about 140°, and is bounded above by the brows and below by the cheeks. Man's total horizontal scan *(below)* is approximately 180° when the eyes are focused on a fixed object *(dotted lines)*. Each eye has a range of about 150°, as shown by the arrows. Where the fields of vision overlap *(center section)*, man has binocular sight. The shaded wedges *(left eye, gray; right eye, color)* indicate the outer fringes of vision.

one of the first hints man has of some things being here and others there by providing a point of reference with a part of himself.

The visual world also is divided by the horizon into up and down—and this horizon is ever present, whether it is the line between earth and sky or between the floor and the wall. The view is further divided into foreground and background, or into figure and ground, an automatic distinction made in every visual experience, however simple. The figure stands out and has the solid and substantial character of a thing or object. It has surface texture, shape, form and localization. The ground, on the other hand, is less substantial. It seems to lie farther back in space and to extend in unbroken fashion behind the figure. These visual elements, the primary distinctions between up and down, here and there, are the base lines of spatial vision. But beyond these the eye makes innumerable other distinctions and is provided with a rich supply of information from which it can reconstruct dimensionality and location. And this information can be catalogued and analyzed with a fair degree of precision to produce a well-founded explanation of the old "mystery" of dimensional sight.

Visual data are made up of spots of color, lines, contours, shadows, and gaps between lines. These data reach the eye and are received by the brain in such specific ways that they constitute what are called "visual cues." Some of these cues depend on the existence of two coordinated eyes, and are known as binocular cues; they are related chiefly to the way the two eyes jointly handle the information they receive.

Harmonizing binocular vision

Although man's two eyes, unlike those of many species, look in the same direction at once and are coordinated to harmonize their two pictures, they are roughly two and a half inches apart from center to center and therefore are not aimed in exactly the same line. If you hold your right hand about 12 inches in front of your nose, the edge of your thumb closest to your face, you can see that the hand is a solid, rounded object with a front and a back, a near side and a far. If you close the right eye, you will see more of the palm and very little of the knuckles. Close the left eye and look with the right; the palm disappears while the knuckles are now clearly in view. Although the pictures from the two eyes are precisely blended, they remain distinct to just that degree that gives roundness and solidity to visual forms, thus creating a powerful binocular cue.

How the visual cortex puts two pictures together so meaningfully is not well understood, although it obviously poses one of the fundamental questions of depth vision. If, for instance, you try to thread a needle with one eye closed, you will see immediately how much your judgment of distance and location depends on two eyes. People who have vision in only one eye do manage to function without a remarkable loss of efficiency, partly because of the richness of other, monocular cues to vision and partly because the rapid movements of the eye can help to compensate for lack of binocularity. Some people even become skillful in fields where binocularity would seem to be indispensable; Wiley Post, the famous airplane pilot of the 1930s whose white eye patch was almost a trademark, was such a rare exception.

Confusing the visual cortex

An odd fact about binocular coordination is that the observer is usually unaware of it and quite incapable of telling which eye is supplying which part of the information. But the optical brain must somehow "know" which part of a scene is being visualized by which eye, because when any confusion about this occurs, the scene becomes strange or even unreadable. In an ingenious experiment first performed in the 19th Century, a hollow tube about two inches across and a foot long is held in front of one eye and pointed at a lighted candle on the other side of the room. This candle is screened from the other eye by the hand, held palm open next to the far end of the tube. Thus one eye looks through the tube, the other looks at the hand. What the observer then sees quite strikingly is a hand with a hole in the palm, through which the flickering candle can be seen. If the open end of the tube is blocked, the candle disappears and only the hand can be seen. The experiment clearly underscores the fact that the brain puts together the two binocular pictures automatically on the basis of physical stimulation, and does not make allowance for possible visual ambiguities.

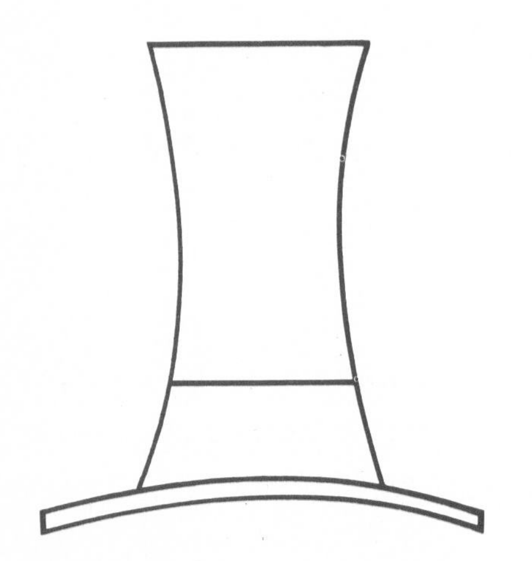

THE TOP-HAT ILLUSION shows how easy it is to misjudge dimensions. Though the hat appears to be much taller than it is wide, in reality the height of the crown and width of the brim are equal. The vertical section intersects the brim, reducing its apparent width. Even more effective in contributing to this illusion of height is the greater bulk of the crown compared with the much thinner brim. For brim and crown to appear equal, the brim should be some 25 per cent wider than that shown.

The most impressive demonstration of the role of binocular vision in depth perception is made with the stereoscope, an instrument that became an extremely popular parlor toy during the Victorian era. This device enables the viewer to look simultaneously at two photographs of the same scene taken from slightly different positions—the difference corresponding to the spatial separation between the two eyes. Since one eye sees one picture, and the other eye sees the other picture, the result is a single image with a compelling three-dimensional quality. Cameras for taking "stereo pairs" were used extensively by reconnaissance aircraft during World War II, and then studied in detail by photo interpreters in an effort to learn the secrets of enemy airfields and factories. One such stereo pair revealed to a sharp-eyed examiner the presence on a German airfield of a V-2 rocket—the first visual proof to British intelligence that such a weapon existed. If this object had been seen only in a single conventional aerial photograph, without the three-dimensional effect of stereoscopic photography, its identification as a rocket would have been much more difficult.

The special effectiveness of stereo photography becomes apparent when the two pictures are brought into single sharp focus, for the result is an illusion of depth throughout the photography. Oddly enough, human vision does not work quite that way when not looking through a stereoscope. To a man staring across a room at a painting on the wall, only the painting is in single sharp image. The other objects in the room, although they may not be consciously registered by the viewer, are perceived as double images. He fails to notice them not only because they are out of focus but also because they tend to be off to the side, on the edges of his field of view. If while focusing on the wall he were to hold up a finger at arm's length in front of him, he would immediately be aware of two fingers—one for each eye—and those fingers would not blend into one unless he focused on them, at which point there would be two paintings on the wall. Close one eye, and doubling disappears. But as long as both eyes are open there is a vast amount of doubling in every scene.

The extent of doubling, and the fuzziness of out-of-focus objects, vary, depending on how far the fuzzy object is from the thing being focused on. Again, returning to the man looking at a painting on the wall, the fuzziest thing in his field of view, and the one with the most extreme doubling, is his own nose. So far apart are the two images of it and so fuzzy are they that unless he thinks about it, he never sees his nose at all while he is looking around. Nevertheless it is there at all times, and it serves as a kind of unconscious base line, a cue to gauging distances.

The separation of the two eyes supplies another kind of binocular cue for judging distance. Because the effectiveness of this separation tends to decrease with distance, the closer the object, the greater the stereo effect. Therefore things that are near to the eyes seem to be more rounded and three-dimensional. At three feet the view of a thumbtack from each eye is quite different, and as a result it fairly jumps with three-dimensionality; move the tack away another 10 feet, and it loses some of its three-dimensional quality. At a quarter of a mile, the view of a tree or building received by one eye is almost identical with the view received by the other. At that distance, the angle between eyes and building is so small that the stereoscopic effect begins to falter, and objects beyond that point seem increasingly flat. This does not mean that man's sense of depth and distance stops utterly at a quarter of a mile. Obviously it does not.

Cues for the one-eyed

Furthermore, man can utilize a number of monocular cues to aid him in gauging distance. So called because they can be interpreted by one eye equally as well as by two, monocular cues depend on the qualities of the objects themselves and not on any stereoscopic effect. Varying lists of cues have been compiled by different scientists, but most vision experts agree on including the following basic categories: linear and textural perspective, relative size of objects, aerial perspective, shadowing, interposition, movement parallax (or relative movement of objects) and upward dislocation.

Linear and textural perspective depends on the fact that surface textures seem to become more dense with distance. The foreground of a freshly plowed field will appear to consist of widely scattered large lumps

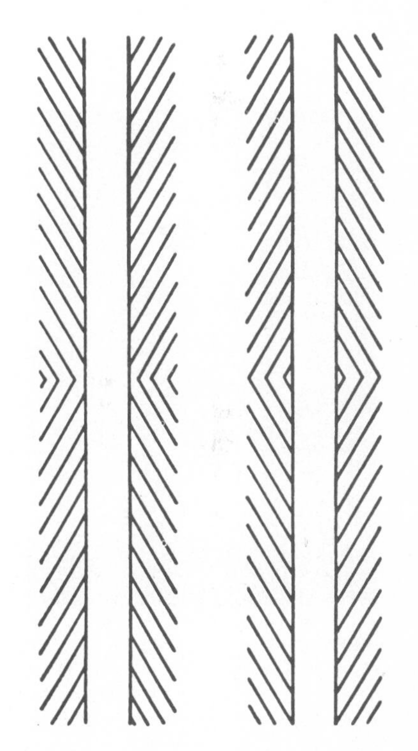

A VISUAL ILLUSION makes these parallel vertical lines appear to spread apart *(left)* and come together *(right)* in bowlegged and knock-kneed fashion. This effect was first described by 19th Century German scientist Friedrich Zöllner, who suggested that diverging lines, like the short ones at the left, lead the eye outward, and make the space between the center of the vertical lines appear greater than it really is. Patterns of converging lines *(right)* have the opposite effect.

of earth; in the distance the eye merges the lumps so closely together that the ground looks like the cut, granular surface of a gingerbread slice. Near the observer a cobblestone street quite obviously consists of large individual stones, but in the distance the cobblestones become so small and close together that the surface seems to be almost as smooth as concrete. Examples of this kind of textural gradation are endless: the flowered pattern of an Oriental rug is sharp and open near the eye, dense and hard to distinguish at the other end; papers and pencils and other paraphernalia on a nearby desk are individually distinct, while objects on a table down the hall are packed together and may sometimes be hard to separate visually. Parallel floorboards, the grain of wood, rows of books on a shelf—all provide graded cues to distance and depth.

Textural perspective also helps to indicate corners, edges and gaps between objects. A change in the steady rate of increase in textural density indicates a curve or bend; a sharp change in the rate suggests a corner, a discontinuity in the change of density indicates a gap or break in the surface.

The relative size of objects is another familiar monocular cue. A six-foot man standing nearby looks considerably larger than a man the same height standing a block away. But this cue is strongly dependent on two other factors: the observer's knowledge of the real size of the object, and the presence of other depth cues. A three-foot dwarf standing 100 feet away might be mistaken for a tall man standing much farther off unless the observer knows the dwarf is a dwarf, or unless there are other hints, such as the size of a doorway next to the dwarf. A train seen at a great distance is recognized as a real train and not a toy close-by, because of the landscape and all the other indications of distance. A child standing nearby is not mistaken for a distant adult, because of clothes and general appearance. These examples indicate the interdependence of cues to give a complete and accurate visual impression of objects in space.

IN EVERY GIRL lurks an old woman, a close examination of this drawing suggests. One usually sees the outline of a young girl's face. But if the eye focuses on the girl's choker necklace for a moment, the left profile of a fierce-looking old crone appears; the girl's choker is her teeth, the girl's chin her nose. The eye notices the more pleasing view first.

Visual tricks to save money

By deliberately withholding or manipulating visual cues that scale size, producers of motion pictures have not only saved enormous amounts of money but have been able to record scenes that could not otherwise be staged. On the screen, the movie patron sees a brilliantly lit passenger liner sailing across a moderately calm ocean. Next, there are some shots supposedly aboard the ship: passengers dancing, drinking, dining, strolling on the decks. Now an ominous note. The scene is the interior of a submarine with an evil-looking captain staring into a periscope. He is looking at the liner. Now he gives the command to fire torpedoes. The weapons can be seen streaking through the water directly toward the ship. Suddenly there is an explosion; the vessel is almost torn in two. Aboard the sinking liner, the panic-stricken passengers don life jackets and rush for the lifeboats through smoke and flame. Then, from a distance, the multimillion-dollar ship is seen to sink into the sea.

The ship is, of course, a scale model of an ocean liner, and the ocean is a studio tank. By keeping the waves and the explosion in scale with the miniature, and by intercutting shots of people and backgrounds in life size, the impression that everything is in full scale is conveyed to the audience. By use of similar optical tricks, King Kong, a giant gorilla, climbs to the top of the Empire State Building and fights off military planes, great cities are burned to the ground, trains are wrecked. As long as everything is in scale—speed and degree of motion as well as all other components of the scene—the illusion is excellent.

One Hollywood producer of a Western film forgot that the illusion could work in reverse. For comedy effect he made up the entire cast with midgets. In keeping with their size, the characters rode ponies instead of horses and acted in miniature sets. However, with little to scale the scenes, all the actors seemed normal-sized, and the joke was lost.

Artistic deception of the eye

Aerial perspective, or haze, is a distance cue long used with great skill and effect by artists and stage designers, who soften and blur the colors and outlines of distant hills to duplicate the atmospheric changes in nature. Conversely, sharpening the outlines of distant mountains in a landscape is the artist's way of indicating a brilliantly clear day, which tends to reduce the distant haze effect. Color, too, changes with distance; Leonardo advised painters that to "distinguish the variations in distance of different buildings which appear placed in a single line . . . you must make the nearest building its real color, but make the more distant ones less defined and bluer." The addition of smog to the modern metropolitan scene has the single dubious advantage of making this distance cue more striking.

Shadowing gives shape and form to objects. A circle drawn on a piece of paper is just a circle, but if shading is applied—lightly at the center, heavily in the outer areas—the circle begins to look like a sphere.

Somewhat related to shadowing is the brightness of an object. Bright objects appear larger and closer than dark ones, which is why stout women are advised to avoid white clothes. An important psychological experiment demonstrates this point: two white balloons of the same size and brightness are placed side by side against a dark background. They appear to be the same distance from the observer, but if the light on one of them is increased, it will appear to be closer; relative brightness has given the cue.

Interposition, the placing of one object in front of another, is an especially useful monocular cue. Obviously, if part of a desk is hidden by a chair, then we can tell immediately that the chair is closer to us than the desk. A related factor is completeness of outline: an interruption in the contour of an object suggests that something is in front of it—although with certain geometric figures or two-dimensional drawings, this can be an important source of ambiguity and confusion.

The relative upward dislocation of an object in a scene is another monocular cue long known to artists: the higher up an object is drawn

WHAT'S WRONG WITH THIS SENTENCE? At first glance, seemingly nothing. But with closer reading the repetition of the word THE becomes obvious. Because we generally read rapidly in word patterns rather than slowly a word at a time, it is easy for the eye to skip over the extra THE and register the familiar sentence "correctly."

within the frame of the picture, the farther away it will appear—even when there is no background to give perspective. Man's natural environment and his angle of vision underlie this phenomenon: the horizon always appears to be higher than the ground on which we stand. This can be vividly observed by standing on the shore and looking out to sea. Thus by habit, man thinks of higher things as more distant, even when the sky's horizon is not there as a reference line.

Movement parallax, or the relative motion of objects in the visual field, is one of the most complicated and difficult of all the monocular depth cues, although it is one that can provide quite accurate information about depth and distance. If you move your head to the right or left while focusing on some spot in the middle distance, near objects will seem to move backward and forward while far ones move to right or left in the same direction as your head movement. Only things at the point of focus stand still. Nearly everyone is familiar with the apparent motion of the landscape seen from a moving train: nearby objects tend to whiz by at a blurring rate, while distant objects move with great slowness or even tend to stand still. Even when the observer is motionless, this cue still operates: if two objects at different distances—say, two airplanes in the sky—pass by at the same speed, the nearer one will appear to be moving faster because it crosses the total angle of vision more quickly than the second plane. Even when no other evidence is available, an observer can usually tell that such objects are at different distances and can even estimate by how much.

THE ILLUSION OF MOVEMENT is created in this portion of a painting titled *Fall*, by Bridget Riley, an optical, or "op," artist. The eye scanning the black, wavy lines sees them moving alternately toward and away from the viewer. The result is a continuous flow of motion, particularly in the lower area of the painting where the contours are closely packed.

The potential for ambiguity

The existence of all these cues, binocular and monocular, may give the impression that there is a straightforward relationship between the detailed information provided by the environment and the visual perceptions man experiences. This is true up to a point. But the visual system and the brain, after all, are not extensions of the world or its servants: they have properties of their own which may bring about transformation in the material received by the eye. Furthermore, the information provided by the eye is not always exact or uncomplicated. Nearly every cue to spatial vision and distance—and thus nearly every visual situation—contains a potential for ambiguity. When the ambiguity arises, it is called an illusion.

Visual illusions are baffling and complicated. They can be described, classified and, in some cases, partly or wholly explained. Nearly all geometric or spatial illusions involve one or more of several basic phenomena. For example, circles always tend to be underestimated in size. Straight lines tend to be overestimated in length. Acute angles are overestimated and obtuse ones are underestimated. A simple square looks taller than it is broad, and the apparent size of a square depends on whether it is standing on a corner or on one side. In fact, this illusion is so powerful than when a square is standing on one corner, we give it an entirely different name: a diamond. Of striking importance is the fact that certain line drawings readily project themselves into the third dimension and can easily reverse their perspective (see page 163 for examples of reversed perspective). Neon signs can easily create an illusion of movement where there is none. A neon image of a small boy, for example, might show him apparently bouncing a ball up and down. Although the ball appears to move, it does not. What happens is that two images of the ball, a high one and a low one, are alternately blinked on and off, and the eye, following these up and down, supplies the illusion of movement. A different kind of illusion is provided by a light that appears to grow larger and come closer as it is made brighter, and to get smaller and farther away when it dims. At night, when an automobile's red brake lights flash on, they make the car seem closer to the following vehicle because the brake lights are brighter than the regular taillights.

The problem of illusions

Illusions have usually been viewed as posing a special problem in the psychology of vision. In the past, such phenomena were referred to as "errors of judgment" or "mistaken interpretations." Today, however, most researchers look upon such labeling as unfortunate because it tended to set the problems of illusion apart from the remainder of psychophysics and from the kind of analysis that is typical of that science. (Psychophysics will be discussed in the next chapter.)

Moreover, to dismiss illusions as errors of judgment or mistaken interpretations seemed to perpetuate the notion that all other perceptions were correct. This distinction may seem reasonable if one thinks of vision as a copying process and then asks if the copy is correct or faulty. Vision is not that simple, however. If by "correct" we mean that the visual system gives a true representation of the physical events in the environment, then we must be prepared to place *all* visual phenomena in the category of illusion.

When the eye fails to see the flickering of movies and television, it is giving an inaccurate rendering of the physical event. When a person is in a poorly lit room for a while, the light source looks dim because the eyes are adapted to it. However, if he comes into the room after a half hour in darkness, the light seems bright. The eyes are making a mistake in registering the physical stimulus. When a mixture of blue and yellow lights is seen as white or gray, because the two colors are complementary and therefore tend to cancel each other out, the eye is again in error. An examination of most of the data of vision would reveal no examples of what could be accurately called correct perception.

In short, an attempt to divide the problems of seeing into "illusions" and "correct vision" simply is not meaningful. What must be discovered is how the eye operates under *all* circumstances. When this is fully understood, the process of vision will be understood, both with respect to those facts and observations which seem intuitively obvious and straightforward, and those which, on the surface at least, seem puzzling and, therefore, are likely to be labeled "mistakes."

GHOSTLY GRAY DOTS appear intermittently at the intersections of the white lines, but nowhere else in the illustration above. This is because the contrast is sharp along the sides of the black squares and the white lines look brighter. However, where the lines intersect, there is more white space, lessening the contrast and creating an illusion of gray spots.

More Than Meets the Eye

While visual perception begins with images the eye actually receives *(opposite),* the complete process involves a series of complex actions. By means of an elaborate mechanism, the tiny, two-dimensional scenes registered by the retina become life-sized, three-dimensional images. The brain's "computer" —the visual cortex—swiftly sorts out and analyzes the nerve signals from the retina before feeding them into a "memory bank." Here, they become visual cues which indicate where an object is, what it is, and its relationship to other objects in the visual field. For example, a yellow sun and a yellow balloon may produce similar cues to size, color and shape; however, only an infant would reach for the sun, because the brain is conditioned from early childhood to "know" that the sun is infinitely larger and more distant. But if the task is to compare two yellow balloons, all of the available cues are examined—how big the balloons are compared to each other and to nearby objects, how the light strikes them, whether they overlap—before a calculated estimate is made as to their size and distance. More often than not, the guess is an accurate one. But when the cues conflict, perception is either uncertain or garbled. The result is often an optical illusion.

THE VIEW FROM THE LEFT EYE
What the left eye actually sees is shown in a photographic restaging of a famous sketch by the 19th Century physicist Ernst Mach. An adaptation of Mach's sketch rests on the reclining body of the mustachioed viewer. The photo displays not only the eye's broad field of vision, but also a number of visual cues that aid the brain to estimate size and distance.

Cues to Size and Distance

The relative sizes and distances of various objects are among the basic visual cues we use to place a scene in its proper perspective. To get this information, the brain draws heavily on past experience. Because the brain is preconditioned to "see" familiar objects at their "correct" size, any variation from that size is a visual cue to distance. Thus, if a particular man is known to be six feet tall, he is always "seen" to be that height. Therefore, as other visual cues give additional information, the brain simply keeps "moving" him until his size harmonizes with the other cues.

Even when helpful visual cues are absent, the brain tries to guess at size and distance. One way is to orient an object in the field of vision. Looking down at it helps give an impression of smallness; looking up at it makes it "big." Another way is to use cues supplied by the eye muscles. If an object can be seen clearly only by conscious focusing of both eyes, it is "near"; if it can be seen just as well without focusing, it is "far."

Because the brain also assumes that similarly shaped objects are always the same size, it can be misled by what it accepts as bona fide cues, as in the large picture opposite. But such errors are usually quickly rectified when other cues are examined and compared. For, during every waking moment, the brain's perception machinery never stops trying to correctly interpret what the eye sees.

SHIP OF GIANTS?
A quick look at this picture suggests that it is an aerial view of an ocean liner. But the point of view changes as soon as the eye spots the abnormally large figure of a man peering from the superstructure. The brain, rejecting the possibility that it is seeing a giant, perceives instead a normal man who now becomes the cue to the size of the scale model ship.

A CONTRAST IN CARS

The two cars at left present conflicting visual cues. They would seem to be two identical autos placed close together except for the presence of a contradictory cue—the narrowing white band—that appears to indicate considerable distance between them. In fact, the car in the foreground is only a small model and it is standing 16 yards in front of a full-sized version. Their true size relationship is revealed when the two are placed side by side *(below)*.

Interpreting the Overlap Cues

When one object overlaps another—and their individual outlines cannot be determined—the undiscriminating eye dutifully records the two-dimensional images of what it sees: a four-armed percussionist *(below)* or a multilegged, two-headed camel *(right)*. But the brain quickly rejects such images as impossibilities and seizes on a more reasonable cue—one that indicates that one object is in front of the other. By establishing such a front-to-back progression, the brain not only identifies what it is seeing, but also adds the missing third dimension of depth.

The most obvious cue to overlapping is the contour edge. The brain assumes that an unbroken contour is in front of the broken contour that it overlaps. But at great distances, or in poor light, outlines often become indistinguishable. Unless the brain can pick up another cue, the scene may remain two-dimensional, as in the case of a distant range of mountains or a landscape at twilight.

A FOUR-ARMED DRUMMER
What appears to be a four-armed man, beating the bass drum and cymbals at the same time, is quickly perceived as one man standing in front of another. The cue is the unbroken contour of the drummer's arms overlapping those of the cymbals player. Although there is only one head visible, it is assumed to be that of the drummer because human figures are always "seen" in their entirety, even without confirming cues.

A TWO-HEADED CAMEL

This vision of a two-headed camel in silhouette exists because of the absence of contour lines. But the brain seizes on the cue of the attached plows going in opposite directions to confirm what it has already suspected: that the picture merely shows two camels passing each other.

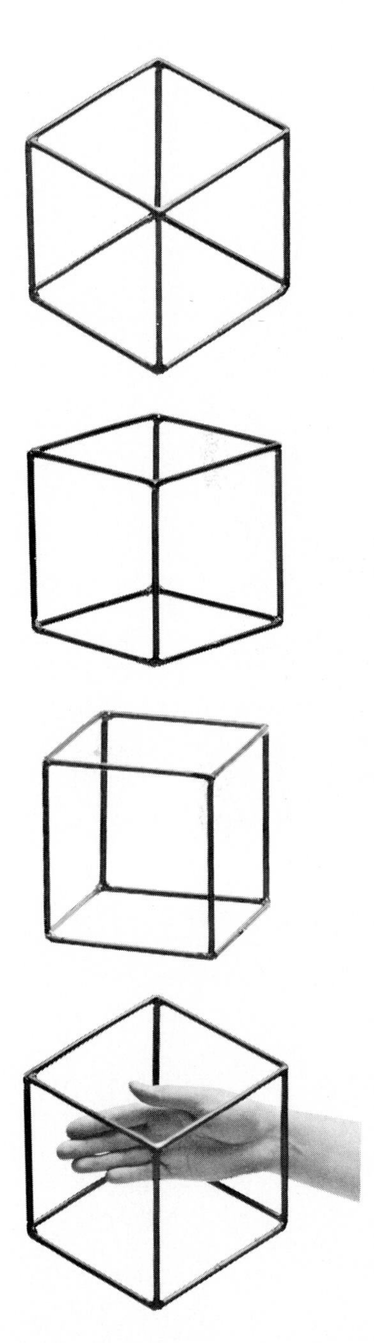

FOUR VIEWS OF A CUBE

The four figures above are all photos of the same wire cube, but each is perceived differently. The top figure appears to be a two-dimensional hexagon, but the next one could be either two- or three-dimensional. The angle of the third figure strongly suggests that it is three-dimensional, while the last—the first repeated—gains depth as soon as a hand is inserted.

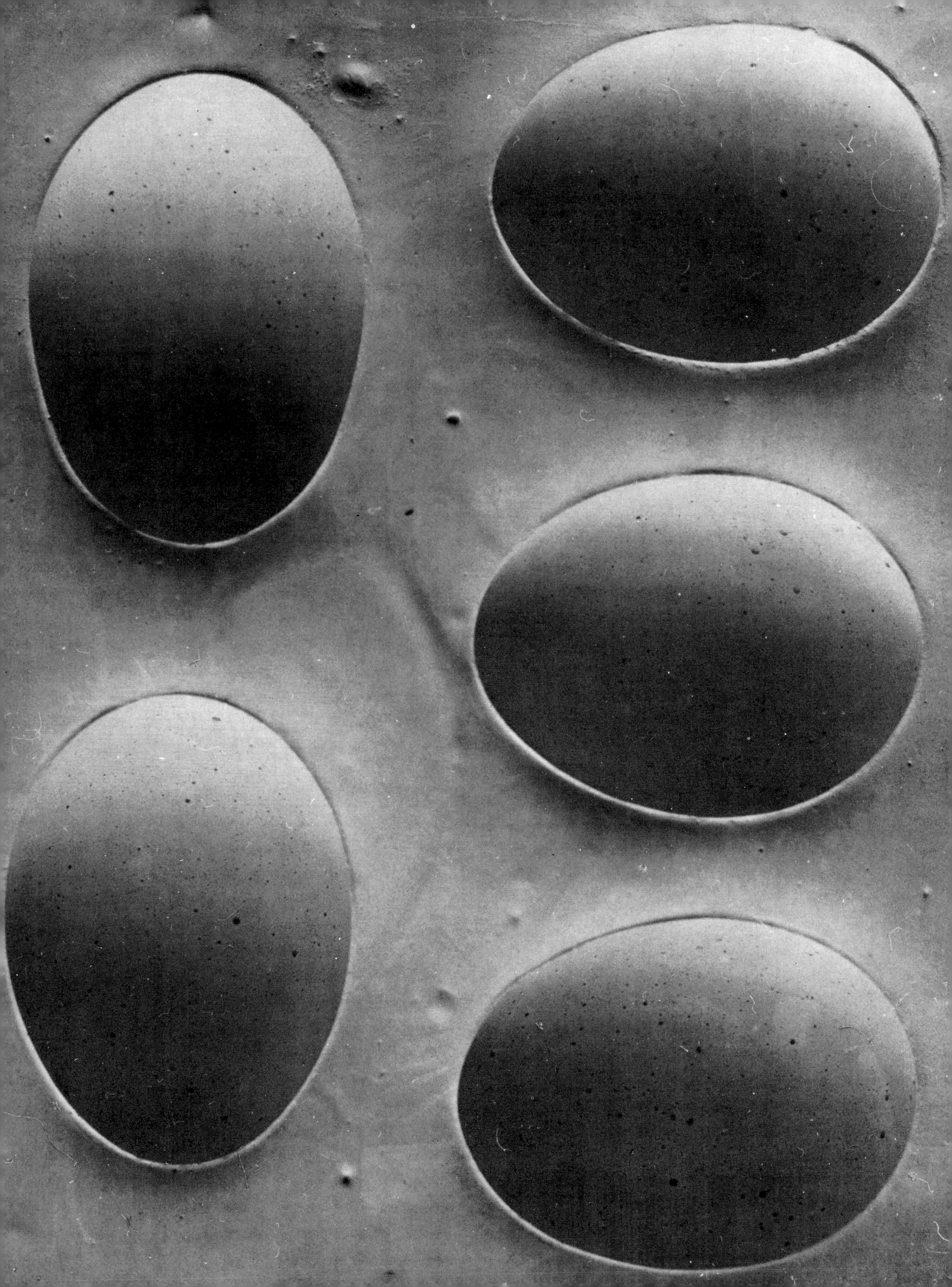

A DECEPTIVE CIRCLE
The ring above is a uniform gray, but the top half appears to be brighter than the bottom half because the darker background provides for a heightened contrast.

Hints from Light and Shadow

Light and shadow, which fall on almost everything the eye sees, provide the brain with valuable cues to angles, curvature and depth. A white circle—if it has the proper shadow on it—is perceived in depth as a white ball. Astronomers have even deduced the shape and size of mountains on the moon by studying their shadows.

However, so accustomed is the visual system to the shadow patterns cast by light from overhead sources—like the sun, streetlights and ceiling fixtures—that it can be confused when light shines from below, as in the photograph on the opposite page. Because the normal shadow pattern is reversed, so is perception. What appear to be mounds are actually depressions. Faces illuminated from below lose familiarity and look frightening, a phenomenon familiar to makers of horror movies and to children going their Halloween rounds with flashlights held under their chins.

The brightness of an object in relation to the surrounding visual field also plays an important part in perception. Bright objects always seem brighter when placed against a dark background, and this illusion is demonstrated by the apparent change of tone of the gray circle at the top of the page when it is seen against two contrasting backgrounds. At night, brightness becomes especially important. Since darkness sharply limits visual cues, the brain relies heavily on the relative brightness of lights to decide whether they are near or far.

SHAPED BY SHADOWS
The picture at left seems to show a container holding five eggs. But there are actually no eggs in the picture, and the brain is being fooled by unaccustomed shadow patterns of light coming from below. In the picture above, taken under normal lighting conditions, two real eggs and three hollows are easily identified. To see the large picture "correctly," turn it upside down.

Seen from the driver's eyes, the hood of the speeding car is perceived as stationary, but the tree-lined road appears to be whizzing by

Linking Sight and Speed

Since the brain considers itself the tracking center of a world in motion, a drive along a country road *(opposite)* presents the kind of problem that must be solved whenever the body is moving amid stationary objects. The brain knows that the trees, grass and road are standing still, yet they are perceived as rushing toward the eye, and their varying speeds are used as cues to depth. Nearby objects are seen as blurs, because the eye cannot adjust fast enough to keep them in focus as they flash by. Others, farther away, seem to move more slowly—or stand still—depending on whether or not the eye is focused directly on them. For example: the two photographs below were taken from a moving car, the top one focused on distant lights and giving a hopelessly blurred view of a sign in the foreground. The bottom picture focuses on the food stand; the street sign "slows down" a little, but the lights in the distance seem to be in motion.

TWO VIEWS FROM A MOVING CAR

With distant focus, a sign and a hot-dog stand go by in a blur; the lights "stand still."

With the stand in focus, the sign "slows down" but the lights "move" the opposite way.

Two Images Blended into One

A SIMPLE STEREOSCOPE
An observer demonstrates the proper way to view the stereo pairs on the opposite page so that they are seen as three-dimensional scenes. A small mirror is held against the right side of the nose, about six inches above the large dot. With the left eye focused on the left picture, the mirror is adjusted until the reflected image of the right picture merges with the left.

While most of the visual cues can be supplied by either eye, there are certain cues to depth and distance that can be obtained only when both eyes are working together. By focusing them on the same object, like the chessboard below, the eyes register images that vary slightly because the eyes themselves are two and a half inches apart. In fusing the two images, the brain notes the slight disparity between them and uses it as a cue to a composite, three-dimensional image.

The ability to combine two different images is called stereoscopic vision, and is what makes a stereoscope work. This device, as popular in Victorian parlors as TV is in modern living rooms, requires two separate photographs of a scene—known as a "stereo pair"—taken from slightly different angles. These photographs are put into a small viewer which permits one to be seen by the right eye and the other by the left. The brain accepts the disparity between the pictures as normal and blends them into a three-dimensional view.

The pictures on the opposite page are stereo pairs, and their three-dimensional effect can be realized with the aid of a small mirror *(left)*. The two pictures of the chessboard show the correct amount of disparity. But in the aerial view of Manhattan, the disparity is exaggerated. This produces a curious stereoscopic effect, drawing the viewer closer to the scene and giving him the erroneous impression that he is looking at a model rather than a real city.

The muscular action of the eyes also plays a role in depth perception. A remarkable and little-understood range-finding process enables us to estimate both the distance to various objects and the distance between the objects themselves. The process, most efficient at distances up to 20 feet, depends for its cue on the muscular convergence of the eyes—their inward movement as they turn to focus. Since the eyes must turn more to see a near object than a far one, the brain "measures" the amount of convergence and adjusts its stereoscopic depth perception accordingly.

SEEING DOUBLE
The photograph above of a blurred chessboard simulates in a single picture the two overlapping images signaled to the brain when both eyes are focused on the white horse at the rear of the board. In the brain, however, this picture is perceived unblurred and in three dimensions by means of stereoscopic vision. To see the board as the brain perceives it, use the stereoscopic viewing technique, demonstrated at the top of this page, on the separated images of the board at right. The other set of pictures, when similarly viewed, shows a panorama of Manhattan that has been deliberately "shortened" for a dramatic effect. The actual disparity at such a distance is almost undetectable.

A TOPSY-TURVY ROOM

A tilting chair inside a tilting room *(left)* provides a special test of perception. The blindfolded subject is unaware that the room is being gently tilted 35° from vertical, and the chair 22°. When the door is closed and the blindfold removed *(below),* the subject is asked to straighten her chair to a horizontal position. Confronted by what appears to be an upright room, complete to pictures hanging "straight" on the walls, she unconsciously orients herself to the surroundings and misjudges badly, as indicated by the level of milk in the pitcher.

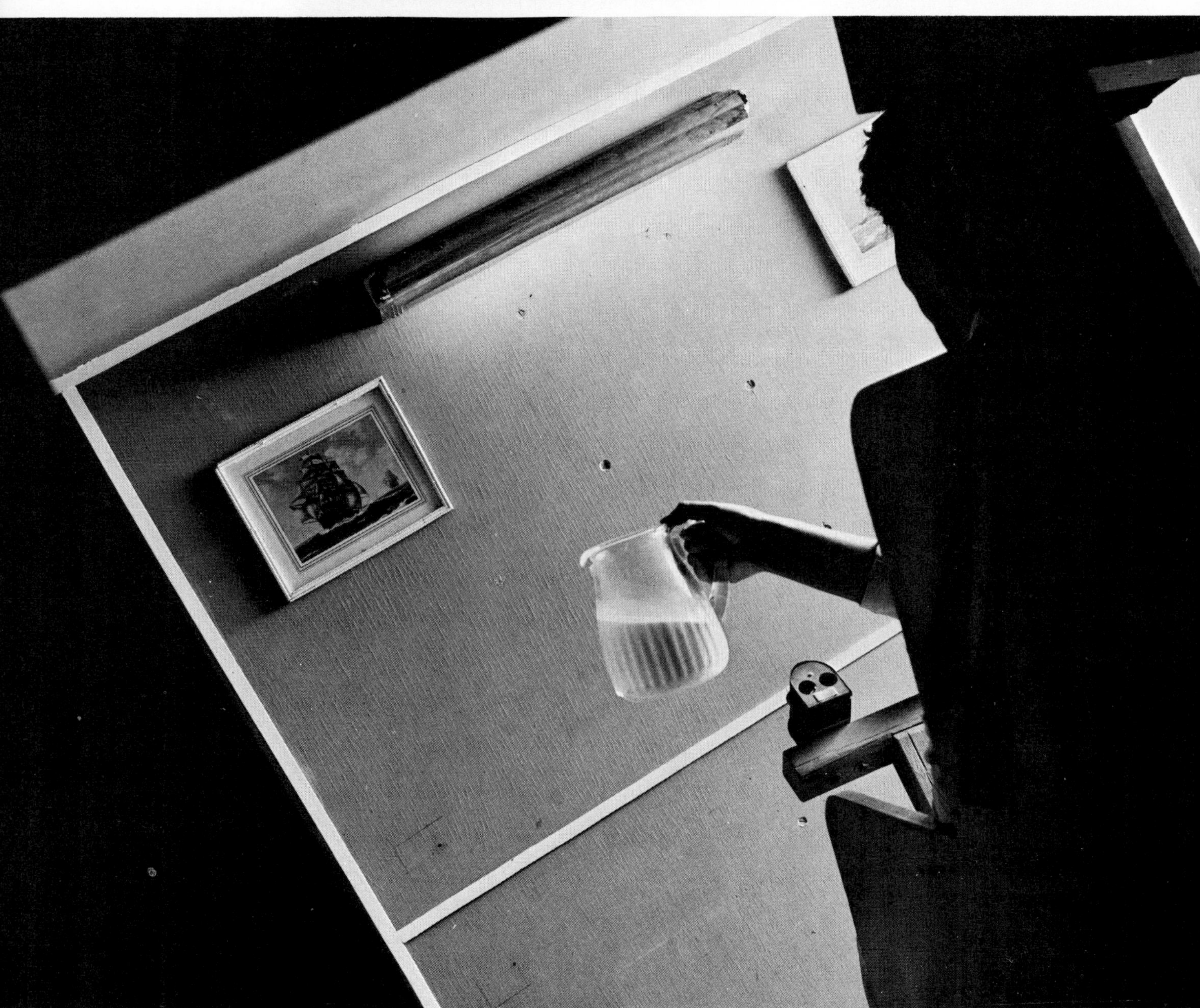

The Tests of Perception

No two people draw the same conclusions from the cue-filled images that are constantly being interpreted by the brain. The process varies with individuals according to what psychologists call "perceptual style."

This style might be compared to the way people use words to express themselves. Just as some habitually use stock phrases while others seek more original terms, so some people are relatively undiscriminating about what they see while others show far more analytical perception. Psychologist Herman A. Witkin has made an extensive study of these perception differences, using both the ingenious tilting room *(at left)* and embedded-figure perception tests like those at the upper right. On the basis of his findings, he has divided his subjects into the "field dependent"—the ones who tend to perceive a scene in its entirety and have difficulty in isolating its parts—and the "field independent"—who can more easily detect individual elements in a scene. The Witkin tests show that most young children have field dependent perception. Among adults men are usually more field independent than women.

Perception seems to be linked to both sociological and psychological conditioning. When embedded-figure tests were given to members of different cultures, some of the swiftest solutions were by Eskimo hunters. Such tests are easy for men who can pick out a polar bear from the thousands of shapes in a distant ice pack.

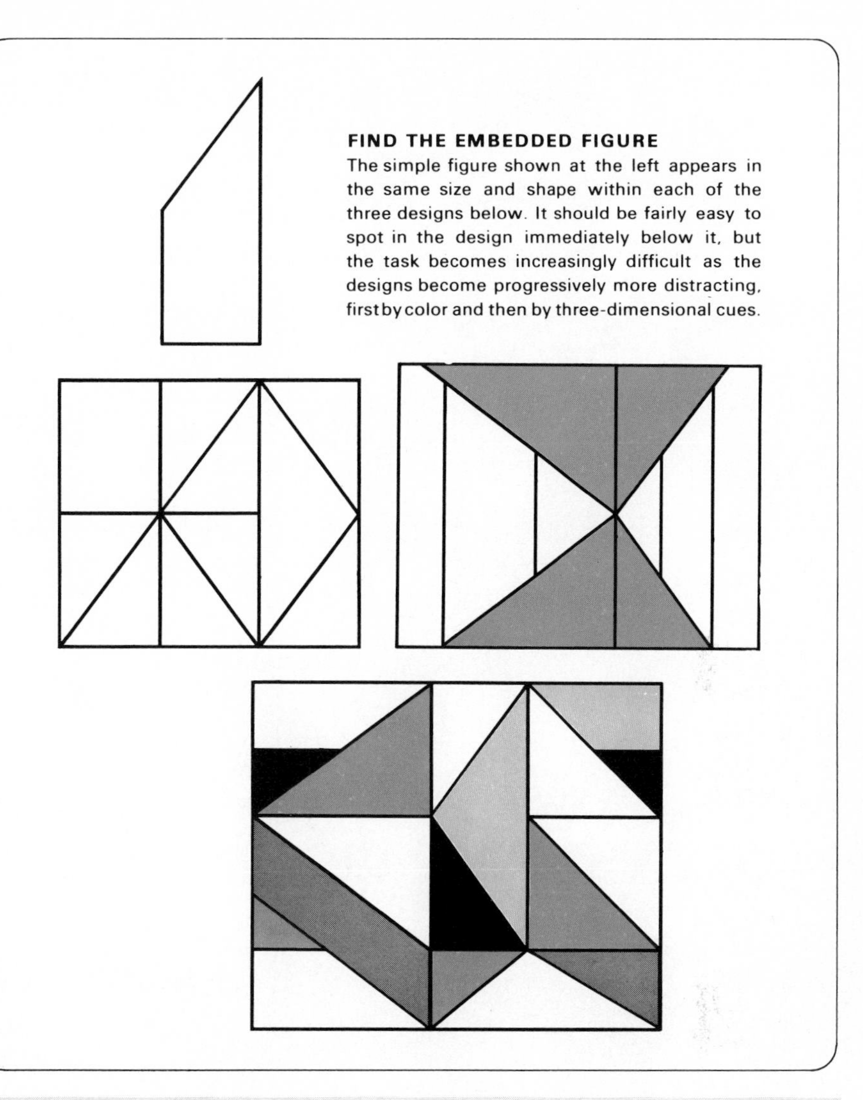

FIND THE EMBEDDED FIGURE
The simple figure shown at the left appears in the same size and shape within each of the three designs below. It should be fairly easy to spot in the design immediately below it, but the task becomes increasingly difficult as the designs become progressively more distracting, first by color and then by three-dimensional cues.

PIECES OF A PICTURE
The object of this perception test is to fill in the missing pieces so that a familiar picture appears. If the test remains puzzling at normal reading distance, try it again from three or four feet before looking at the answer below.

A horse and rider.

Cues That Confuse

Human vision is a highly adaptable system. The brain routinely processes data from the eyes, relying on visual cues to perceive an acceptable, if not always accurate, picture of the world. But occasionally the system breaks down. For there are sights, like the one at the left, that are simply beyond comprehension. Here, an imaginative artist has planted so many conflicting cues to perspective, distance and direction, that it is impossible to tell up from down.

Visual impossibilities, unknown in direct vision, can be created on paper in such a way that at first glance they appear logical. But as they are examined more carefully, the cues create confusion. The staircase below neither rises nor descends; the three-pronged bolt and its bracket and nuts *(opposite)* are all inconceivable. The brain struggles briefly to make sense of them, but eventually accepts them for the illusions that they are.

When given conflicting but equally acceptable cues, however, the visual system interprets them impartially. The wire coil, stacked blocks and fish pattern *(opposite)* all can be viewed from two directions, and the brain alternates from one view to the other.

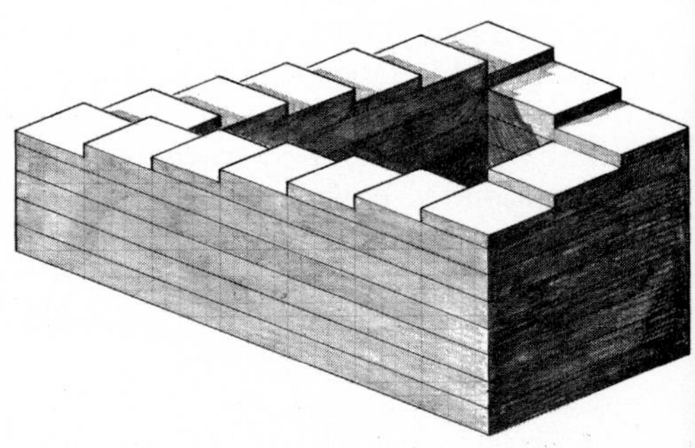

STAIRCASES TO NOWHERE
In the surrealistic drawing at left, staircases run off at impossible angles and directions because the artist has deliberately distorted the visual cues. While it is possible to draw such a scene —and even make parts of it tantalizingly logical —it is impossible for it to exist in three dimensions. The same can be said for the simpler but equally impossible figure above. It is inconceivable that a staircase should end where it begins, no matter which direction is followed.

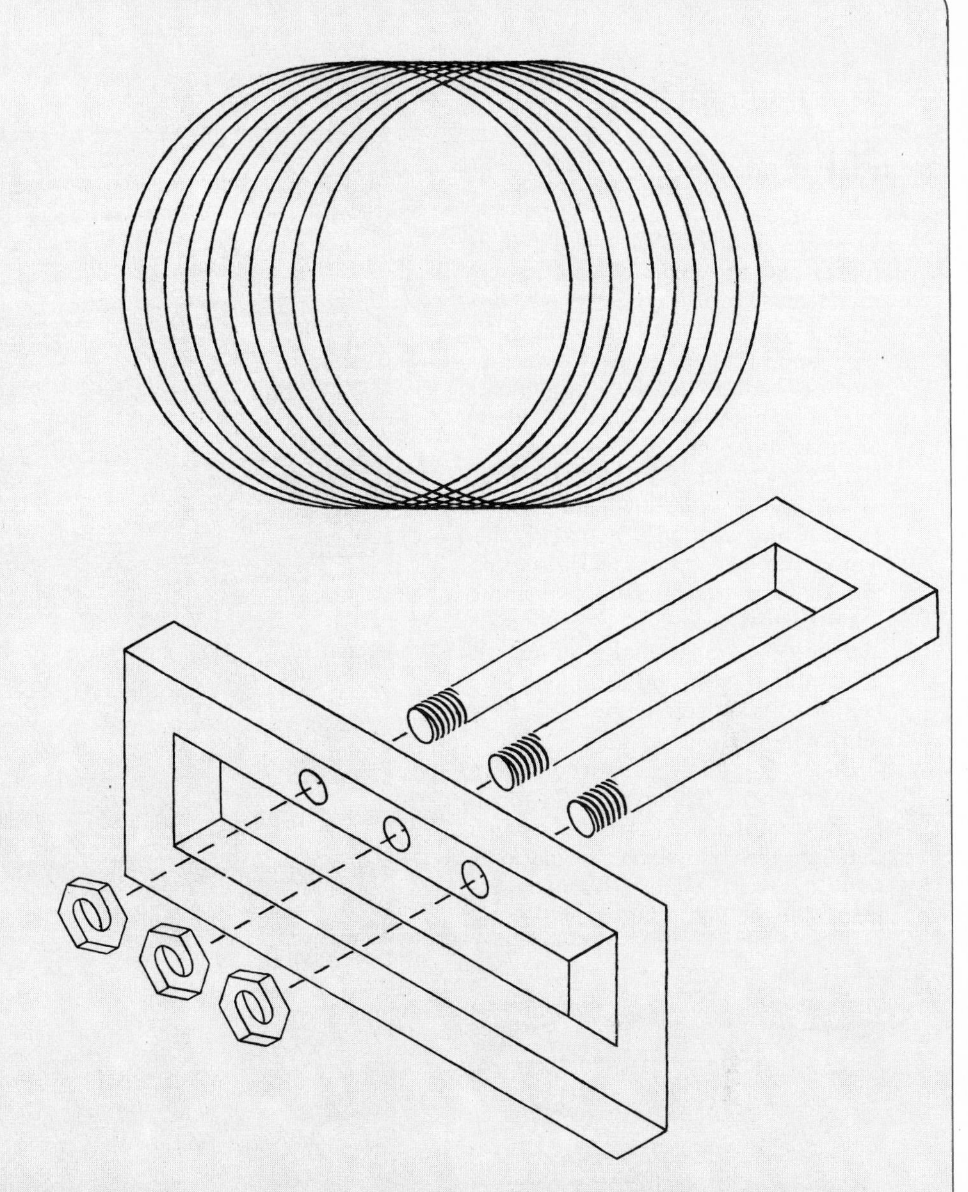

PLAYING TRICKS ON THE EYE
Confusing cues are sometimes rationalized. The stack of blocks above can be perceived with the white sides at either the top or bottom, a phenomenon called reversible perspective. The phenomenon also makes the coil *(top, right)* seem to change position. The fish in the pattern below appear to swim now in one direction, then the other. But the fork, bracket and nuts *(right)* are rejected by the brain as impossible figures.

A Fascination for Faces

Probably nothing fascinates people more than the sight of another human face. One of the first images recognized by an infant is its mother's face, and throughout life the brain's memory center identifies individuals by their particular facial features. Looking into a crowd, like the one at right, the eyes automatically scan the scene rapidly, searching for a familiar face. If one is found, it quickly becomes the center of visual attention and the scene assumes new meaning—an occurrence that psychologists attribute to "emotional loading." It is a familiar sensation to anyone who has ever unexpectedly spotted a celebrity in a crowd.

Faces are often perceived where there are none. The man in the moon is an example, but faces have been detected in clouds, rock formations, buildings, and even in sights transformed by newly fallen snow *(below)*.

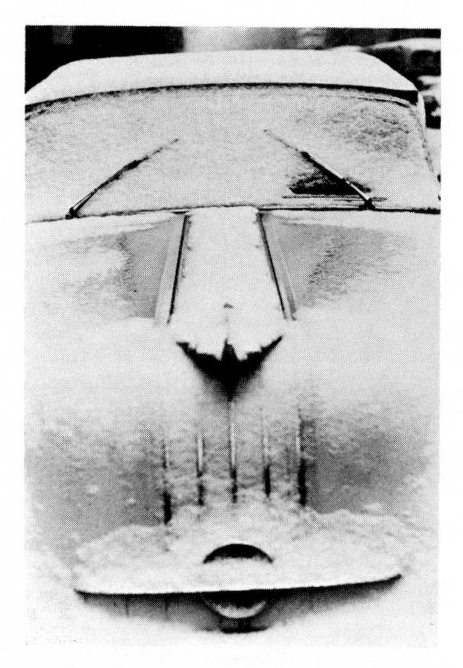

FIND THE FACES
Most observers viewing the photograph above will quickly perceive facelike characteristics: eyes, eyebrows, nose, mustache and mouth. But it takes a bit longer to perceive what the picture really shows: the snow-covered front of a car. The faces in the crowd at right are real enough, but can you spot one you know?
The late President John F. Kennedy.

8

Seeing with the Brain

Precursors of the movies, these 19th Century "fantascopes" were the first devices to use persistence of vision for illusions of movement. The figures are animated when the disks are spun and observed in a mirror through slots along the edges.

ONE OF THE BELIEFS of 19th Century visual science was that the image on the retina is a good copy of the scene before the observer, and what the observer sees is also a good copy of the image on the retina. But continuing scientific study usually uncovers complications, as well as simplifications, and the 20th Century has learned that vision is not so straightforward. The three facets of vision—the scene, the retinal image and the visual impression—quite often do not have a one-to-one-to-one relationship with each other.

This is not a matter of illusion. Examples of noncorrespondence can be found throughout all of vision. A light of a given intensity appears much brighter in a dark room than in daylight. This is the reason why stars can be seen at night but not during the day; the difference between their brightness and that of the sunlit sky is so small that man cannot detect it. A light of a certain wavelength which appears as one color most of the time may seem to change color when the intensity of the light source is changed. A reddish yellow, for example, will apparently become pure yellow when the light intensity is increased. Perhaps the most obvious case of noncorrespondence is that of three-dimensional vision. The scene is three-dimensional, the retinal image is flat, the visual impression is three-dimensional.

But noncorrespondence does not mean chaos. It does not imply that vision constantly plays tricks or that the visual apparatus is a catch-as-catch-can affair which often results in mistakes. The differences and the similarities between what is physically "there" and what man actually sees are both part of the very fabric of vision; they apply to everybody everywhere in much the same way. On the whole, the rules are consistent and orderly.

The search for these rules involves every area of visual science, from the study of the behavior of light waves to the investigation of the anatomy of the eye to the photochemistry of the retina. One branch of the science of vision—psychophysics—attempts to merge all the various fields and to seek out the rules of vision by weighing the physical stimulus against the resulting action of various parts of the visual system, from the cornea to the cortex. In short, psychophysics tries to bridge the large gap between the physics of light and the behavior of living organisms by defining with mathematical precision the connection between physical stimuli—lines, points, wavelengths, gradients of texture—and "what man sees." The purpose is to amass the wealth of information from which general rules may then emerge.

Psychophysics began to become a full-fledged science in the 19th Century when Gustav Fechner established experimental methods whereby a clear behavioral unit of measurement, the "just noticeable difference," could be accurately calculated. This is simply the smallest difference between two stimuli that can be detected by the observer; for example, how many more candles have to be added to a row of candles for the total light to appear brighter.

From these beginnings there has grown up a vast scientific effort to pin down the facts of the visual process in every aspect, from the determination of how many quanta, or photons, are needed to make the eye see light to the explanation of why poor children think quarters are bigger than rich children do. Most of the major subjects of the psychophysics of vision, however, can be roughly classified under a handful of conditions that are the prerequisites for visual perception. For instance, for vision to take place, it must first of all involve an object big enough to be seen. Second, the light source must be intense enough to produce some kind of response, this intensity varying with the particular test conditions, such as whether the observer's eyes are at that moment adapted to the dark or the light. Third, the stimulus must last long enough to ensure that the response has time to take place and, of course, the object must be different enough from its surroundings to be distinguished for what it is.

The arc of acuity

The problem of discrimination—known as acuity—is not simply a question of whether something can or cannot be seen. Acuity is also the capacity to discriminate the fine details in an object or scene; the eye doctor's test chart, with its rows of smaller and smaller letters, is a familiar acuity test. One unit of measurement in acuity is angular. One is considered to have normal acuity if one can resolve details of an object that creates a visual angle of one minute of arc. An angle of one minute of arc is the angle made by a one-inch target viewed at 100 yards. At 20 feet, the usual distance for testing acuity, this means a target of less than a tenth of an inch. If the person being tested can see an object of this size at 20 feet, he is said to have visual acuity of 1.0. If he needs something bigger, like the end of a pencil, before he can make it out at that distance, his acuity is less than 1.0, perhaps .75.

Acuity involves one or more of at least four tasks: detection—determining whether the object is there; recognition—being able to name the object or specify something about it, such as distinguishing between a letter O and a C; resolution—being able to make out a separation between elements in a pattern, such as recognizing four dots as dots and not as a straight line; and finally, localization—the ability to detect small displacements of part of the object, such as a seemingly vertical line whose top half slants slightly left or right.

An enormous number of physiological factors in the retina, the optic nerve and the brain control acuity. It is fairly well agreed that a fundamental role is played by the retinal mosaic, that is, the spatial separation of the rods and cones. However, it is now recognized that other factors must also be considered. For example, fairly large objects can be seen in very dim light while small ones nearby remain invisible until the light is made considerably brighter—thus involving the second condition of vision, intensity of light. This phenomenon constantly regulates human activity. Adequate night-lighting on a highway, for example, where only large objects such as another car or a pedestrian are of interest to the driver, requires a light intensity of only .3 foot-candles (a foot-candle is the amount of light given by a standard candle to a surface at a distance of one foot). But if that motorist wanted, instead, to sit in his room and read a book with comfort, he would need a lamp producing at least 30 foot-candles.

Several explanations have been offered as to why an increase in light improves the visibility of small objects. There is, of course, considerable variation in the sensitivity of the rods and cones in the retina. As long as the light is very weak, only the rods are activated, and as a result the performance of the visual apparatus is extremely limited. But as the light gets stronger, the cones begin to be affected, and this provides an increasingly rich pattern on the retina and thus finer resolution of detail.

There is another theory that involves chance "hits" on the retina by a single quantum of light. According to this theory, the more light there is, the more quanta will pour into the eye, and the more likely they are to hit receptors in the retina, each one of which can register where there is light and where there is no light.

As researchers move to other problems in vision, and particularly where color vision is involved, the subject becomes increasingly complicated. To begin with, some colors seem to be brighter than others. "Brightness" is, of course, a subjective term that man uses to describe one of his responses to color. Newton correctly said that the yellows, near the middle of the visible spectrum, were the brightest and affected the eye most strongly. (This is true even though equal amounts of energy may be radiated at each of the other wavelengths.) Next came red and green, then blue and violet, which were far down on the scale, nearest to invisibility, and consequently the darkest. Why this was so, Newton did not know.

A problem with telescopes

The problem was first dealt with in an orderly way in the 19th Century by the German optician Joseph von Fraunhofer. Fraunhofer was bothered by colored edges, known as chromatic aberrations, that were produced by the lenses he made. These colored fringes were most annoying, since they gave varyingly colored borders to the objects seen through his telescopes. In order to eliminate the aberrations, he realized that he would first have to learn something about the relative intensity of colors.

Fraunhofer devised an ingenious apparatus with a viewing field on which he could observe lights of varying intensities. He divided the field in half in such a way that one side showed only white light and the other side showed whatever color he chose to examine. By regulating the intensity, or physical energy, of the white light, he could make it exactly match the brightness of the colored light. After he had tested all the colors in this way, he was able to arrange them, in order of their relative brightness, on what is now called a luminosity curve. From this it was only a step to the explanation of the old phenomenon, noted earlier in this book, that each color of light must have a certain minimum intensity before it can be seen at all. When this minimum-intensity factor is combined with the wavelength of the color, and the result plotted on graph paper, a visibility curve results. The word "visibility" is used because if at any point a given wavelength has less than the required minimum amount of energy the eye sees nothing—there is not enough energy for that particular wavelength to produce a reaction in the human visual system.

Actually there are two sets of visibility curves. This is because there are two sets of receptors in the retina, the rods and cones, and each kind has greatest sensitivity in a different part of the spectrum. The rods are more sensitive than the cones throughout the spectrum, except in the far red end. In the red portion the rods and cones are about equally sensitive. In addition to this difference in overall sensitivity, the rods and cones have different regions of the spectrum to which they are most sensitive. For the cones it is the greenish yellow band; for the rods it is the bluish green part. It is important to remember that the eye has a two-level system of sensitivity, for this system is critical to an understanding of many of the problems of visual psychophysics.

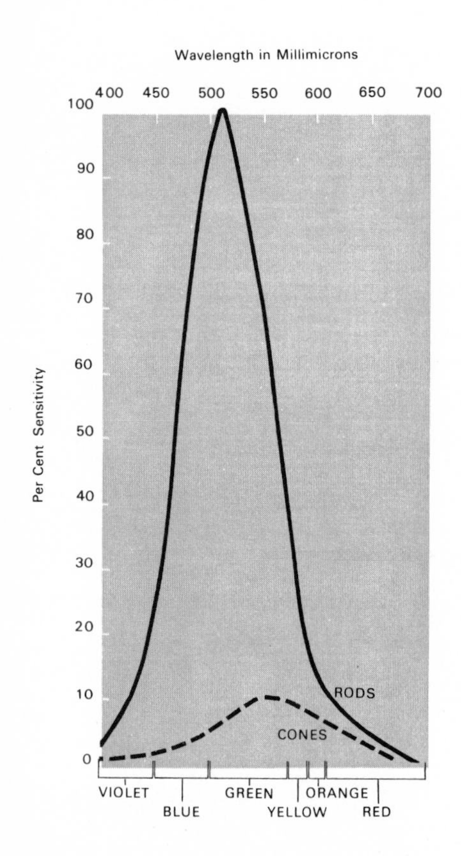

VISIBILITY CURVES compare the sensitivity of rods and cones to light of various colors. As the high rise of the solid line shows, rods are far more sensitive than cones, the greatest sensitivity being in the area of blue-green. The cones *(dotted line)* have little sensitivity to violet but peak in the yellow-green section. At the red end, they respond proportionately more strongly than the rods, which exhibit a drastic reduction in sensitivity.

The threshold of vision

One of these problems concerns the extent of the eye's sensitivity. Studies have revealed that the rods will respond to a blue-green light that provides only about a half-dozen quanta to the eye. This is almost inconceivably dim, and in comparison with other work-energy measurements is so small as to appear meaningless. The chirp of a cricket, by comparison, uses about 20 trillion times as much energy as is contained in this minimum bit of light. It has been calculated that the mechanical energy of a pea falling one inch, if converted into luminous energy and parceled out in units of quanta, would produce enough quanta to give a faint impression of light, not only to every man living on the earth today, but to every man who *ever* lived.

In short, the eye is fantastically sensitive. And when this sensitivity is related to the torrent of light energy that streams from the sun every year, it seems a wonder that man is not blinded by the light of the world. One good reason is that while it may take only five or six quanta of blue-green light to trigger a response on the retina, there must be many more quanta than that pouring into the eye for those five or six quanta to reach the retina. Selig Hecht, a physiologist, and his associates have calculated that the minimum flash that can be seen is 10 to 25 times that strong when measured *outside* the eye, i.e., between 50 and 150 quanta. About 90 per cent of these quanta get lost by reflection or absorption as they pass through the cornea, the lens and eye liquids and the retina. So, of the original 50 to 150 quanta entering the eye, only about half a dozen or so will actually have any effect.

Equally as important to vision as intensity of light is its duration and location. In one famous experiment, the optic nerve of an eel was placed across two electrodes in such a way that they would record and measure any stimulation of the retina. These measurements showed that the intensity of the light, the amount of retinal area stimulated and the duration of the flash were inversely proportional. A very intense light shining on a small portion of the retina for a very short time had the same effect as a dimmer light covering a wider area for the same period.

There are, however, exceptions to this inverse-proportion relationship, one of which was first suggested by experiments with certain drugs that exaggerated the normal responses of the eye. Strychnine, for example, tends to increase the sensitivity of the eye to faint light. Under the heightening effect of strychnine, there is a transmission of impulses across nerve junctions and a consequent spread of nerve excitation sideways over a larger area of the retina than would be the case without the drug.

This possibility—that one part of the retina might help trigger off another part—was confirmed by Haldan Hartline in his experiments with the optic nerve of a frog. Hartline moved a tiny exploring light over various areas of the frog's retina in an attempt to find out whether—and exactly where—light would produce a response in a single nerve fiber. He discovered several things: first, there were very sensitive spots that could excite a single nerve fiber; second, the nerve fiber seemed to be connected in some way to the general area around the most sensitive spot as well as to the spot itself; third, the nerve responded better when the surrounding area as a whole was stimulated than when the spot alone was stimulated; fourth, it took a very small amount of light to produce a good response in the nerve if several of these receptive areas were stimulated at the same time.

Sight from pooled responses

What is the significance of these findings? Simply that they give added evidence about the different functions performed by the rods and cones. Thus it is evident that when several of these receptors pool their activity, they succeed in getting off a signal to the nerve that is strong enough to be useful—and which, without pooling, might have excited no nerve response, and no sensation of light. The part of the retina most capable of this kind of pooling of low light responses is in the corners of man's eyes, where the rods are most plentiful, and this explains why human peripheral vision is so sensitive. Thanks to pooling, man can perceive things out of the corners of his eyes and also detect motion in very poor light—but in neither of those conditions can he make out with any certainty the details of what he is looking at. The detail work, the acute part of vision, is taken care of by the cones, particularly those in the sensitive center of the retina (the fovea), which require a fairly high level of illumination for best performance in their kind of pinpoint activity.

With the sensitivity provided by the eye's two kinds of receptors and the pooling action of the rods, it has been difficult to understand why—with the vast numbers of quanta pouring into it—the eye does not produce a chaos of constantly twinkling and bursting lights. This becomes even harder to understand when it is learned that the nerve fibers in the eye often "fire" quite spontaneously without any stimulation from the outside. In fact, there is a fairly constant random firing of this type. It is known as background "noise." Although this might seem to add to the general confusion in the eye, apparently the visual system is capable of concentrating on the signals that rise above this noise level, and thus can discriminate between random firing and signals that actually come from light. To do this, the brain, of course, must not be confused by the random firing; and one way it avoids confusion is by depending on the pooling of signals mentioned above. Several confirming signals from separate receptors are necessary to convince the visual system it is receiving a genuine light stimulation coming in from the outside. Each signal serves as a kind of witness testifying to the truth that the other receptors are telling, whereas a single random firing would have no corroboration from other witnesses and would be ignored.

Signals recognized and ignored

Another way the system sorts out and controls the low-level signals is by refusing to acknowledge any that do not last for a minimum amount of time. There again, a single random firing is over and done with so quickly that the visual system can afford to ignore it, whereas one that persists will begin to make an impression. In short, it takes the eye a certain fraction of a second to organize and integrate low-level signals, and if they do not last long enough, the brain does not recognize them.

Proof that there is such an integration lag was supplied by Carl Pulfrich. (Curiously enough, while his experiment required binocular vision, Pulfrich himself was blind in one eye.) A piece of string with a weight at the end is swung from side to side like a pendulum in front of the eyes. The viewer looks at this pendulum with both eyes, but with one eye covered by a piece of dark glass or a piece of exposed photographic film—anything that is fairly dark but that can still be seen through. When viewed in this fashion the pendulum no longer seems to be swinging straight back and forth, but appears to swing in an ellipse. The explanation is complicated but it depends chiefly on the fact that the dark glass causes the covered eye to become dark-adapted, which makes a very slight delay in the message reaching the brain from this eye. So the uncovered eye sees the weight immediately, while the dark-adapted one sees it slightly in the past tense. As the weight speeds up in the middle of its pendulum swing, the filtered eye sees it farther and farther behind its real position, and when the two versions are put together binocularly, the result is an apparent elliptical motion.

The fact that the dim light takes longer to get its message through to the brain is of more than just academic interest. Retinal delay may produce a lengthening reaction time among automobile drivers in dim lights, and may worsen the performance of any delicate task undertaken in poor light. It is one of the reasons why, before the introduction of powerful lighting systems, baseball games were called off at dusk; in spite of the fact that the spectators were still able to see the overall play in twilight, the players could not follow the ball, which sometimes moves at a speed of nearly 100 miles per hour.

Thus, throughout all visual phenomena there are important differences between the way the eye behaves when it is dark-adapted and when it is light-adapted—when it is depending chiefly on the rods or chiefly on the cones. Therefore, the relationship between the energy of the light, the length of time it is shining on the retina and the area where it shines is not always quite the same.

For instance, the relationship does not hold below the visual threshold; a very low-energy light remains invisible no matter how long one looks at it. The eye is limited in the duration of time over which it can accumulate, or add up, energy; therefore the energy-time relationship does not cover long durations. According to one theory, this may be because of a peculiarity of retinal photochemistry known as the back-reaction. Rhodopsin—the light-sensitive pigment in the rods—is broken down chemically when it is acted on by light. However, the breakdown is reversible; at a certain point the rhodopsin begins to be restored. This period between breakdown and beginning of restoration is very short—in the range of one hundredth of a second—and is called the "critical duration." As long as the light stimulus is as short as or shorter than the critical duration, the product of intensity and duration will determine whether the light is seen or not. But beyond the critical duration, intensity is the only thing that matters. Thus, a very weak light shining for a very brief time will barely be seen by the eye or will not be seen at all; if it shines for just a little longer, the eye can see it; longer yet, the light seems to become brighter. But if it keeps on shining for a very long time, it does not continue indefinitely to seem brighter and brighter; it soon reaches a ceiling beyond which its brightness is not affected by time.

EARLY "MOVIE" ENTHUSIASTS were fascinated by the hand-operated tachyscope, which produced the illusion of movement with a series of scenes mounted on a large rotating disk. The successive photographs of action were illuminated by flashes of light coordinated with the turning of the wheel, with a brief period of darkness between pictures, a variation of the way the modern movie projector functions. Because the human eye retains an image longer than it is actually there, and blends it with the next, the viewer saw movement. The tachyscope, invented in the late 19th Century, was one of the many similar machines built in that period.

Flickering and visual blending

Whether light shines steadily or intermittently also makes an enormous difference in what kind of visual response it produces—and if the light is intermittent, its rate becomes critical. When a revolving disk painted half black and half white is turned slowly at first and then gradually faster and faster, the even, rhythmical pulsations of light and darkness at the beginning will soon give way to an unsteady, wavering flicker that is uncomfortable to the eyes. But when the disk is revolving fast enough the flicker disappears and the observer sees a uniform gray. The white and black stimuli at this speed follow each other so quickly that the effect of one white patch lingers, or "spills over," into the next, producing a blend. The point at which flicker stops and a uniform gray is seen is known as the "critical fusion frequency," and is measured by the number of cycles per second. It is one of the pillars of psychophysical knowledge, and is the source of some extremely complicated visual experiences.

Intermittent stimulation, for example, appears to be another factor crucial to acuity—vision being best when the frequency of the flashes is either so low that each flash can be seen individually, or so high that fusion occurs. In the middle, in the range where flicker is visible, acuity is at its worst.

Usually, man is not even aware that intermittent stimulation is a common feature of everyday vision. Fluorescent lights, for example, are not the steadily glowing energy sources they appear to be but are flickering at a rate so fast that fusion is reached and the light seems constant. Only when the tube begins to wear out does one see the annoying blips that result from a slowing-down of the flicker rate. Television is achieved by a highly complicated form of intermittent visual stimulus. The picture is built up in strips which are designed to keep flicker at a rapid enough level to achieve an image without annoyance.

The darkened movie screen

Flicker, when properly controlled, can be used to advantage. The best-known use of it is, of course, in the motion picture, which creates an illusion of movement by showing in rapid succession a series of still pictures separated by dark intervals. In fact, a motion picture screen—though it appears to be constantly lit—is dark about half the time. But we see the movie as continuous and "live" because of the persistence of vision. The excitation that takes place in the eye outlasts the stimulus of the lighted portions of the film, through a kind of inertia in the retina—not only the inertia of rousing, or starting up, but also the inertia of stopping, or "ringing off." This lag usually amounts to a few hundredths of a second, although it can be lengthened by decreasing the amount of light in the surroundings. That is one reason why movie theaters are always darkened. In addition to keeping the spectator's eyes from straying to distracting sights around the theater, the darkness is needed to slow down the eye's response so that it will not be aware of the dark intervals between frames.

These are intriguing phenomena, but they should not be allowed to overshadow the more important fact that intermittence is fundamental to the way man actually sees—to the way in which his visual apparatus sorts out and organizes problems of spatial dimension and detail.

Intermittence is of two main types. There is the kind that is produced from outside, either by fluctuations in the light source itself, or—much more commonly—by changes in the pattern of light areas brought about by sharp edges in the scene, as where a brightly lit object ends abruptly and the area next to it is in dark shadow. As far as the brain is concerned, such a fluctuation is just as much intermittence as a flickering neon light is, and both are external.

Even more important is what might be called internal intermittence, caused by movement of the image across the retina as a result of movements of the eyes or head. The brain's task is to make sense of the signals triggered by these movements, and the story is by no means as simple as it would seem when the problem is first considered.

For years, people thought that the seeing of movement was one of the more straightforward of visual phenomena. At one moment an object appears in one place on the retina; at the next it appears somewhere else. The retina signals to the brain that the visual image has been displaced in space and time; therefore, it must have moved. But there are some features of movement vision that do not fit this simple formula. Sometimes man sees movement when there is none, and sometimes he fails to see it when it takes place, as when he is in a high-flying airplane and is staring out at a cloudless sky.

The distinction between real and apparent movement was made by a number of scientists in the very early 1800s, and was studied by such notable investigators as Johannes Purkinje, Peter Mark Roget (the man who devised the *Thesaurus*) and Michael Faraday, the "father of electricity." One of the most vivid movement effects described in this era was the "waterfall illusion." If a sightseer gazes at the moving water of a fall and then looks at the rocks beside the water, the rocks appear to move up. If he stares out of the window of a moving train for a while and the train stops, the station will then appear to go forward.

Since then, researchers have found another example of apparent movement—the autokinetic phenomenon—that occurs wholly in the visual system itself. In an otherwise totally dark room an observer is shown a fixed pinpoint of light, which he looks at as steadily as possible. He is asked to describe its movements. After a brief time, during which the light appears to be steady, he begins to report that it is moving in wide gyrations, sideways, up and down, drifting, gliding and darting. What has happened is that the visual stimulus has been divorced from all the normal steadying points of reference and the eye reacts to it in a most erratic fashion.

Short circuit in the brain

In his historic report on apparent movement, Max Wertheimer, a German, suggested that the phenomenon may be the consequence of a "physiological short circuit" in the brain. With exactly the right time interval, he said, excitation at one point might be drawn over to excite another point, thus giving the illusion of movement.

But apparent movement is a special case. The common experience of real movement vision is the important thing, and it is gradually becoming clear that this is a three-stage affair involving detection and processing at all three stages: first in the retina, next in the nerve fibers, and finally in the cortex. The linkage in these three stages is extremely subtle, and recent studies have produced knowledge about them that had hitherto not even been suspected.

For one thing, the retina is now revealed to have a wide variety of transmission nerve cells, each responding to different kinds of signals. For example, a frog appears to have at least four kinds of nerve cells, or ganglia, in its retina. Each kind responds in a different way to what

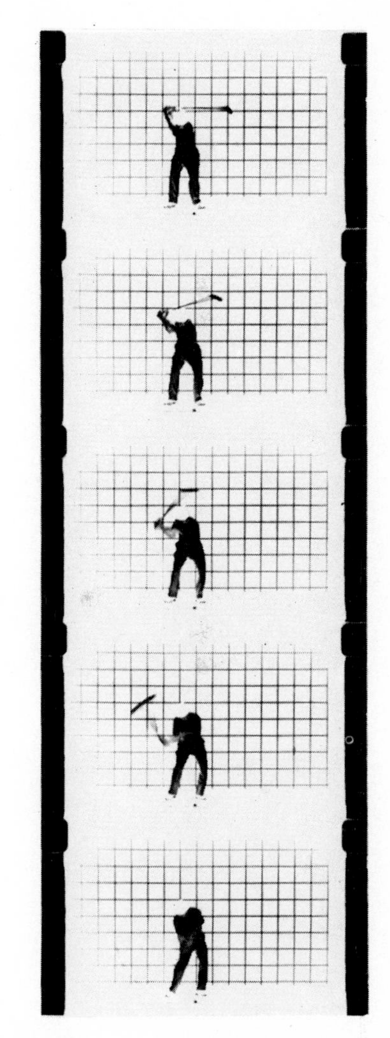

THE MOTION IN MOTION PICTURES is achieved by projecting still photographs at a set speed with a dark interval between pictures. These consecutive frames from a 16-millimeter movie film show a golfer from the moment he is at the top of his backswing until he hits the ball. If this film were projected at a rate of 24 frames per second, the viewer would have the illusion of seeing the golfer in action as he makes the downswing.

is going on out in front of its eye. One kind fires off a signal only when there is a decrease in light—when there is a dimming or darkening of whatever the frog is observing—and thus presumably it conveys information about large dark shapes. A second kind of cell fires only in response to the movement of such large shapes. These cells are called event detectors, to distinguish them from yet another kind of cell that fires only in response to the movement of very small things with clearly defined edges. Thus, a frog looking at the surrounding scene would become aware of large, shadowed objects with fuzzy edges like trees or bushes with certain of its nerve cells, and small, sharp-edged things like insects with others. This information is enriched and refined by yet another kind of nerve cell that fires only in response to sharply contrasting edges of light and dark.

A frog's view of the world

With all these ways of "looking" at things, and with all of them based either on movement or on contrasts between light and dark, the frog gets a rather rich and detailed impression of the surrounding scene. But this information must be analyzed to be useful. For most animals this type of processing begins in the retina, by means of an enormously intricate connecting-up of the various cells, much as the various elements of a computer are connected together for data-processing purposes. This partially analyzed visual information is then passed on via the optic nerve to the brain. The rate at which this information is processed and passed along is also believed to have some significance for the reflex centers of the brain, and therefore to have an effect on the action of the animal. In any case, the information reaches the cortex, where final analysis takes place—and that final step produces the phenomenon called vision. Unfortunately, much of what goes on in the brain is little understood, which is why men can only speculate about how things look to other animals.

The problem is complicated by the fact that animals differ in the amount of processing that takes place and where in the visual system it occurs. For instance, processing in the frog brain is done by only a few kinds of cells and is relatively crude. But a cat may have dozens, if not hundreds, of different kinds of brain cells for analyzing information from the retina. The functions of a few of these have already been worked out; one kind, for example, deals with the movement of long, narrow shapes. Thus, the cat disposes of the problem of recognizing blades of grass in its brain, whereas that is taken care of by the frog largely in its eye.

This brief description of some of the things that go on in the visual apparatus of the frog and cat has dealt only with things moving or changing outside the eye, which are registered as images moving across the retina. They are, in short, traveling objects passing in front of a stationary retina. But what happens when the eye or the head moves? If a man turns his head slowly and smoothly to track a moving object, keeping it constantly in focus, where is the signal of "image moving across the retina" going to come from? Furthermore, when he moves his eyes to focus on one object, why does not everything else in the scene appear to swing in the opposite direction? Those objects—if the eye sweeps across them—should appear to be moving. But they do not; what man sees is a succession of stable objects in a stable environment. The room does not reel.

These two puzzling aspects of movement vision are closely related, and they emphasize once again the important role played by the brain. It has been suggested by Sir Charles Sherrington, a British physiologist and Nobel Prize winner, that the scene remains stable during head or eye movement because at the same time that the visual signals which this movement produces are being transmitted, there is another set of signals canceling them out—this second set being triggered by the eye-movement muscles. One trouble with this proposal is that the neural signals from the eye muscles would take longer to get to the brain than the visual signals from the retina, and man would get a visual jolt at the start of every eye movement until the signal could catch up with the motion. An earlier suggestion, proposed by Helmholtz, is that the situation is exactly the reverse: the retinal "sweep" signals are corrected not by signals from the eye-movement muscles to the brain, but by signals from the brain to the muscles.

This can be demonstrated by closing one eye and pressing gently with a finger at the corner of the other. When the eye is moved in this way, without the use of its own muscles, the world does indeed swing dizzily. The image moving across the retina is sending its signals, but they are not being corrected by brain signals to the eye muscles.

This conjunction of eye and brain explains not only why the eye sees movement when tracking, but why the world remains stable when man swings his view across a scene. And it again makes it clear that the brain is not—as once believed—merely a passive instrument that receives and "reads" visual data, but is an active partner with the eye in the process of seeing.

Road signs for researchers

So the science of psychophysics, in close conjunction with the many other sciences that relate to vision, already has piled up an impressive collection of data that point to some specific rules of vision. Through such studies, a number of unsupported theories and unproved generalities about vision are being eliminated, and through exact measurements and carefully correlated data, researchers are receiving strong indications as to where the true solutions may lie. In this endlessly fascinating but enormously complicated field of vision, the search for many "true solutions" will be long and arduous. But thanks in a great measure to psychophysics, research will move at a faster pace than ever before. As Edwin G. Boring, a famous psychologist, has said, "Problems cannot be solved until they are discovered."

The Craft of the Artist

No two people see anything exactly alike. Even when the eye is performing perfectly and reproducing on the retina an exact image of the object seen, the brain interprets that image according to a complex series of associations based on past experience. Thus, a woman's face may appear more beautiful to her husband and children than it does to strangers, while a flower that seems brilliant to an Eskimo may look pale to a Polynesian. It is the expression of the image born in the mind's eye that has been the goal of painters over the centuries. For, as the remarkable pair of pictures opposite shows, the artist "sees" far more than does a camera.

The artist's problem is to transfer onto a two-dimensional surface his emotional response to the movement, forms and colors of the three-dimensional world around him. To height and width he may choose to add the illusion of depth in order to complete the desired translation. The artist may elect to use any of a number of techniques and styles ranging from cameralike realism to total nonobjectivity, from stark, black-and-white line drawings to vivid masses of color. But his ultimate objective always remains the same: the creation of a visual image as he both sees and translates it.

TWO VIEWS OF A MODEL
The young woman shown in two versions opposite was photographed in the same pose painted by Henri de Toulouse-Lautrec. But the Lautrec portrait of her emphasizes some details—such as her carriage, hair and chin line—and ignores others while adding vibrant colors to produce a much different interpretation than the image recorded by the camera.

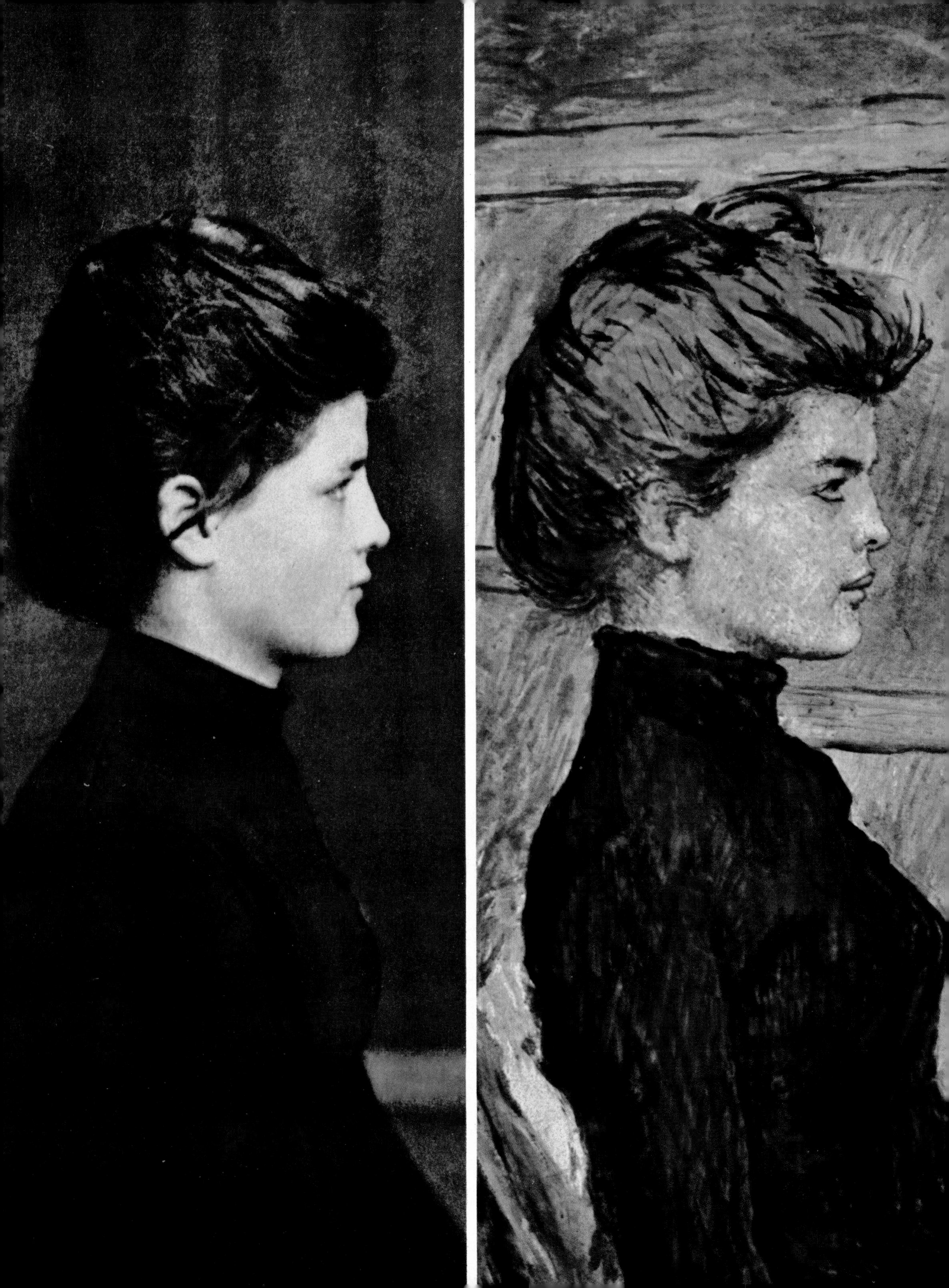

A HANDFUL OF LINES

This preliminary portrait sketch of Albert Einstein, by Hans Erni, shows how a few deftly drawn lines can suggest a wealth of detail. The artist has caught not only Einstein's sad eyes and unruly hair, but also his characteristic finger positions and casual, unpressed clothing.

VARIETIES OF LINE

This drawing of the French village of Saintes Maries by Vincent van Gogh shows the versatility of the line in creating a visual image. The straight lines of the wall, the thick, swirling curves for foliage, the dots on the path suggesting texture—all help to convey the scene.

Images from Lines

The simplest artistic expression of what the eye sees is something that does not exist in nature—the line. Both the child who draws houses by scrawling a few lines and the artist who pencils a portrait sketch are indulging a quirk of the human mind—the assumption that three-dimensional shapes can be described by two-dimensional lines. Just as the mind is willing to supply lines where there are none—i.e., a circle to represent a ball—it is also ready to grasp an image delivered by lines alone. Artists have used this technique since prehistoric times and the oldest known pictorial works of art are the line drawings of animals scratched into cave walls some 20,000 years ago. Over the centuries artists have also learned to create human figures and entire scenes by means of a few deft strokes. Lines can produce an accurate sketch *(top, opposite)*, convey a sense of texture *(below, opposite)* and, in the hands of a master craftsman like Albrecht Dürer, they can become a powerful, self-sufficient means of artistic expression *(left)*.

A CARVED SAINT
The German master Albrecht Dürer used only a series of lines in this woodcut of St. Christopher. Short lines indicate the roundness of the saint's staff, curved lines represent his lumpy knees, and cross-hatching on the underside of his cape makes it seem to billow in the wind.

Drama from Light and Shadow

SHAPED BY SHADING
This Madonna's face, painted by Italian Renaissance artist Carlo Crivelli, is shaped by the delicate use of light and shadow. The viewer's eye blends the flat left side with the shadowed right to obtain an image of a rounded whole.

The interplay of light and shadow is one of the artist's most effective tools for representing on canvas the world he sees. The technique was perfected by the giants of the Italian Renaissance, who realized that the eye sees brighter objects as being closer than dimmer ones. They learned to use varying contrasts of brightness and shadow to create the illusion of depth among figures and objects.

The angle at which painted light strikes an object, together with the resulting shadow, also can give a feeling of volume and roundness. A face seems flat when viewed under harsh frontal light; however, when illuminated by a soft sidelight *(left)*, the bright side of the face gains contours as the eye "fills in" the shape suggested by the shadows on the other side.

A third use of light and shadow is to bring a sense of mood to what would otherwise be simple duplication of an image. Men have always associated light with warmth and "good," while shadows traditionally represent darkness and "evil." By establishing a light source either outside or within a painting *(below and opposite)*, the artist creates a mood by lightening or darkening important sections of the picture. A particularly dramatic technique, often used for saints and other religious figures, is to make light seem to emanate from the figure itself. The unnatural radiance adds a spiritual quality more effective than the ancient device of painting a halo encircling the head.

THREE USES OF LIGHT
In this scene from his Sistine Chapel ceiling, Michelangelo used light and shadow to show depth, form and mood. Light from above and slightly to the rear emphasizes the strength and shape of the fortune-teller's left arm and lends foreboding to her harshly outlined profile.

LIGHT FROM WITHIN

A candle provides both the light source and focus for this masterpiece by the 17th Century French artist Georges de la Tour. The candle's flame not only illuminates the child's face, but also provides a striking illusion of depth by projecting forward the lighted parts of both figures. The furrowed brow and veined arms of the man —St. Joseph—are emphasized by the light, while the rest of his body melts into shadows.

DESCRIPTIVE COLOR

In this 16th Century portrait by the Belgian artist Bernard van Orley, the descriptive colors duplicate the scene with the same precision found in a color photograph. Van Orley's aim was to record colors; he made no attempt to interpret them or to elicit any particular mood.

The Vital Role of Color

The eye sees in color, and the artist, by simply painting an apple red or a sky blue, can add to the illusion of reality in much the same way as a child colors with crayons. This is "descriptive" color, favored by early Renaissance artists. They painted a red object red; though they might mix in other tints to suggest a shadow, the finished object was still red.

But artists are not restricted to so literal a use of color. They may want to paint a face green or a tree purple to achieve a desired emotional impact. Blues and greens are cool and soothing, and tend to recede; reds are hot and exciting, and bright red jumps forward. By placing pure colors next to one another, instead of mixing them, artists can produce almost infinite variation in tint and tone. This effect is evident in the work of Georges Seurat *(right)*, consisting entirely of minute colored dots.

EMOTIONAL COLOR

The German painter Emil Nolde used colors to evoke emotional responses in this Expressionist work, *Christ among the Children*. The children are gaily colored in contrast to the elders, who are made to appear somber in dark tones. The serenity of Jesus is transmitted by His blue robes, which also make Him the focal point by offsetting light and dark colors on either side.

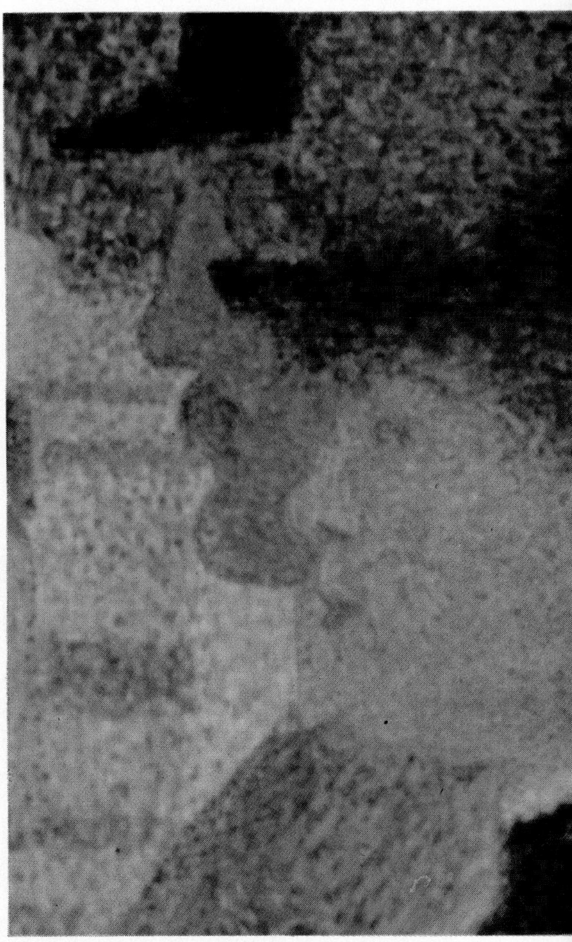

DOTS OF COLOR

Thousands of tiny colored dots in this painting by Georges Seurat, some of which can be seen in the detail above, blend into a variety of subtle tints when seen from a distance. It took Seurat two years to complete the painting by means of this painstaking technique, called pointillism.

SEEING A SILHOUETTE
This silhouette of his own profile by the modern artist Marcel Duchamp shows how the eye reacts to a recognizable figure. Although the picture contains only two flat-painted surfaces, the silhouette is assumed to be in the foreground.

Lines and Massed Colors

A blank rectangle of canvas has no visual meaning until an artist draws something on it. Then two things take place: a perceptible form appears, and that form is seen as the foreground of the picture. The effect is comparable to the one experienced when a dark, dimensionless sky is suddenly transformed as the moon appears from behind a cloud. Instantly the sky becomes a background setting. This phenomenon, familiar to painters throughout the ages, is the basis of techniques developed by artists like Henri de Toulouse-Lautrec and Henri Matisse. Both men used strong, spare lines and masses of solid color against flat planes to achieve results like the ones shown here. By keeping colors to a minimum, and by using colors to create shapes, these artists achieved a stark, dramatic quality often missing in other, more subtle techniques. Matisse, Vlaminck, Rouault and Braque adopted styles that seemed so crude and shocking at the time that they were called *fauves*—wild beasts. Today, with the shock impact gone, their paintings are prized examples of modern art.

AN ANCIENT TECHNIQUE REUSED
Matisse heavily outlined the figures to move them forward; the flat green and blue tones recede to become hillside and sky. Although trained as a conventional artist, Matisse deliberately developed a primitive style, explaining: "The whole arrangement . . . is expressive. The placement of figures . . . the empty spaces . . . the proportions, everything plays a part."

VIVID SHAPES AND COLORS
Exaggerated shape and contrasting flat colors provide a strong impact in this theater program by Toulouse-Lautrec. But to supply perspective, the artist used the table which, with its silverware and wine decanter, provides a foreground against which the figures can be seen in depth.

L'ARGENT
Comédie en 4 actes de M. Émile FABRE
(EN PROSE)
DISTRIBUTION :
Reynard. . . . . . . MM. Arquillière
Laurent, son fils . . . . Larochelle
Roux, son gendre. . . . Antoine
Bousquet . . . . Paul Edmond
Madame Reynard. . . . Mmes Henriot
Mathilde Roux . . . . . Brienne
Irma. . . . . Luce Colas
Julienne. . . . . Zapolska
De la part de M. Emile FABRE.
Paris. Imp. Eugène Verneau, 108, rue de la Folie-Méricourt.

The Effect of Overlapping

The three paintings on these pages represent three different eras and art forms, yet each uses the same technique—overlapping—to produce an illusion of depth. The eye always assumes the figure or object being overlapped is more distant than one seen in its entirety. Utilizing this effect, the three artists have made certain things appear closer than others by the simple device of overlapping one on the other.

The ancient Egyptians, who knew little about perspective, used overlapping almost exclusively to show depth *(below)*. Later artists used the same method to indicate the front-to-back progression when representing large groups in close proximity, as in the scene at center. Although this painting and the modern work at the far right present unnaturally tilted surfaces, thus easing the artist's task, the eye uses overlapping as its clue to depth and sequence.

AN EGYPTIAN TECHNIQUE
Five identical Egyptian maidens, weeping in a funeral ceremony, show how overlapping alone establishes depth. The flat, superimposed profiles of the women's faces and figures give the desired illusion of a shoulder-to-shoulder line of mourners, ranging away from the viewer.

DEPTH WITHOUT DISTORTION
A three-dimensional effect is achieved in this 15th Century painting by Giovanni di Paolo even though all the figures are drawn to the same scale. The bottom figures appear to be in the foreground because they overlap those in the middle, who in turn overlap the top figures and cast them into the background of the scene.

IN A MODERN SETTING
By overlapping certain objects with others in the painting above, the French Cubist Georges Braque has provided a conventional indication of their arrangement in a rather unconventional setting—a table that the viewer can see from both the side and the top at the same time.

Realism and Perspective

Not until the artists of the Italian Renaissance combined geometry with art to produce perspective was it possible for a painting to achieve a degree of realism rivaling that of direct vision. To attain such a remarkable three-dimensional illusion, the artist must first draw a series of precise, parallel lines that seem to converge at a single point on the horizon. Between these lines are painted figures or objects that steadily diminish in size. The key to perspective is this decreasing size, the same phenomenon that can be seen by looking down a long, straight highway. The surface seems to narrow, and cars on it get smaller until cars and highway vanish at a point on the horizon. Perspective is clearly illustrated by the pattern of progressively shrinking architectural details in the painting at right. But in dealing with irregular shapes, like a human figure, perspective is often more difficult to attain. In the painting below, the artist had to drastically foreshorten the reclining figure of Christ in order to achieve the visual effect he desired.

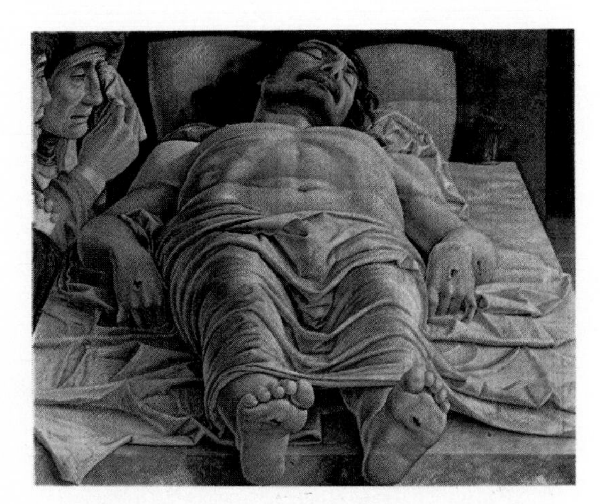

TWO VIEWS OF PERSPECTIVE
The unusual painting of Christ *(above)* by Andrea Mantegna is an example of deliberate distortion for a realistic effect. Mantegna viewed the body from in front of the outstretched legs, foreshortening the limbs and trunk to achieve a dramatic result. In the painting at the right, the arched interior of a Dutch church by Emanuel De Witte, the nave seems to extend far into the distance as the alternating columns and patches of light steadily grow closer and smaller.

The Evolution of the Eye

ALTHOUGH THE EVOLUTION of the vertebrate eye has been called the most important development that enabled man's remote ancestors to rise from the twilight of the ocean floor to the sunlight of dry land, modern scientists can only guess at how it was accomplished. Some believe that the eye developed as an outgrowth of the brain; others theorize that primitive eyes came first, with the brain evolving as their message center. The sketches below, drawn from studies by the American anatomist Stephen Polyak, reflect the latter view. Polyak's progression, tracing the eye development of a hypothetical vertebrate animal, is partially based on his examinations of human embryos, which are believed to duplicate the various stages of evolution as they grow from single cells to complex vertebrate organisms.

SIX STEPS TO VISION

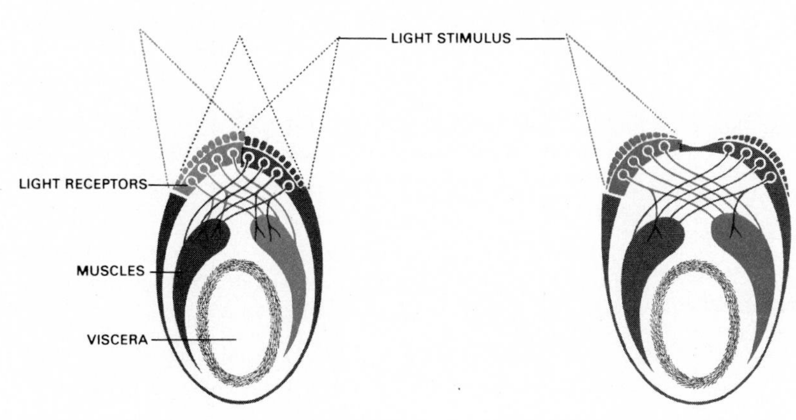

Eyes may have begun in small aquatic organisms 1.5 billion years ago as a single patch of light-sensitive cells *(top)* sending nerve signals directly to the muscles. Light or shadows from the right have the effect of triggering escape movement to the left *(black system)*; those from the left control right movement *(color system)*.

As the organism gains more mobility on the ocean floor, its single eye divides into right and left halves to permit a more direct cross-linkage between the light receptors and the muscles under their control. Here a light signal from the left—possibly the shadow of a predator—is being sent to the motor muscles on the right side.

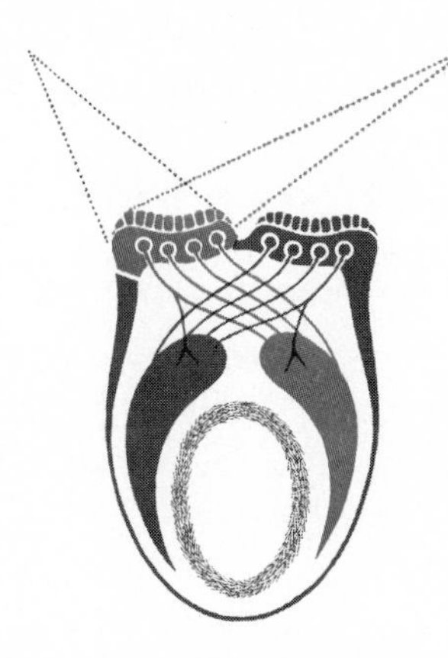

In this third stage, the light-sensitive cells are indented and face in the same direction, an arrangement that permits better forward visibility but works poorly when light comes from the side. For example, the left eye cannot distinguish between the two signals shown; neither offers a clue to the direction of possible danger.

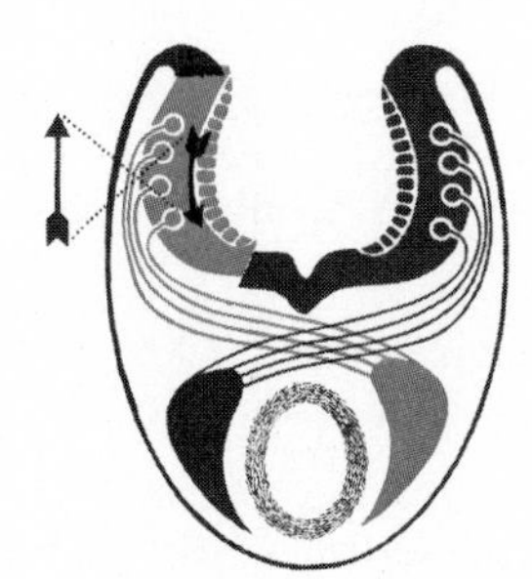

A turning point comes when the cells fold in to face each other, forming light-sensitive plates (future retinas) which get light from the sides instead of the front. Crude images of objects *(arrows)* are formed on the plates by the lens-like action of the animal's transparent body, which concentrates the light passing through it.

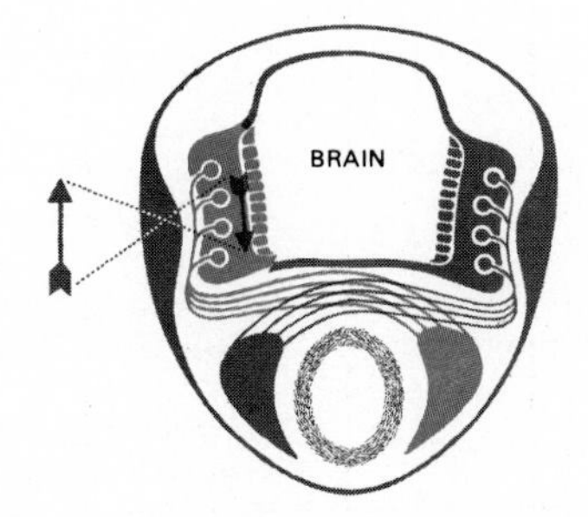

Now enclosed within a newly formed head, the eyes are separated by the developing brain, which serves to coordinate and interpret the messages from the retinal plates. The skin shield, evolving into the lenses of the eyes, produces a significant improvement; the eyes can detect form and detail as well as light and shadow.

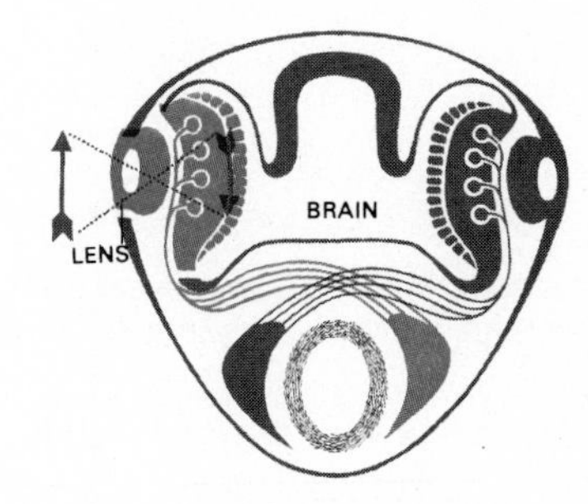

This relatively modern visual system—actually half a billion years old—may have enabled man's marine ancestors to move about freely in the ocean and aided their eventual emergence onto land. The eyes, which form clear images through fully developed lenses, are now dependent on the brain to convert signals into action.

A Vocabulary for Vision

ACCOMMODATION. Changing the shape of the eye's lens to focus on near and far objects.

ACUITY. The capacity to discriminate fine details of objects.

ADDITIVE COLOR MIXTURE. The creation of a new color by overlapping beams of colored light or by blending different colors in the eye.

AERIAL PERSPECTIVE. A visual cue to relative distances, in which objects lose detail and their color shifts toward hazy blue according to the distance between them and the eye.

AFTERIMAGE. A visual effect occurring after a light stimulus has been removed. This effect can be either positive (when the brightness or color is the same as the stimulus) or negative (when the brightness or color of the image is the opposite of the stimulus).

ANGLE OF INCIDENCE. The angle at which a light ray strikes a surface, measured between the incoming ray and a line perpendicular to the surface.

ANGLE OF REFLECTION. The angle at which a light ray is reflected from a surface, measured between the ray and a line perpendicular to the surface.

AQUEOUS HUMOR. A watery liquid between the lens and cornea which supplies some nutriment to the cornea.

ASTIGMATISM. A vision defect usually caused by uneven curvature of the cornea.

BIPOLAR CELLS. A layer of nerve cells in the retina which receive stimulation from the photoreceptors and pass it on to the next layer, the ganglion cells.

BLIND SPOT. The point of exit of the optic nerve from the retina. There are no rods or cones at this point and therefore no response to light.

BRIGHTNESS. A subjective description of light intensity.

CATARACT. A general term covering any partial or complete clouding of the lens.

CHOROID. The middle membrane of the eye, between the retina and outer coating, which supplies blood to the eye.

CILIARY BODY. The group of muscles which regulates the shape of the lens for near- and far-vision.

COLOR BLINDNESS. An inexact term covering all major deviations from normal color vision. The most common form is *dichromatism,* sensitivity to only two distinct colors rather than the three needed to match all the colors in the spectrum.

COLOR CONSTANCY. The tendency to perceive a familiar object as the same color under different light conditions.

COMPLEMENTARY COLORS. Two spectral colors which add together to make white or gray.

COMPOUND EYE. A light-receptor system, generally found in insects, that contains a number of similar units. Each unit, called an ommatidium, takes in a small segment of the field of vision and contributes its bit of nerve activity to the mosaic composed by the brain.

CONES. Plump photoreceptor cells in the retina which provide color sensitivity and detail.

CORNEA. The transparent coating of the eyeball over the iris and pupil. The cornea is part of the eye's focusing system.

DARK AND LIGHT ADAPTATION. The eye's adjustment in sensitivity to changing light conditions. This adjustment is accompanied not only by changes in the size of the pupil, but also by chemical changes in the visual pigments.

DIFFRACTION. The spreading of light around the edges of an obstacle.

DIFFRACTION GRATING. A device, usually an opaque screen with narrow, equally spaced transparent lines, which spreads out light waves into spectra. The number of lines usually ranges from 5,000 to 30,000 per inch.

ELECTROMAGNETIC SPECTRUM. Waves of electric and magnetic energy traveling at the speed of light. This energy takes many forms, including light, heat, X-rays and radio waves.

FIGURE AND GROUND PHENOMENON. The interpretation of certain parts of an enclosed area as foreground figures and the remainder of the area as background.

FOVEA. A small depression in the central part of the retina which contains only cones and is responsible for acuity.

GANGLION CELLS. The third important layer of the retina, which receives stimulation from the bipolar cells and transmits impulses to the optic nerve.

GLARE. A harsh, uncomfortably bright light or reflection.

HUE. The distinctive color by which each narrow band of light wavelengths is perceived.

HYPEROPIA. Farsightedness, or ability to focus only on objects at a distance (see MYOPIA).

INTERFERENCE. The combined effect of overlapping light waves, causing bright bands when the waves intersect crest to crest and trough to trough, dark bands when they meet crest to trough.

IRIS. Contractile eye tissue behind the cornea which regulates the amount of light entering the eye.

LATERAL GENICULATE BODIES. Way stations in the brain for optic nerve fibers from the retina. A critical region of nerve tissue for all visual functions of higher organisms.

LENS. A transparent oval body behind the iris which adjusts the eye's focus for near- and far-vision.

LIGHT. A small band in the electromagnetic spectrum, ranging from about 400 to 700 millimicrons, which contains all of the visible colors (see ELECTROMAGNETIC SPECTRUM).

LINEAR PERSPECTIVE. The depth cue of parallel straight lines seeming to converge at a distant vanishing point.

MACULA. The pigmented central area, or "yellow spot," of the retina.

MILLIMICRON. A measure of length equal to one twenty-five millionth of an inch, or one billionth of a meter.

MOVEMENT PARALLAX. The relative motion of near and far objects perceived when either the object or the observer is moving.

MUNSELL COLOR SYSTEM. A classification of color in terms of three attributes, hue, value and chroma. By this system, any color can be specified by numbers and letters.

MYOPIA. Nearsightedness, or ability to focus only on objects near the eye (see HYPEROPIA).

NICTITATING MEMBRANE. Also called the "third lid," a vertical, often transparent fold of skin used to lubricate and protect the eyes of many reptiles, birds and mammals.

OPTIC CHIASMA. The intersection of the two optic nerves, one from each eye. At this point in the human system, the optic nerve fibers divide, half from each eye crossing over to join half from the other eye. The two newly formed bundles continue on to the lateral geniculate bodies.

OPTIC NERVE. A bundle of nerve fibers which carries light-generated impulses from the eye to the brain.

OPTICAL ILLUSION. A visual perception in which there is an unusual discrepancy between the stimulus and the object perceived.

PERSISTENCE OF VISION. A brief continuation of a visual effect beyond its stimulus, representing a kind of inertia of the visual system.

PHOTOELECTRIC EFFECT. The effect light has on certain substances, usually metals, causing them to give off electrons.

PHOTON. The smallest unit by which the energy of light can be measured.

PHOTOPIGMENTS. Molecules which selectively absorb and reflect different wavelengths of light.

PHOTORECEPTORS. Cells at the back of the retina containing light-sensitive pigments. When light is absorbed, these pigments undergo a reaction which triggers the nerve impulses resulting in vision (see CONES and RODS).

POLARIZED LIGHT. Light waves vibrating in a single plane rather than in all directions.

PRESBYOPIA. Loss of flexibility in the lens owing to aging. The lens thus cannot focus well for near-vision.

PRIMARY COLORS. Any set of three colors whose mixture in various proportions will produce white and all colors in the visible spectrum. The most common primaries are red, green and blue.

PSYCHOPHYSICS. The study of the relationship between physical stimuli and the psychological or behavioral response.

PUPIL. The hole in the center of the iris that governs the amount of light passing to the interior of the eye. The size of the opening is controlled by the iris.

REFRACTION. Bending of a light ray when passing from one transparent medium into another of different density.

RETINA. The innermost layer of the eye where light-sensitive rods and cones are located.

REVERSED PERSPECTIVE. A change in the perception of the dimensions of an object, bringing background into the foreground and vice versa.

RHODOPSIN. Also called visual purple, a light-sensitive pigment of the rods. It bleaches in the light and regenerates in the dark.

RODS. Straight, thin photoreceptors which respond to low levels of illumination and give black and white responses.

SATURATION. Refers to the purity or richness of a color. One measure is how much white or gray is in the mixture.

SCATTERING. The deflection of light by particles. This effect is most pronounced for high frequencies such as blue light, giving the sky a blue hue.

SCLERA. The "white," or thick outer coating of the eyeball.

SIZE CONSTANCY. The perception of familiar objects as being unchanged in size, regardless of the distance at which they are seen.

SPATIAL INDUCTION. Also called simultaneous contrast. The contrast of one part of the visual field with an adjacent area, affecting the perception of black, white and colors.

SPECTROPHOTOMETER. A device to measure the amount of each color, or wavelength, in the light reflected by an object.

STEREOSCOPIC VISION. Perception of the visual field in three dimensions through a mixture of images from each eye.

SUBTRACTIVE COLOR MIXTURE. The absorption and reflection of light by two or more superimposed pigments or dyes, creating a new color.

TEXTURAL PERSPECTIVE. The crowding and blending of details—like the pebbles in a field—as they are seen from increasingly greater distances.

VISUAL CORTEX. That part of the cerebral cortex in the brain primarily responsible for interpreting signals from the eye.

VISIBILITY CURVE. A graph illustrating the eye's sensitivity to light at each wavelength in the visible spectrum.

VITREOUS HUMOR. A thick, transparent jelly which fills the cavity between lens and retina, giving the eye its shape.

WAVELENGTH. The distance between two similar points of a given wave.

FURTHER READING

General

Asher, Harry, *Experiments in Seeing*. Basic Books, 1963.
Boring, Edwin G., *Sensation and Perception in the History of Experimental Psychology*. Appleton-Century, 1942.
Geldard, Frank A., *The Human Senses*. John Wiley, 1953.
Graham, Clarence H., ed., *Vision and Visual Perception*. John Wiley, 1965.
†Gregory, Richard L., *Eye and Brain*. McGraw-Hill, 1966.
*Helmholtz, Hermann von, *Popular Scientific Lectures*. Dover Publications, 1962. *Treatise on Physiological Optics*. Dover Publications, 1924.
Kahn, Fritz, *Man in Structure and Function* (2 vols.). Alfred A. Knopf, 1947.
Murchie, Guy, *Music of the Spheres*. Houghton Mifflin, 1961.
*Southall, James P. C., *Introduction to Physiological Optics*. Peter Smith, 1937.

The Eye

Davson, Hugh, ed., *The Eye* (Vol. II). Academic Press, 1962.
Matthews, L. Harrison, and Maxwell Knight, *The Senses of Animals*. Museum Press, 1963.
*Platt, Rutherford, *The River of Life*. Simon and Schuster, 1956.
Polyak, Stephen, *The Vertebrate Visual System*. University of Chicago Press, 1958.
Walls, G. L., *The Vertebrate Eye and Its Adaptive Radiation*. Hafner, 1942.
Wolff, Eugene, *The Anatomy of the Eye and Orbit* (5th revised edition). Saunders, 1961.

Light

*Bragg, William, *The Universe of Light*. Peter Smith, 1940.
†Mach, Ernst, *The Principles of Physical Optics*. Dover Publications, 1926.
†Monk, George S., *Light, Principles and Experiments* (2nd edition). Dover Publications, 1963.
*Ruechardt, Eduard, *Light: Visible and Invisible*. University of Michigan Press, 1958.
Sears, Francis W., *Optics* (3rd edition). Addison-Wesley, 1949.

Color and Color Vision

Burnham, Robert W., R. M. Hanes and C. James Bartleson, *Color: A Guide to Basic Facts and Concepts*. John Wiley, 1963.
†"Color as Seen and Photographed." Kodak Color Data Book E-74 (2nd edition). Eastman Kodak Co., 1962.
Evans, Ralph M., *An Introduction to Color*. John Wiley, 1948.
Hering, Ewald, *Outlines of a Theory of the Light Sense*. Harvard University Press, 1964.
†Teevan, Richard C., and Robert C. Birney, eds., *Color Vision*. Van Nostrand, 1961.

Visual Perception

*Arnheim, Rudolf, *Art and Visual Perception*. University of California Press, 1964.
Bartley, S. Howard, *Principles of Perception*. Harper & Row, 1958.
Beeler, Nelson F., and Franklyn M. Branley, *Experiments in Optical Illusion*. Thomas Y. Crowell, 1951.
Gibson, James J., *The Perception of the Visual World*. Houghton Mifflin, 1950.
Ittelson, William, *Visual Space Perception*. Springer, 1960.
Tolansky, Samuel, *Optical Illusions*. Pergamon Press, 1964.
†Vernon, M. D., *The Psychology of Perception*. Penguin Books, 1962.
Woodworth, Robert S., and Harold Schlosberg, *Experimental Psychology* (revised edition). Holt, Rinehart & Winston, 1954.

History of Photography

Gernsheim, Helmut, and Alison, *History of Photography*. Oxford University Press, 1955.
Newhall, Beaumont, *The Daguerreotype in America*. Meredith, 1961. *The History of Photography, 1839-1965*. Doubleday, 1964.
Pollack, Peter, *The Picture History of Photography*. Abrams, 1958.
Taft, Robert, *Photography and the American Scene*. Peter Smith, 1938.

*Also available in paperback edition.
†Only available in paperback edition.

ACKNOWLEDGMENTS

The editors of this book are indebted to the following persons and institutions: R. Tucker Abbot, Department of Mollusks, Academy of Natural Sciences of Philadelphia; Rudolf Arnheim, Sarah Lawrence College, Bronxville, New York; Karen Bates, Bausch & Lomb, Inc., Rochester, New York; Faber Birren, Color Consultant, New York City; Robert Bretz, Assistant Curator, Collections, George Eastman House, Rochester, New York; Ramon Castroviejo; Noel deLeon; Ivan Dunaief, Bronx Eye and Ear Infirmary, Bronx, New York; Ralph Evans, Director of Photographic Technology, Eastman Kodak Company, Rochester, New York; Richard L. Gregory, Department of Psychology, Cambridge University, Cambridge, England; Gordon Hendricks; Gerald Howett, National Bureau of Standards, Gaithersburg, Maryland; William Ittelson, Department of Psychology, Brooklyn College; Dean Judd, National Bureau of Standards, Gaithersburg, Maryland; Lazare Kaplan and Sons, Inc., New York City; Harry J. Keegan, Physicist, National Bureau of Standards, Gaithersburg, Maryland; Kenneth L. Kelly, Physicist, National Bureau of Standards, Gaithersburg, Maryland; Bert S. Kleinsinger, Bronx High School of Science, New York City; Miriam Levensohn, Greenwich House, New York City; John Meaney, Curator, Gernsheim Collection, University of Texas, Austin; Munsell Color Company, Inc., Baltimore; Beaumont Newhall, Director, George Eastman House, Rochester, New York; I. Nimeroff, Physicist, National Bureau of Standards, Gaithersburg, Maryland; James Rainwater, Department of Physics, Columbia University, New York City; Harris Ripps, Associate Professor of Ophthalmology, New York University School of Medicine, New York City; John Rohrbach, Department of Physics, New York University, New York City; Constance P. Warner; and Herman A. Witkin, State University of New York, Downstate Medical Center, Brooklyn.

INDEX

Numerals in italics indicate a photograph or painting of the subject mentioned.

A

Aberrations, chromatic, 169
Absorption of light, partial, by pigment molecules, and resultant color, *56*, 98-99, 128; simulation with filters, *110-111*
Accommodation, of eye lens, 56-57, 58, *89*
Acuity, 168, 174; retinal area of greatest, *76*
Acuity tests, *chart* 58, *59*, 168
Adaptations of animal eyes, *10*, *22-23*, *28-29*, 60
Additive mixing of color, 98, *112-113*
Aerial perspective, as cue in depth vision, 143, 145
Aerial photography, stereoscopic, 142
Afterimage, in color vision, 124, *132*
Aging, eye defects due to, 55, 59, 61, 90, 91
Amateur photography, beginnings of, *70-71*
Amoeba, light sensitivity of, 16
Anableps, bifocal eyes of, *23*, 60
Anaconda snake, eye of, *22*
Angle of reflection, 31, *32*, *42-43*
Angle of refraction, 32, *33*, *44-45*
Angles, visual illusions in viewing of, 146
Animal eyes, 10-11, 16, *17*, *20-29*, 53, 56; of browsers, 11, 16, 58; compound, *20-21*, *25*, 60, *61*; evolution of, 10, 11, 16, *18-19*, *193*; of insects, 20, *21*, 60, *61*; lids and lashes, *26-27*, 59; numbers of, in various species, 20, 58; oldest fossil, *20*; placement of, 10, 11, 16, *24-25*, 58; of predators, 11, 16, *22-23*, *27*, 58, *77*; pupil shapes, *22-23*; rod pigment of, 78; simple, *20*; specialized, *10*, *22-25*, *28-29*, 58-59, 60; of spiders, *20*, 58. *See also* Birds; Fishes; Marine life
Animal vision, 9, 16, 18, 20; color, 126; nocturnal, 11, 16, 22-23, *28-29*, *77*; retinal *vs.* cortical analysis of nerve signals, 176; stereoscopic, 11, 58
Animal visual systems, 176; *Copilia*, 18, *19*
Aperture, camera, *54*
"Aperture color" experiments, 121
Apes: color vision of, 126; placement of eyes of, 58
Aqueous humor, 53-54, 55, 84
Archer, Scott, 66
Aristotle: concept of light of, 31; his doubt in emanation theory of vision, 53
Art: perspective in, 147, *187*, *190-191*; surrealism, *162*; techniques for indicating depth and distance, 145-146, *182-183*, *187-191*; techniques for indicating shape, 145, *180-181*, *182*, 186. *See also* Line drawings; Painting
Artificial light *vs.* sunlight, 99, 106, *107*
Astigmatism, 59, 82, *86*; test, *60*
Atmospheric particles, effect on sunlight, *30*, 100-101, *102*
Autochrome photography, *72-73*
Autokinetic phenomenon, 175

B

Babylonia, ancient, eye surgery in, 61
Back-reaction, of rhodopsin, 173
Balance, sense of, 11-12
Bats, eyes of, 28
Bees, vision of, 20; color, 126
Berkeley, George, Bishop, 139
Bifocals, 60, *90*, 91
Binocular cues, in depth vision, 141-143, 146, *158-159*
Binocular vision, 58, 80, *81*, 141-143; coordination, 141-142; range, *140*
Bipolar cells, in retina, *76*, 80, *94*
Birds, 22; eyelashes of, 26; nictitating membrane of, 26, *27*; of prey, eyes and vision of, 11, 16, *23*, *27*, *77*; robin, 10
Black, 136; caused by complete light absorption, 99, 110, *111*; in color TV, 112
Bleaching effect, in color perception, 136
Blind spot, 80, *92*, *93*; locating, *93*
Blindness: due to brain injury, 75; due to cataracts, 61; due to cornea damage, 86; in one eye, remaining vision, 141-142
Blue (color): cause of hue of sky, 100, *102*; coolness and recession of, 184, *186*; creation of, *110*; a fundamental color in perception, 123, 133; low brightness of, 120, 169; of man-made materials, 99; as primary spectral color, 98, 110; saturation of, 120; sensitivity of rods *vs.* cones to, 77, *graph* 170
Blue-green. *See* Cyan
Blue light: refraction of, 33; wavelength of, 120
Boll, Franz, 75, 78
Boring, Edwin G., 177
Box camera, invention of, *70*, 71
Braille, Louis, 14
Braille alphabet, *14*
Brain, in visual system, 9, 14-15, 75, 80-81, 120, 126, 136, 168; analyzing role of, 9, 14-15, 126, 130, 140, 141-142, 148, 150, 152, 155, 157, 158, 162, 172, 174-175, 177; in animals, *19*, 176; transmission of visual signals to, *76*, *79*-80, *81*, 93, 125, *130*, *132*, *133*, 134, 136, 140
Brain injury, 75
Braque, Georges, 186; painting by, *189*
Brightness of color, 116, 119-120, 169; relative, *155*, 169
Brightness of objects, and judging distance and size, 145, 147, 155, 182
Brown, Paul K., 125
Brown (color), creation of, 112
Burning glass, 32, 60

C

Camel, eyelashes of, 26
Camera: comparisons of eye to, 53, *54*, 55, 56, 76, 82, *88*; early, wet-plate *vs.* dry-plate, 69; first Kodak, *70*, 71; focusing, 54, 56, *88*; Muybridge's 12-lens, *69*; refraction principle in, *45*
Camera obscura, 62
Carotene, 78-79, 99
Cataract, 61
Cats: brain's part in vision, 176; eye of, *22*, 28; pupil of, 23; stereoscopic vision of, 58
Celestial goldfish, eyes of, *24*
Cells, light-sensitive, as forerunner of eye, 16, *18*
Cellulose acetate film, 71
Chameleon, eyes of, *17*, 58-59
Chiasma, optic, 80, *81*
Chlorophyll, 98-99
Choroid, *84-85*, *94*
Christ among the Children, Nolde, *184*
Chroma of color, *116-117*
Chromatic aberrations, 169
Ciliary muscle, 57, 58, 84, *85*, *89*
Circles, visual illusion in viewing of, 146
Collodion, 66, 67
Color(s): absorption *vs.* reflection of, 98-100, *107*, *110-111*, 128; additive mixing of, 98, *112-113*; analysis by spectrophotometer, *100-101*, 119; brightness, 116, 119-120, 169; chroma, *116-117*; complementary, 123-124, 147; cool *vs.* hot, 184; creation of, 98-103, 104, *105-117*; desaturation of, 122; of distant objects, 145; effects in sky, 100-101, *102*; hue, *116-117*, 119, 120; intensity of light and, 120, 167, 169-170; iridescence, 102-103; of man-made materials, 99, *116-117*; in nature, 98-99, 110, *116*; nomenclature of, 116; pigment mixing, *111*; primary, artists', 97-98; primary, spectral, 98, 110, 123; prismatic, *129*; relationship of wavelength and frequency to, 36, *107*, 119, 120; relative brightness of, *155*, 169; saturation, 116, 119, 120; source of, 36, 97, 98-99, *128*; spectral *vs.* pigment, 98; spectrum, 33, 97, *108-109*, *128*; subtractive mixing of, 98-99, *110-111*; transmission of, 99; use of, in painting, 119, *184-187*; value, *116-117*; wavelengths, 98, *107*, 120, 123. *See also* Pigment color
Color blindness, 124-125, 133; in animals, 28, 77; test, *127*
Color coding, industrial, *118*
Color constancy, 120-121
Color photography: history of, *72-73*; indoor, 106
Color printing, *114-115*
Color receptors, in human eye, 76, 77, 122-124, 125, 128, *130*, *133*; defects, 124-125; testing, *134-135*
Color scale, Helmholtz's, *131*
Color television, 112, 115
Color vision and perception, 76, 77, 82, 94, *95*, 103, 119-125, 126, 128, *130-137*; afterimage in, 124, *132*; in animals, 126; "aperture" experiments, 121; bleaching effect in, 136; composite theory of, 125, 126, *133*, 134; constancy of, 120-121; defects (*see* Color blindness); differentiation of hues, 122; four fundamental colors, 123, 133; Hering (opponent-process) theory of, 123-124, 125, 126, *132-133*, 134, 136; loss of, in dim light, 76, 82, 94, *95*; memory color, 121; nerve function in, Hering theory, 124, 125; physiology of, 119, 120, 122-125, 126, *130*; psychology of, 119, 120-121, 126, 133; psychophysical aspects, 136, 169-170; sensitivity of rods *vs.* cones, to different parts of spectrum, 77, *graph* 170; subjectivity of, 119, 178; tests, *127*, *134-137*; Young-Helmholtz (trichromatic) theory of, 122-123, 124, 125, 126, *130*, 133, 134, 135
Color wheel, *129*
Colored light: luminosity curve, 169; minimum-intensity factor, in vision, 170; reflection of, 99-100, 106, *107*; refraction of, 33; relative brightness of, 169; wavelengths, 98, *107*, 120
Complementary colors, 123-124, 147
Compound eyes, *20-21*, *25*, 60, *61*
Compton, Arthur H., 39
Concave lenses, 32, *35*, *44*, *91*
Conch, queen, eyes of, 24, *25*
Cones, photoreceptors, *76-77*, *94*, 168, 169, 171; function of, 76, 94, 171; number of, in human eye, 76; proportion to rods, in man *vs.* owl, *77*; sensitivity of, in different parts of spectrum, 77, *graph* 170; testing of, *134-135*; visual pigments of, 78-79, 94, 120, 122, 125. *See also* Color receptors
Conjunctiva, 84, *85*
Contact lenses, 61
Convergence, muscular, of pair of eyes, 158
Convex lenses, 32-33, *35*, *44*, *91*; in camera, *45*
Copepods, one-eyed, 58
Copilia, visual system of, 18, *19*
Cormorant, double-crested, eye of, *23*
Cornea, 53, 54, 55, 56, 84, *85*, *86*, *89*; defects of, 59, 60, 86; function of, 53, 55, 86; surgery, *86*
Corpuscular theory. *See* Particle theory of light
Cortex, 81, 125, 176; visual, *81*, 120, 141, 148
Crab, fiddler, eyes of, 24, *25*
Critical duration, of rhodopsin back-reaction, 173
Critical fusion frequency, 173
Crivelli, Carlo, painting by, *182*
Cues, visual. *See* Visual cues
Cyan (color): creation of, *110*, *112*; primary pigment color, 98
Cyclops, one-eyed, 58
Cypridinids, eyespots of, *18*

D

Daguerre, Louis J. M., 62, *65*
Daguerreotypes, *63*, *65*, 66
Dalton, John, 124-125
Dark and light adaptation of eye, 77-78, 172-173
Da Vinci, Leonardo. *See* Leonardo da Vinci
De Broglie, Louis, 39
Deer, eyes of, 11, 58
De Morgan, Augustus, 102
Depth illusion: in art, 145-146, 178, *180-183*, *186-191*; in photographs, *138*
Depth perception, 139, 140-141, 143-146, *151-159*; binocular cues to, 141-143, 146, *158-159*; of infants, 12; monocular cues to, *138*, 142, 143-146, *150-157*; of previously blind people, 14. *See also* Stereoscopic vision
Desaturation of color, 122
Desert animals, eyelashes of, 26, *27*
Detection, visual, 168
Deuteranopia, 124
De Witte, Emanuel, painting by, *190-191*
Diamond: rainbow colors of, *108*, 109; velocity of light in, 44
Diamond beetle, wings of, 103
Diffraction, 35, 37, 38, 39, *46-47*, 103, *109*
Distance of objects, judging, *138*, 139, 140-141, 143-146, 148, 150, *151*, 158
Distance vision. *See* Far vision
Divisionism, painting technique, 119
Dogs, eyes of, 58
Doubling of out-of-focus objects, 143
Dragonfly, vision of, 16, 20
Drawings. *See* Line drawings
Dry-plate photography, *68-69*
Duchamp, Marcel, painting by, *186*
Ducks, nictitating membrane of, 26
Dürer, Albrecht, woodcut by, *180-181*
Dye and dyeing: artificial, 99, 116; natural, *98-99*

E

Eagle: bald, eyelashes of, *27*; vision of, 16
Ear, cooperation with eye, 11-12
Earthworm, light sensitivity of, 16
Eastman, George, *70*, 71
Eel: American, eye of, *23*; vision experiment with, 170-171
Egyptian painting, *188*
Einstein, Albert, 9, 39, 50, *180*
Electric eye, use of photoelectric effect in, 38, 50
Electric light, 99, 106, *107*, 174
Electric ray, eye of, *22*
Electrode probes of visual cortex, 75, 81
Electromagnetic radiation: discovery of, 38; particle *vs.* wave theory, 39
Electromagnetic spectrum, 38, 39, 98
Emanation theory of vision, 53
Emotional loading, 164
Energy conversion in visual system, 75-76, *78-79*, 80, 93, 94
Energy-time relationship in vision, 170-171, 173
Erni, Hans, sketch of Einstein by, *180*
"Errors of judgment" in vision, a misnomer, 147
Euclid, 53, 139
Euglena, eyespots of, 18
Event detectors, 176
Evolution of eyes, 10, 11, 16, *18-19*, *193*; adaptations, *22-23*, *28-29*
Eye: basic process in, 53; compound, *20-21*, *25*, 60, *61*; energy conversions in, 75-76, *78-79*, 80, 93, 94; evolution of, 10, 11, 16, *18-19*, *193*; focusing for three-dimensional vision, 11, 58; simple, *20*; specializations, 10-11, 16. *See also* Animal eyes; Human eye
Eye defects, 59-61, 82, *90-91*; astigmatism, 59, 82, *86*; astigmatism test, *60*; cataracts, 61; color blindness, 124-125, 133; color blindness test, *127*; cornea damage, *86*; due to aging, 59, 61, 90, 91; farsightedness (hyperopia), 54, 59, 82, *91*; measuring, 60; nearsightedness (myopia), 59, 82, *91*; presbyopia, 59, 91
Eye muscles, 54, 57, 59, *84-85*, 177; of iris, 54, 87; of lens (ciliary), 57, 58, 84, *85*, *89*
Eye surgery: ancient Babylonia, 61; ancient Greece, 53; corneal, *86*; India, 1000 B.C., 61; lens removal for cataract, 61
Eyeglasses, 44, 61; bifocal, 69, *90*, 91; history of, 59-60, 91; lenses, *91*; number of wearers, in U.S., 82; polaroid, 38, *49*
Eyelashes, *83*; animal, 26, *27*; function of, 59, 82
Eyelids, 54, *83*; animal, *26-27*, 59; function of, 59; movement of, 58, 82
Eyespots, *18*

F

Fantascope, *166*
Fantz, Robert L., 12
Far vision: acuity tests, *chart* 58, *59*, 168; lens accommodation for, 56-57, *89*; defective (*see* Nearsightedness); diminished stereo effect, 143; pupil adjustment for, 54
Faraday, Michael, 175

Farsightedness (hyperopia), 54, 59, 82, *91;* correction by glasses, *91*
Fauvism, *186-187*
Fechner, Gustav, 167
Fenton, Roger, 66, 67
Fiddler crab, eyes of, 24, *25*
Field dependents and independents, 161
Figure-ground phenomenon in art, *186-187*
Film, roll, invention of, *70-71;* color, 72
Fire-bellied toad, eye of, *23*
Fishes, eyes of: aiming of, 10; focusing of, 56; lack of eyelids of most, 26; placement of, 24; puffer eyelid, *27;* rod pigment of, 78; special adaptations, *10, 22-23,* 60
Flicker, in intermittent stimulation of eye, 173-174
Flounders, eyes of, *22-23,* 24
Fluorescent light, 99, 106, *107,* 174
"Flying gnats" in vitreous, 61
Flying squirrel, eyes of, *28*
Focusing, camera, 54, 56, *88*
Focusing of eyes, 11, 53-54, 55-58, 86, 88, *89;* defective, 59-60, *86,* 90, *91;* for far vision, 56-57, *89;* for near vision, 56-57, 59, *89;* selectivity in, 14, 142-143, *156-157;* for stereoscopic vision, 11, 58
Foot candle, unit of measurement, 169
Form perception, 138, 141, 143, *144,* 145, *152-153, 154-155;* in infants, 12
Fossilized eye, oldest, *20*
Fovea, *76-77,* 81, *84, 92,* 93, *94,* 171; tissue test, *135*
Franklin, Benjamin, 60, 90
Fraunhofer, Joseph von, 169
Frequency of light, relationship to wavelength, 36
Frog: brain's part in vision, 176; retinal nerve cells of, 175-176; vision experiment with, 171; Wied's, eyelids of, *26*
Fuzziness of out-of-focus objects, 143, *156-157*

G

Galileo Galilei, 32
Gamma rays, 38, 98
Ganglion cells, in retina, *76,* 80, *94,* 125, 175-176
Giant gecko, eye of, *23*
Gibson, Eleanor, 12
Glare, *48-49;* causes of, 49; response of eye to, 54
Glass: refraction of light by, 31-*33,* 44, *45;* velocity of light in, 44
Glasses. *See* Eyeglasses
Godowsky, Leopold, 72
Goethe, Johann Wolfgang von, 97
Gold leaf, color of, 99, 103
Goldfish: celestial, eyes of, *24;* color vision of, 126
Grande Jatte, La, Seurat, 119, *184-185*
Greece, ancient: concepts of light in, 31; concept of vision, 53, 89; eye surgery, 53
Green (color): coolness and recession of, 184, *186;* creation of, *110-111;* a fundamental color in perception, 123, 133; in nature, 98-99; as primary spectral color, 98, 110; relative brightness of, 169; sensitivity of rods *vs.* cones to, 77, *graph* 170
Green light, wavelength of, 98, 120
Green whip snake, eye of, *22,* 23
Gregory, Richard L., 14
Grimaldi, Francesco, 34-35
Guitar fish, eye of, *22*
Gulf flounder, eye of, *22*

H

Harris, Moses, 129
Hartline, Haldan, 171
Harvard University, 80, 125
Hawk, eye of, 11, 16
Haze, as cue in depth vision, *138,* 145
Hearing, sense of, 11
Hecht, Selig, 170
Helmholtz, Hermann von, 52, 60, 82, *130,* 133, 139, 177; and color vision, 122, 130, *131*
Hering, Ewald, 123, 124, 126, *132,* 133
Hering theory of color vision, 123-124, 125, 126, *132-133,* 134, 136
Hero of Alexandria, 31
Highway lighting at night, 168-169
Holmes, Oliver Wendell, 139
Honeybee, vision of, 20
Horizon, 141, 146
Horizontal scan of human vision, *140*
Horse, eye of, 58
Horsefly, eye of, *20-21*
Hubel, David H., 75, 81
Hue: changes in, causes, 120; defined, 116, 119; examples, Munsell color tree, *116-117;* human perception of, 122; and wavelength, 120
Human eye(s), 9, 11, 53-61, 82, *83-95;* adaptability of, 11, 82; blind spot of, 80, *92, 93;* coloring of, 54, *56,* 86; comparisons of camera to, 53, *54,* 55, 56, 76, 82, *88;* dark and light adaptation of, 77-78, 172-173; distance between, 141, 143; energy conversions in, 75-76, *78-79,* 80, 93, 94; focusing, 11, 14, 53-54, 55-58, 86, 88, *89;* focusing defects, 59-60, *86,* 90, *91;* light control of, 53-55, 57, 58, 84, 86, *87;* mobility of, 14-15, *52,* 57-58, 59, 77; model, *52;* muscular convergence of, 158; nervous control of, 57-58, 177; parts of, 53-57, 59, *84-95;* placement of, 11, 58, 81; precision of, 11; range of, *140;* selectivity in focusing of, 14, 142-143, *156-157;* sensitivity of, 170-171; structure of, *84-85;* unconscious movements of, *57. See also* Eye defects; Eye surgery
Human vision, 9-10, 11-15, 75-81, 119; acuity, *76,* 168, 174; ancient Greek concept of (emanation theory), 53; basic processes of, 53, 75-76, 79-80, *81;* daylight, 76, 77, 82, 94, *95;* depth perception, 12, 14, *138,* 139, 140-141, 143-146, *151-159;* distance perception, *138,* 139, 140-141, 143-146, 148, 150, *151,* 158; episodic character of, and blending of images, 14-15; external conditions of, 168-169, 170-171; form perception, 12, 139, 141, 143, *144,* 145, *154-155;* horizontal scan of, *140;* impairments of, 75, 78-79 (*see also* Eye defects); of infants, *8,* 12-13; integration with other senses, 11-12, 13; at night, 76, *77-78,* 82, 94, *95,* 172; noncorrespondence of three stages of, 139, 167; of previously blind people, 13-14; psychophysics of, 136, 147, 167-177; stability during movement, 15, 177; subjectivity of, 119, 161, 178; 20/20, *chart* 58, *59;* vertical range of, *140. See also* Binocular vision; Color vision; Far vision; Near vision; Stereoscopic vision
Human visual system, 9, 11, 14-15, 75, 80-81, *83-95;* analyzing role of brain, 9, 14-15, 126, 130, 140, 141-142, 148, 150, 152, 155, 157, 158, 162, 172, 174-175, 177; and color vision, 124, 125, *130, 132, 133,* 134; energy conversion in, 75-76, *78-79,* 80, 93, 94; and stereoscopic vision, 139, 141-142, 158; transmission of signals to brain, *76, 79-*80, *81,* 93, 125, *130, 132, 133,* 134, 136, 140
Hummingbirds, iridescent colors of, 102-103
Hurvich, Dr. and Mrs. Leo, *136-137*
Huygens, Christian, 32, 33, 34
Hyperopia (farsightedness), 54, 59, 82, *91;* correction by glasses, *91*

I

Iguana, eyelashes of, *27*
Illusions, visual, *142-147,* 148, *162-164. See also* Movement, illusions of
Incandescent light, *107*
India, cataract operations, 1000 B.C., 61
Infants, vision of, *8,* 12-13
Insects: compound eyes of, 20, *21,* 60, *61;* iridescence of wings, 102-103
Intensity of light, 119; and brightness, 120, 169; and color, 119, 120, 167, 169-170; as condition of vision, 168-169, 170; and hue, 120; minimum factor, 170; and saturation, 120; unit of measurement, 169
Intensity-time relationship in vision, 170-171, 173
Interference, 36, 38, 39, *47,* 103
Interference pattern, 36, *37*
Intermittence: external, 174; internal, 174-175
Intermittent stimulation of eye, 173-174
Interposition, as cue in depth vision, 143, 145, *152-153;* in art (overlapping), *188-189*
Iridescence, 102-103
Iris of eye, *54,* 59, *83,* 84, *85,* 86, *87, 88;* coloring of, 54, *56,* 86; function of, 54; origin of word, 54
Ishihara test, *127*

J

Jackson, William H., *66*
James, William, 14
Japanese goldfish, eye of, *24*
Johns Hopkins University, The, 75, 125, *134-135*

K

Kennedy, John F., *165*
Kodachrome film, 72
Kodak camera, first, *70,* 71
Kühne, Wilhelm, 78

L

Lateral geniculate body, 80-*81,* 120, 125
La Tour, Georges de, painting by, *183*
Lemur, vision of, 58
Lenard, Philipp, 38, 39
Lens of eye, *54, 55,* 59, 61, 84, *85,* 89; accommodation of, 56-57, 58, *89;* accommodation deficiencies, 59, *91;* in animals, 22; effect of aging on, 55, 59, 61, 91; function of, 54, 55-56, *89;* removal of, for cataract, 61; structure of, *55,* 56, *88*
Lenses, optical, 32-33; camera, *54,* 56; concave, 32, *35, 44, 91;* convex, 32-33, *35, 44, 45, 91;* polaroid, 38, *49;* polishing, 60
Leonardo da Vinci, 139, 145; color concept of, 97; drawing of human head by, *74*
Light: artificial, *vs.* sunlight, 99, 106, *107;* candle, 99; conversion by photosynthesis, 76; conversion to electrochemical reactions, in eye, 75-76, *78-79,* 80, 93, 94; diffraction phenomenon, 35, 37, 38, 39, *46-47,* 103, *109;* double nature of, 39, 79; electromagnetic nature of, 38, 39; fluorescent, 99, 106, *107,* 174; frequency-wavelength relationship, 36; history of concepts of, 31, 33-39; incandescent, *107;* intensity of, and color, 119, 120, 167, 168-169; intensity of, unit of measurement, 169; interference phenomenon, 36, *37,* 38, 39, *47,* 103; partial absorption and reflection by pigment molecules, and resultant color, *56,* 98-100, 110, 128; partial transmission of, by certain materials, 99; photoelectric effect of, 38-39, *50-51;* photon (particle) nature of, 39, 50, 79; polarization of, 37-38, *48-49;* reflection of, *30,* 31, *32,* 33, *42-43, 44, 45;* refraction of, 31-*33,* 34, *44-45;* scattering phenomenon, *56, 96,* 100-101, *102;* total internal reflection of, 33, *41;* velocity of, 38, 44, 103; velocity of, and refractive index, 32, 34; wave theory of, 31, 33-35, *36-37,* 38-39, *46-49,* 79; wavelength of, 98. *See also* Colored light; Light spectrum; Sunlight
Light and shadow, use in painting, *182-183*
Light meter, photographic, *50*
Light quantum, 39, 50; minimum required for visibility, 170
Light-sensitive cells, as forerunner of eye, 16, *18*
Light spectrum, 33, *108-109, 128;* Newton's discovery of, 33, 97, 128; primary colors of, 98, 110; sensitivity of eye to different parts of, 77, *graph* 170
Line drawings, 145, 178, *180-181;* reversible perspective in, 147, *163;* surrealist, *162*
Linear and textural perspective, as cue in depth vision, *138,* 143-144, *151*
Lippershey, Hans, 32
Lizards: eyelids and lashes of, 26, *27,* 59; eyes of, *23*
Localization, visual, 168
Lumière brothers (Louis Jean and Auguste M.L.N.), 72
Luminosity curve, 169

M

Mach, Ernst, sketch of monocular vision by, *149*
MacNichol, Edward F. Jr., 125, 134, *135*
Macula, *84, 92,* 93
Maddox, Richard L., 69
Magenta (color): creation of, *110, 112;* primary pigment color, 98
Mammalian eyes, 16, 22
Mannes, Leopold, 72
Mantegna, Andrea, painting by, *190*
Marine life: compound eyes, 20, *25;* microscopic, vision of, *18-19;* placement of eyes, *24-25. See also* Fishes
Mariotte, Edmé, 80
Marks, William B., 125
Matisse, Henri, painting by, *186*
Maxwell, James Clerk, *123;* and color photography, 72; discovery of electromagnetic spectrum, 38; studies of color perception, 103, 122
Memory, and vision, 81
Memory color, 121
Metals, photoelectric effect on, 38, *50-51*
Michelangelo, detail of Sistine Chapel ceiling, *182*
Michelson, Albert A., 102-103
Mirages, *34,* 44
Mirror reflection of light, *42-43, 45*
"Mistaken interpretation" in vision, a misnomer, 147
Mole rat, eyes of, *28*
Moles, eyes of, 28
Monkeys, placement of eyes of, 58
Monocular cues, in depth vision, *138,* 142, 143-146, *150-157;* aerial perspective (haze, color), 143, 145; interdependence of, 144; interposition, 143, 145, *152-153, 188-189;* linear and textural perspective, 143-144, *151;* movement parallax, 143, 146, *156-157;* relative size of objects, 143, 144, *150-151;* shadowing, 143, 145, *154-155, 182-183;* upward dislocation, 143, 145-146, *188-189*
Moon, halo of, 102
Mother-of-pearl, color of, 99, 103
Motion pictures: illusion of motion in, 147, 174, *175;* manipulation of visual cues in, 144-145, 155; precursors of, *166, 173*
Motion studies, Muybridge's, *68-69*
Movement, illusions of, 146, *156-157,* 175; in fantascope, *166;* in motion pictures, 147, 174, *175;* in op art painting, *146;* in tachyscope, *173*
Movement parallax, as cue in depth vision, 143, 146
Movement vision, 175-177
Mudskipper, eye of, *10*
Munsell, Albert, 116
Munsell color tree, *116-117*
Murex brandaris, snail, *98*
Muscles. *See* Eye muscles
Muscular convergence of eyes, 158
Muybridge, Eadweard, 68, 69
Myopia (nearsightedness), 59, *91;* correction by glasses, *91*

N

Near vision: lens accommodation for, 56-57, 59, *89;* defective (*see* Farsightedness); pupil adjustment for, 54; stereo effect, 143
Nearsightedness (myopia), 59, *91;* correction by glasses, *91*
Negative afterimages, 124, *132*
Neon light. *See* Fluorescent light
Neon signs, illusion of movement of, 147
Nerve, optic, 80-*81, 84,* 93, 120, 125, 168
Nerve cells and fibers, retinal, *76,* 80, *93, 94,* 120, 125, 175-176; background noise of, 172; response of, experiments, 171
Nerve control of eye, 57-58, 177
Nerve function in color vision, Hering theory, 124, 125, 134
Nerve head, optic, *84, 92, 93*
Newton, Sir Isaac, 35, 103, 126, 128, *129,* 134, 169; on color vision (*Opticks*), *121*-122, 129, 130; discovery of light spectrum by, 33, 97, 128; his theory of light, 34, 121
Newton's rings, 35, 36
Nictitating membrane, 26, *27*
Niépce, Nicéphore, 64, 65, 72
Night-prowling animals, eyes of, *22-23,* 28, *29, 77*
Nighttime driving, 147, 168-169, 172
Nitrocellulose film, 71
Nocturnal vision, 11, 16, 22-23, *28-29, 77;* limited in man, 76, *77-*78, 82, 94, *95;* retinal delay in, 172-173
Noise, background, in retinal nerve fibers, 172
Nolde, Emil, *Christ among the Children, 184*
Nurse shark, eye of, *22*

O

Octopus, eye of, *22*
Oil slicks, color effect of, 102, 109
One-eyed animals, 58
One-eyed vision, human, 141-142
Op art painting, *146*
Ophthalmoscope, 60
Opponent-process theory of color vision, 124, 125, *132-133*
Opsin, 79
Optic chiasma, 80, *81*
Optic nerve, 80-*81, 84,* 93, 120, 125, 168

Optic nerve head, *84, 92, 93*
Optical illusions. *See* Illusions, visual; Movement, illusions of
Opticks, Newton, *121*-122
Orange (color), 123; creation of, *110;* in nature, 99
Orley, Bernard van, portrait by, *184*
Overlapping, as depth cue, 145, *152-153;* in art, *188-189*
Owl: nocturnal vision of, 11, 16, 28, *77;* stereoscopic vision of, 58

P

Paint pigments: mixing of, *111;* primary colors, 97-98
Painting, 178, *179, 182-191;* fauvism, *186-187;* op art, *146; vs.* photography, *179;* pointillism, 119, *184-185;* techniques for indicating depth and distance, 145-146, *182-183, 186-191;* techniques for indicating shape, 145, *182*, 186; use of color, 119, *184-187;* use of light and shadow, *182-183;* use of line, *186-187*
Paolo, Giovanni di, painting by, *188-189*
Particle (corpuscular) theory of light, 31, 33-34, 38, 39, 79; Newton and, 34; and photoelectric effect, 38-39, *50-51;* Pythagorean, 31
Penguin, king, eye of, *23*
Perception, visual, 139-148, *149-165;* emotional loading in, *164-165;* illusions in, *142-144*, 146-*147*, 148, *162-164* (*see also* Movement, illusions of); tests, *160-161*. *See also* Color vision and perception; Depth perception; Distance perception; Form perception; Psychophysics
Perception cues. *See* Visual cues
Perceptual style, 161
Periophthalmus, eyes of, 10-11
Peripheral vision, *76*, 77, 81, 171
Perspective: in art, 147, *190-191;* in depth vision, 143-144; reversible, in line drawings, 147, *163*
Phonograph record, color effects of, *109*
Photoelectric effect, 38-39, *50-51*
Photography, 62, *63-73;* amateur, beginnings of, *70-71;* color, *72-73*, 106; daguerreotypes, *63, 65*, 66; depth illusion cues in, *138;* dry-plate process, *68-69; vs.* painting, *179;* roll-film, *70-71*, 72; stereoscopic, 142, 158, *159;* wet-plate process, *66-67*, 68, 69. *See also* Camera; Light meter
Photon(s), 39, *50-51;* minimum required for visibility, 170; role in visual process, *79*-80
Photoreceptors: in human retina, 76-77, 78, 79-80, 84, *94*, 120, 122 (*see also* Color receptors; Cones; Rods); photography, 62
Photosynthesis, 76
Pigment, visual, in retinal photoreceptors, 76, 77, 78, 94; bleaching and regeneration of, 78-79; role in visual process, *78-79*, 80, 94, 122, 125 (*see also* Color receptors)
Pigment color(s), 97, 98, 103; creation of, 98-99, *110-111;* primary, 97-98
Pigment epithelium, *94*
Pigment molecules: in man-made materials, 99, *110-111;* in nature, *98*-99, 110
Pink (color): creation of, 112; low saturation of, 120
Planck, Max, 39
Plate photography, *63-69;* color, *72-73*
Pointillism, 119, *184-185*
Polarization of light, 37-38, *48-49*
Polaroid glasses, 38, *49*
Predatory animals, eyes and vision of, 11, 16, *22-23, 27*, 58, *77*
Presbyopia, 59, 91
Primary colors: artists', 97-98; spectral, 98, 110, 123
Printing, color, *114-115*
Prism, spectral separation by, 33, *108*, 109, *128*
Prismatic color wheel, *129*
Protanopia, 124
Psychophysics of vision, 147, 167-177; of color vision, 136, 169-170; of intermittent stimuli, 173-175; of movement vision, 175-177; sensitivity studies, 170-173; units of measurement, 167, 168
Pufferfish, eyelid of, *27*
Pulfrich, Carl, 172
Pupil of eye, 54, 59, *83*, 84, *85, 88;* adjustment of, 54, 58, 78, *87;* animal, special adaptations, *22-23;* emotionally based widening of, 54-55
Purkinje, Johannes, 175
Purple (color), 123
Pythagorean concept of light, 31

Q

Quanta, 39, 50; minimum required for visibility, 170
Quantum theory, 39
Queen conch, eyes of, 24, *25*

R

Rabbit, placement of eyes of, 16, 58
Raccoon, placement of eyes of, 58
Radio waves, 38, 98
Rainbows, 44, 102, 104; experiment, *128*
Ray, electric, eye of, *22*
Rayleigh, Baron John, 102
Reading, mechanics of, *145*
Rearward vision: rabbit, 16; squirrel, 10
Recognition, visual, 168
Red (color): creation of, *110;* a fundamental color in perception, 123, 133; a hot color, 184; human perception of, 122, *132, 133;* of man-made materials, 99; in nature, 99; as primary spectral color, 98, 110; relative brightness of, 169; sensitivity of rods *vs.* cones to, 77, *graph* 170
Red-blue. *See* Magenta
Red light: refraction of, 33; wavelength of, 98, 120
Red-yellow light, reflection of, 106, *107*
Redundancies, in interpretation of visual stimuli, 15
Reflection of light, 31, 32, *42-43, 44, 45;* angle of, 31, *32, 42-43;* by atmospheric particles, *30*, 100-101; colored light, 99-100, 106, *107;* partial, by pigment molecules, and resultant color, *56*, 98-100, 110, 128; scattering phenomenon, *56, 96*, 100-101, *102;* total internal, 33, *41*
Reflectors, 99; role of surface structure of, in color creation, 99, 104, *108-109*
Refraction of light, 31, 33, 34, 35, *44-45;* angle of, *32, 33, 44-45;* of colored light, 33; in eye, 55-57, 86, *89, 91;* measurement of, 119
Refractive index(es), 32, 33; of cornea, 55; and velocity of light, 32, 34
Reichenbach, Henry M., 71
Renaissance painting, *182, 184, 188-191*
Resolution, visual, 168
Retina, 53, 54, 57, 59, 80, 81, *84-85*, 86, *92-94*, 168, 169; area of greatest acuity, *76;* dark and light adaptation in, 78, 172-173; description of, 76, 77, 93; effect of strychnine on, 171; function of, 75, 84; image inversion on, *54, 89*, 140; origin of word, 76; tissue tests, *134-135;* two-dimensionality of, 139
Retinal cells. *See* Cones; Rods
Retinal delay, in dim light, 172-173
Retinal nerve cells and fibers, *76*, 80, *93, 94*, 120, 125, 175-176; background noise of, 172; response of, experiment, 171
Retinene, 79; effect of light on molecules of, *78-79*
Rhodopsin, *78, 79*, 173
Riley, Bridget, painting by, *146*
Robin, vision of, 10
Rods, photoreceptors, *76-77, 94*, 168, 169, 171; function of, 76, 94, 171; number of, in human eye, 76; pooling action of, 171-172; proportion to cones, in man *vs.* owl, *77;* sensitivity of, in different parts of spectrum, 77, *graph* 170; visual pigment of, *78-79*
Roget, Peter Mark, 175
Rouault, Georges, 186

S

St. Christopher, Dürer, *180-181*
Saturation of color, 116, 119, 120
Scallop, eyespots of, *18*
Scattering of light, *96*, 100-101, *102;* and eye coloring, *56*
Scheiner, Christopher, 53
Sclera, *84-85*
Sea gull, eyes of, 58-59
Sea water, cause of color of, 101-102
Sehpurpur, 78
Sensory perception: development in infancy, 12-13; integration of senses, 11-12, 13
Seurat, Georges, *La Grande Jatte*, 119, *184-185*
Shadow, edges of, 34-35, 37, 46, *47*
Shadowing, and form perception, 145, *154-155, 182-183*
Sherrington, Sir Charles, 177
Shrews, eyes of, 28; tree shrew, 58
Simple eyes, *20*
Sistine Chapel ceiling, Michelangelo, detail, *182*
Size of objects: apparent, in relation to brightness, 145; as condition of vision, 168-169; judging, 139, 144, 148, *150;* relative, as cue in depth vision, *138*, 143, 144, *150-151, 190-191*
Skate, eye of, *22*, 23
Sky coloring, cause of, 100-101, *102*
Snails, eyes of, 24, *25*
Snakes: eyes of, *22*, 23; lack of eyelids of, 26, 59
Snell, Willebrord, 31-32
Snellen, Herman, 58
Snellen chart, *58, 59*
Soap bubbles, rainbow colors in, 35, 36, 102, 104, *109*
Spectacles. *See* Eyeglasses
Spectral colors, 33, 98, 103, *108-109, 128-129;* creation of, 98; primary, 98, 110, 123
Spectrophotograph, *101*
Spectrophotometer, *100*, 101, 119
Spectroscope, *131*
Spectrum. *See* Electromagnetic spectrum; Light spectrum
Speed, as cue to depth vision, *156-157*
Speed of light, 38, 44, 103
Spiders, eyes of, *20*, 58
Squares, visual illusions in viewing of, 146
Squid, eye of, *23*
Squirrel, eyes of, *28;* placement, 10
Stereoscope, 142, *158*
Stereoscopic photography, 142; stereo pairs, 142, 158, *159*
Stereoscopic (three-dimensional) vision, 11, 58, 81, 139-146, 158, 167; in animals, 58; basic requirements for, 58; binocular cues for, 141-143, 146, *158-159;* doubling of out-of-focus objects, 143; interdependence of cues, 144; unit of measurement, 167
Straight lines, visual illusion in viewing of, 146
Strychnine, increase of sensitivity of eye by, 171
Subtractive mixing of color, 98-99, *110-111*
Sun, differences in appearance of, *96*, 100-101
Sunglasses, polaroid, 38, *49*
Sunlight: *vs.* artificial light, 99, 106, *107;* and color effects, 98-99, *102;* and photosynthesis, 76; reflection of, by mist particles, *30;* scattering phenomenon, *96*, 100-101, *102;* spectrum, 97, *128*
Sunrise, 100-101
Sunset, 44, *96*, 100-101, *102*
Surface structure of materials, role in color creation, 99, 104, *108-109*
Surgery. *See* Eye surgery
Surrealism, *162*

T

Tachyscope, *173*
Talbot, Fox, *64-65*, 66
Tarsier, eyes of, *29*
Taste, sense of, 13
Tears, 59
Telescopes, 32, 82, 169
Television, 147, 174; color, 112, 115; use of photoelectric effect in, 38
Tennyson, Alfred Lord, 61
Tests: acuity, *chart* 58, *59*, 168; astigmatism, *60;* color vision, *127, 134-137;* Ishihara, *127;* perception, *160-161;* Snellen, *chart* 58, *59*
Textural perspective, as cue in depth vision, 143-144
Three-dimensional vision. *See* Depth perception; Stereoscopic vision
Three-receptor theory of color vision, 122-123, 124, 125, *130*, 133, 134, 135
Toads, specialized eyes of, 11, *23*
Total internal reflection, 33, *41*
Touch, sense of, 11, 13
Toulouse-Lautrec, Henri de, paintings by, *179*, 186, *187*
Transmission of color, 99
Tree-climbing animals, eyes of, 11, 58
Tree shrew, vision of, 58
Trichromatic theory of color vision, 122-123, 124, 125, *130*, 133, 134, 135
Trilobite eye, fossil, 20
Tritanopia, 124
20/20 vision, *chart* 58, *59*
Twilight: color effects in sky, 101; vision problems in, 77, 94, *95*, 172-173
Tyrian purple, source of, *98*

U

Ultraviolet light, and photoelectric effect, 38
University of Pennsylvania, *136-137*
Upward dislocation, as cue in depth vision, 143, 145-146, *188-189*

V

Value of color, *116-117*
Van Gogh, Vincent, drawing by, *180*
Velocity of light, 38, 44, 103; and refractive index, 32, 34; relationship to frequency and wavelength, 36
Vertical range of human vision, *140*
Violet (color): low brightness of, 169; sensitivity of eye to, *graph* 170
Visibility curves, *graph* 170
Vision: ancient Greek concept of (emanation theory), 53; basic processes of, 53, 75-76, 79-80. *See also* Animal vision; Binocular vision; Color vision; Far vision; Human vision; Near vision; Nocturnal vision; Stereoscopic vision
Visual cortex, *81*, 120, 141, 148
Visual cues, *138*, 141, 148; binocular, 141-143, 146, *158-159;* distortions of, *162-163;* interdependence of, 144; monocular, 142, 143-146, *150-157*
"Visual purple," rod pigment, 78
Visual systems. *See* Animal visual systems; Human visual system
Vitamin A, and vision, 78-79
Vitreous humor, 54, 55, 57, 61; function of, 84
Vlaminck, Maurice de, 186
Volcanic eruptions, effect on twilight colors, 101

W

Wald, George, 80, 125
Wasp, vision of, 20
Water: causes of colors of, 101-102; refraction of light by, 31-32, 44, *45;* velocity of light in, 44
Water droplets, rainbow colors of, 102, 109
Waterfall illusion, 175
Waterfowl, nictitating membrane of, 26
Wave theory of light, 31, 33-35, *36-37*, 38-39, 79; Aristotelian, 31; and diffraction and interference, 35-36, *37*, 38, 39, *46-47;* Huygens and, 32, 34; Maxwell and, 38; and polarization, 37-38, *48-49;* temporary triumph over particle theory, 38; Young and, 35-36, *37*
Wavelength of light, 98; absorption *vs.* reflection by pigment molecules, and resultant color, 98-100, 110; and color saturation, 120; and hue, 120; and photoelectric effect, 39; relationship to frequency and color, 36, *107*, 119, 120; of various colors, 98, *107*, 120, 123
Weather prediction, sky coloring and, 101
Wertheimer, Max, 175
Western Reserve University, 12
Wet-plate photography, *66-67*, 68, 69
White: caused by complete light reflection, 99, *106;* in color TV, 112, *113;* human perception of, 122, *130, 133*
Wied's frog, eyelids of, *26*
Wiesel, Torsten N., 75, 81
Wilson, R. R., 101
Winter flounder, eye of, *23*
Witkin, Herman A., 161
Wolves, stereoscopic vision of, 58

X

X-rays, nature of, 39

Y

Yellow (color): brightness of, 120, 169; creation of, *110, 112;* a fundamental color in perception, 123, 133; human perception of, 122, *133;* not a primary spectral color, 98; as primary pigment, 98, *111;* sensitivity of rods *vs.* cones to, 77, *graph* 170
Yellow light: produced by combination of red and green light, 98; wavelength of, 98
Yellow-orange (color), in nature, 99
Young, Thomas, *130;* and color vision, 103, 122, 126, 130, 133; experiment on nature of light, 35-36, *37*
Young-Helmholtz theory of color vision, 122-123, 124, 125, 126, *130*, 133, 134, 135

Z

Zöllner, Friedrich, 143

PICTURE CREDITS

The sources for the illustrations which appear in this book are shown below. Credits for the pictures from left to right are separated by commas, from top to bottom by dashes.

Cover—John Murello.

CHAPTER 1: 8—David Linton. 10—Drawing by Leslie Martin. 13—Drawings courtesy Greenwich House. 14—Drawing by Mana Maeda. 17—Fritz Goro. 18—Yata Haneda courtesy Yakasuka City Museum—Constance P. Warner. 19—Philip Clark. 20, 21—Left Andreas Feininger—Constance P. Warner courtesy Smithsonian; right Constance P. Warner. 22, 23—Constance P. Warner except bottom extreme right Fred H. Wylie from Annan Photo Features. 24—Laurence Perkins from Annan Photo Features. 25 through 28—Constance P. Warner. 29—United Press International.

CHAPTER 2: 30—From *The World Through My Eyes* by Andreas Feininger used by permission of Crown Publishers Inc. 32, 33—Drawing by Otto van Eersel. 34, 35—Drawing by Otto van Eersel adapted from *Physics Tells Why*, by Overton Luhr copyright 1946 The Ronald Press Company, New York. 36, 37—Drawings by Otto van Eersel. 41—Fritz Goro. 42—Ken Kay. 43—Hank Walker, Ken Kay. 44 through 49—Ken Kay. 50, 51—Albert Fenn, Albert Fenn designed by Matt Greene.

CHAPTER 3: 52—Derek Bayes. 54—Drawing by Donald Crews adapted from *Eye and Camera*, by George Wald p. 33 © August 1950 by Scientific American Inc., All rights reserved. 55—Drawing by Nicholas Fasciano, adapted with permission of Alfred A. Knopf, Inc. from *Man in Structure and Function* by Fritz Kahn, © 1943 by Fritz Kahn. 56—Drawing by Donald Crews. 57—Drawing by Donald Crews adapted from *Control Mechanisms of the Eye* by Derek H. Fender © July 1964 by Scientific American Inc., All rights reserved. 58—Courtesy American Optical Company. 59—Drawing by Donald Crews. 60—Courtesy American Optical Company. 61—Drawing by Donald Crews adapted from *The Eye*, Vol. 2, *The Visual Process*, edited by Hugh Davson, Academic Press Inc., New York, figure 3, page 328. 63—Bavarian National Museum courtesy The Museum of Modern Art. 64, 65—Courtesy Kodak Research Laboratory, Harrow, Middlesex, England; original in Gernsheim Collection; drawing by Charles Mikolaycak, courtesy George Eastman House. 66—Smithsonian Office of Anthropology, Bureau of American Ethnology Collection; Denver Public Library, exhibited in The Museum of Modern Art's *The Photographer in the American Landscape*, September 24-November 28, 1963. 67—Ben Rose courtesy George Eastman House—Roger Fenton, courtesy The Science Museum, London. 68—Top two rows originals by Eadweard Muybridge copied by Ben Rose courtesy George Eastman House; bottom three rows Eadweard Muybridge courtesy George Eastman House. 69—George M. Quay courtesy University of Pennsylvania Archives—Matt Greene, originals by Eadweard Muybridge courtesy George Eastman House. 70, 71—Copied by Ben Rose courtesy George Eastman House except top left Ben Rose courtesy George Eastman House. 72, 73—Original by Niépce de Saint Victoire courtesy George Eastman House, original by Louis Lumière copied by Dmitri Kessel.

CHAPTER 4: 74—Royal Collection, Windsor Castle copyright reserved. 76, 77—Drawings by John and Mary Condon. 78—Drawings by John and Mary Condon adapted from *Light and Life*, by George Wald p. 102 © October 1959 by Scientific American Inc., All rights reserved. 79—Drawings by John and Mary Condon adapted from *Afterimages* by G. S. Brindley © October 1963 by Scientific American Inc., All rights reserved. 80, 81—Drawings by John and Mary Condon. 83—Ben Rose. 84, 85—Elliott Herman. 86—From figures 154 B and 154 D in Dr. Roman Castroviejo's *Atlas of Keratectomy and Keratoplasty* published by Salvat Editores, S.A., Barcelona—Bob Gomel. 87—Ben Rose. 88—Julius Weber, Albert Fenn (2). 89—Drawings by Otto van Eersel. 90—Bob Gomel. 91—Drawings by Otto van Eersel. 92—Dr. Harris Ripps. 93—Julius Weber—Bob Gomel. 94—Julius Weber, Toichiro Kuwabara, M.D., Associate Professor of Pathology, Harvard University. 95—N. R. Farbman.

CHAPTER 5: 96—Don Strittmatter. 98—Drawing by Leslie Martin. 99—Alan Clifton photo by permission of the Clarendon Press, Oxford. 100—Drawing by John and Mary Condon. 101—Graph courtesy E. I. Du Pont. 102—Drawings by Donald Crews and Joel Margulies. 105, 106—John Zimmerman. 107—John Zimmerman—drawing by George V. Kelvin. 108—John Zimmerman—Fritz Goro. 109—Andreas Feininger, Ken Kay—John Zimmerman, Ken Kay. 110, 111—Fritz Goro except right John Zimmerman. 112, 113—John Zimmerman. 114, 115—Norman Parkinson. 116, 117—Victor Waldrop, John Zimmerman.

CHAPTER 6: 118—Courtesy American Telephone and Telegraph Company. 121—Courtesy New York Public Library. 123—Culver Pictures. 127—Courtesy Kanehara Shuppan Company Ltd., Tokyo, and Matalene Surgical Instrument Company, New York. 128—Zentralbibliothek, Zurich. 129—The Granger Collection—Faber Birren and the Holyoke Lithograph Company Inc. 130, 131—Courtesy the Royal Society, London, Derek Bayes, Derek Bayes courtesy the Ronan Picture Library, London, Derek Bayes, drawing by John Condon. 132—Dr. Leo M. Hurvic, drawings by John Condon. 133—Drawing by John Condon. 134—Drawing by John Condon—Ben Rose. 135—Ben Rose, William Dobelle, Johns Hopkins University. 136, 137—Ben Rose.

CHAPTER 7: 138—Dmitri Kessel. 140—Drawing by Nicholas Fasciano. 142, 143—Courtesy of Pergoman Press, Oxford. 144—Adapted from an illustration in *One for a Man, Two for a Horse* by Gerald Carson, Doubleday and Co., 1961. 145—From *Science Puzzlers* by Martin Gardner © 1960 by Martin Gardner and Anthony Ravielli. Reprinted by permission of the Viking Press, Inc. 146—*Fall* (1963) by Bridget Riley, reproduced courtesy the Trustees of the Tate Gallery. 147—Drawing by Mana Maeda. 149—Ben Rose courtesy Wax Museum Enterprises; drawing from *The Perception of the Visual World* by James G. Gibson, published by Houghton Mifflin Company. 150, 151—Bill Ray, Ben Rose courtesy Ford Motor Company (2). 152—Ed Stein. 153—Lee Lockwood from Black Star, Ben Rose courtesy Brooklyn College Psychology Department. 154—Zyonko Glyck. 155—Drawing by Mana Maeda, adapted from *Eye and Brain: The Psychology of Seeing* by R. L. Gregory, World University Library, McGraw-Hill, New York, p. 72—Zyonko Glyck. 156 through 160—Ben Rose. 161—Drawing by Otto van Eersel—from Norman L. Munns's *Psychology*, published by Houghton Mifflin Company. 162—*House of Stairs* by Maurice Escher from the collection of C.V.S. Roosevelt, Washington, D.C., drawing courtesy L. S. and R. Penrose and the *British Journal of Psychology*. 163—Top; copied by Otto van Eersel from illustrations by Fred H. Lyon in *Experiments in Optical Illusion* by Nelson F. Beeler and Franklyn M. Branley; © 1951 by Thomas Y. Crowell Company, New York; center copied by Otto van Eersel from Don Mackey's optical illusion printed in North American Aviation's *Skywriter* of February 18, 1966; courtesy Braun and Company, Inc.; bottom drawing by Otto van Eersel. 164, 165—Louis Stettner, Lynn Pelham from Rapho-Guillumette.

CHAPTER 8: 166—Derek Bayes courtesy Science Museum, London. 169—Courtesy Bausch & Lomb, Inc. 170—Copied by Raymond Ripper, based on figure 13-3 in *Optics* by Francis W. Sears, Addison-Wesley Publishing Company, 1949. 173—The Bettmann Archive. 179—Helene Vary by Edita, Lausanne, detail of *Portrait D'Helene* by Toulouse-Lautrec courtesy Kunsthalle Bremen photograph by Walter Sanders. 180, 181—Study of Albert Einstein by Hans Erni—*Cottages des Saintes Maries 1888* by Vincent Van Gogh courtesy Kunstarchivarntz Haag Upper Bavaria, *St. Christopher* by Albrecht Dürer photograph by John Freeman courtesy British Museum. 182—Detail of *The Madonna* by Carlo Crivelli Pinacoteca di Brera Museum, Milan, photograph Marzari—detail of the Cumaean Sibyl by Michelangelo, Sistine Chapel ceiling photograph by Bruno del Priore, Rome. 183—*St. Joseph the Carpenter* by Georges de la Tour courtesy the Louvre Museum photograph Giraudon. 184, 185—Portrait of *George van Zelle* by Bernard van Orley The Brussels Royal Museum of Fine Arts—*Christ among the Children* by Emil Nolde, collection The Museum of Modern Art New York, gift of Dr. W. R. Valentine, details of *A Sunday Afternoon on the Grand Jatte* by Georges Seurat courtesy The Art Institute of Chicago photograph by Jahn and Ollier. 186—*Autoportrait de profil, 1958* by Marcel Duchamp courtesy the Galleria Schwarz Milan photograph by Bacci—*Dance* by Henri Matisse collection The Museum of Modern Art New York gift of Governor Nelson A. Rockefeller in honor of Alfred H. Barr. 187—*L'Argent* theater program by Toulouse-Lautrec; *Loys Delteil le Peinte Graveur Illustre* courtesy Bibliothèque Nationale, Paris photograph by Eric Schaal. 188, 189—Details from the tomb of the Vizier Ramose; Thebes Photograph Hassia, *Paradise* by Giovanni di Paolo courtesy the Metropolitan Museum of Art, Rogers Fund, 1906, *The Round Table* by Georges Braque courtesy the Phillips Collection, Washington D.C. photograph by Henry Beville. 190, 191—*Dead Christ* by Andrea Mantegna courtesy Pinacoteca di Brera, Milan photograph by Dmitri Kessel, *Interior of a Church* by Emmanuel de Witte courtesy Boysmans-van Beuningen Museum, Rotterdam. Appendix: 193—Drawings by Otto van Eersel adapted from *The Vertebrate Visual System* by Stephen Polyak, M.D., edited by Heinrich Klüver The University of Chicago Press © 1957 by the University of Chicago. © 1955 under the International Copyright Union. Back cover—Raymond Ripper.

PRODUCTION STAFF FOR TIME INCORPORATED

John L. Hallenbeck (Vice President and Director of Production), Robert E. Foy, Caroline Ferri and Robert E. Fraser
Text photocomposed under the direction of Albert J. Dunn and Arthur J. Dunn